D0524441

WJEC
A2 Physics

Study and Revision Guide

Nigel Wood • Iestyn Morris • Gareth Kelly

Revised edition published in 2012 by Illuminate Publishing Ltd, P.O. Box 1160, Cheltenham, Gloucestershire GL50 9RW

Orders: Please visit www.illuminatepublishing.com
or email sales@illuminatepublishing.com

British Library Cataloguing in Publication Data

A catalogue record for this book is available from the British Library

ISBN 978-1-908682-05-5

Printed in England by 4edge Ltd., Hockley, Essex, UK.

09.13

The publisher's policy is to use papers that are natural, renewable and recyclable products made from wood grown in sustainable forests. The logging and manufacturing processes are expected to conform to the environmental regulations of the country of origin.

Every effort has been made to contact copyright holders of material reproduced in this book. If notified, the publishers will be pleased to rectify any errors or omissions at the earliest opportunity.

This material has been endorsed by WJEC and offers high quality support for the delivery of WJEC qualifications. While this material has been through a WJEC quality assurance process, all responsibility for the content remains with the publisher.

Editor: Geoff Tuttle
Cover and text design: Nigel Harriss
Text and layout: The Manila Typesetting Company

Permissions

p59 Tom McNemar/Fotolia; p124 gdvcom/Fotolia.

Acknowledgements

We are very grateful to the team at Illuminate Publishing for their professionalism, support and guidance throughout this project. It has been a pleasure to work so closely with them.

The authors and publisher wish to thank:
Len Belton for his thorough review of the book and expert insights and observations.

Contents

How to use this book   5

Knowledge and Understanding

PH4 **Oscillations and Fields**   **7**
   4.1   Momentum and force   10
   4.2   Circular motion   15
   4.3   Oscillations   18
   4.4   Gases   25
   4.5   Thermodynamics   30
   4.6   Electric fields   36
   4.7   Gravitation: fields and potentials   42
   4.8   Orbits in gravitational fields   47

PH5 **Magnetism, Nuclei and Options**   **55**
   5.1   Capacitance   57
   5.2   B-fields   65
   5.3   Electromagnetic induction   77
   5.4   Radioactivity and radioisotopes   90
   5.5   Nuclear energy   97

OPTION A **Further Electromagnetism and Alternating Currents** **104**
   Induction, transformers and self-induction   105
   Phasor diagrams and ac circuits   108
   Resonance in an LCR circuit   111
   The quality (Q) factor of a resonance circuit   113
   CR circuits as low- and high-pass filters   116

OPTION C **Materials**   **119**
   Hooke's law   120
   Young modulus   121
   Material structure   126
   Polymers and their mechanical properties   129

OPTION D **Medical Measurement and Medical Imaging** **131**

X-rays 132

Ultrasound 133

Magnetic resonance imaging 135

Electrocardiograms (ECG) 137

Nuclear radiation in medicine 138

PH6 **Experimental Physics** **142**

6.1 Uncertainties 143

6.2 Graphs 144

6.3 Planning investigations 151

Practice questions **152**

Exam Practice and Technique **157**

Exam practice and skills 157

Questions and answers 161

Quickfire answers **176**

Practice question answers **180**

Index 186

How to use this book

The authors of this book are senior A level Physics examiners. We have written this study guide to help you understand what is required to do well in your studies. The contents of the guide are structured to help you to success in WJEC A level Physics.

There are notes for the externally assessed units:

PH4 – Oscillations and Fields

PH5 – Electromagnetism, Nuclei and Options*

and for the internally assessed unit

PH6 – Experimental and Synoptic Assessment

* This book contains notes for option A (Further Electromagnetism and Alternating Currents), option C (Materials) and option D (Medical Measurement and Imaging).

Knowledge and Understanding

The **first section** of the book covers the key knowledge and skills required for the examination.

In addition, we have given some pointers to help your revision:

- Many Physics terms are defined – you should also refer to the WJEC document 'Terms, Definitions and Units'.

- There are 'Quickfire' questions designed so that you can test your own progress.

- We have given advice based on our experience of what candidates need to do to raise their grades.

Exam Practice and Technique

The **second section** of the book covers the key skills for examination success and gives examples of candidates' actual responses to past-paper questions. This section also explains about key terms which examiners use when they set questions and how you should respond to them.

A complete range of question types is given. Each question has two answers of different standards and there is also a commentary to explain why the candidates received the marks they did.

The **practice questions** section which precedes the examination questions has a series of practice questions covering units PH4, PH5 and PH6. These are not past paper questions but are designed to give you pointers in your examination preparation. There are model answers to these questions, i.e. responses which the examiners would consider to be ideal.

The most important thing is that you take responsibility for your own learning and examination preparation. This will include making your own notes as you go through the course and consulting textbooks and other sources. The WJEC website, www.wjec.co.uk, has the specification, guidance notes, past papers and mark schemes. Remember that preparation for examinations is an **active** process – not just reading and learning, but making notes and practising the techniques which you will need to attain the highest possible grade.

We wish you every success.

Nigel Wood   Iestyn Morris   Gareth Kelly

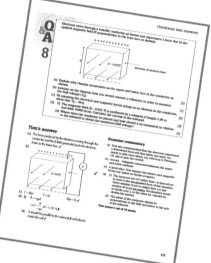

Knowledge and Understanding

PH4 Oscillations and Fields

The PH4 unit demands a higher level of mathematical analysis than the AS course. It investigates the closely related topics of vibrations and circular motion, exploring the phenomena of forced vibrations and resonance. The relationship between momentum and Newton's laws of motion is clarified. The thermal physics topic looks at the relationship between molecular motion and gas properties and introduces the first law of thermodynamics. The mathematics of electrostatic and gravitational fields is introduced and the unit finishes with the application of several of the unit's concepts to the exploration of the universe, concentrating on extra-solar planets and dark matter.

PH4 is assessed by a 1½-hour examination.

Revision checklist

Tick column 1 when you have completed brief revision notes.

Tick column 2 when you think you have a good grasp of the topic.

Tick column 3 during final revision when you feel you have mastered the topic.

			1	2	3	Notes
p10	**4.1**	**Momentum and force**				
p10		Momentum				
p12		Bodies exerting forces on each other				
p13		Elastic and inelastic collisions				
p14		Calculating the force of light on a body				
p15	**4.2**	**Circular motion**				
p15		Measuring angles in radians				
p15		Angular velocity				
p16		Centripetal acceleration				
p18	**4.3**	**Oscillations**				
p18		Simple harmonic motion				
p19		Variation of displacement with time for a body in SHM				
p20		Examples of using $x = A \sin(\omega t + \varepsilon)$				
p21		Velocity of a body in SHM				
p21		Acceleration of a body in SHM				
p22		Energy interchange in SHM				
p23		Damped oscillations				
p24		Forced oscillations				

			1	2	3	Notes
p25	**4.4**	**Gases**				
p25		Molecules				
p26		Squeezing a gas: what we find				
p26		Temperature				
p27		The ideal gas equation				
p28		Gas pressure according to kinetic theory				
p29		The mean kinetic energy of molecules				
p30	**4.5**	**Thermodynamics**				
p30		Internal energy				
p30		p–V diagrams for a gas				
p31		Energy flows into and out of a system				
p32		The first law of thermodynamics				
p34		Cycles of changes				
p35		Solids and liquids				
p36	**4.6**	**Electric fields**				
p36		Electric field strength				
p37		Coulomb's law				
p37		E due to a point charge				
p38		Electric potential and electrical potential energy				
p38		Field strength and potential difference				
p39		Electric potential due to a point charge, Q				
p39		Potential gradient				
p40		Electric field strength due to a number of charges				
p40		Electric potential due to a number of charges				
p41		Electric field lines				
p41		Equipotentials				
p42	**4.7**	**Gravitation: fields and potentials**				
p42		Gravitational field strength				
p42		Newton's law of gravitation				
p43		g due to a point, or spherically symmetric mass				
p43		Gravitational potential and gravitational potential energy				
p44		g and gravitational potential difference				
p45		Conservation of energy in a gravitational field				
p45		Escape speed (or escape velocity)				
p46		Field strengths and potentials due to more than one body				

				1	2	3	Notes
p47	**4.8**	**Orbits in gravitational fields**					
p47		Kepler's laws of planetary motion					
p47		Circular orbits					
p48		Using orbit theory for satellites and planets					
p49		Rotation of galaxies, and dark matter					
p50		Binary systems					
p51		Measurements of velocity by Doppler shift					
p52		Determining a binary system from one body's orbit					

Momentum and force

Momentum

Some of the most important laws of Physics involve **momentum**.

The momentum, p, of a body of mass m, moving with velocity v, is defined by:

$$momentum = mass \times velocity$$

that is $p = mv$.

It is a vector (with the same direction as the velocity).

Unit: $kg\,m\,s^{-1} = N\,s$ (newton second).

>> **Pointer**

The unit $N\,s$ is equivalent to $kg\,m\,s^{-1}$ because $N = kg\,m\,s^{-2}$, so $N\,s = kg\,m\,s^{-1}$.

Example

A cricket ball of mass 0.160 kg is thrown vertically upwards with an initial speed of 14.0 m s^{-1}. After 2.5 s it has a downward velocity of 10.5 m s^{-1}. Calculate its change in momentum.

Change in momentum = final momentum – initial momentum

$$= 0.160 \times 10.5\ N\,s\downarrow - 0.160 \times 14.0\ N\,s\uparrow$$
$$= 1.68\ N\,s\downarrow - 2.24\ N\,s\uparrow = 1.68\ N\,s\downarrow + (-2.24\ N\,s\uparrow)$$
$$= 1.68\ N\,s\downarrow + 2.24\ N\,s\downarrow = 3.92\ N\,s\downarrow$$

So the ball's change in momentum is 3.92 N s downwards.

>> **Pointer**

In the example, note how –2.24 N s upwards is the same as +2.24 N s downwards. A useful trick with vectors!

This change in momentum is brought about by the continued action of the downward gravitational force. This is one case of a general law...

Newton's second law of motion

The rate of change of a body's momentum is proportional to the resultant force acting on it, and the direction of the change is that of the resultant force.

Mathematically, $F_{res} = \dfrac{\Delta p}{\Delta t}$ or $F_{res} = \dfrac{\Delta(mv)}{\Delta t}$ or $F_{res} = \dfrac{m_2v_2 - m_1v_1}{\Delta t}$.

>> **Pointer**

In Newton's second law, F_{res} is the same as ΣF, meaning the *vector* sum of individual forces.

- The constant of proportionality has been put as 1. This applies if we work in SI units, measuring force in newton (N).
- If the body's mass doesn't change while the force acts, then we can put $m_2 = m_1 = m$, and so:

$$F_{res} = \frac{mv_2 - mv_1}{\Delta t} = \frac{m(v_2 - v_1)}{\Delta t} = m\frac{\Delta v}{\Delta t},\quad \text{that is}\quad F_{res} = ma.$$

>> **Pointer**

If F_{res} is changing, then $\dfrac{\Delta p}{\Delta t}$ gives the mean value of F_{res} over the interval Δt.

In other words: resultant force = mass × acceleration.

This should be familiar!

Examples of applying Newton's second law

(1) Calculate the mean resultant force on the cricket ball in the example on the previous page.

$$F_{res} = \frac{\Delta p}{\Delta t} = \frac{3.92\,Ns}{2.5\,s} = 1.6\,N$$

To 2 s.f. this is equal to mg, so the mean force of air resistance on the ball must be small!

(2) A momentum–time graph is given for a car making a short journey eastwards along a straight road.

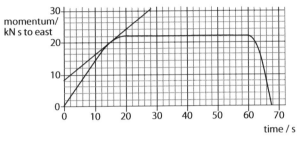

- Calculate the resultant force on the car over the first 10 seconds.

$$F_{res} = \frac{\Delta p}{\Delta t} = \frac{14\,kN\,s}{10\,s} = 1.4\,kN \text{ (to the east)}$$

- Calculate the resultant force on the car *at* 15 s.

Between 10 s and 20 s, the rate of change of momentum isn't constant, so we have to draw a tangent to the graph at $t = 15$ s.

Then F_{res} = slope of tangent = $\dfrac{(30.0 - 8.0)\,kN\,s}{(27.5 - 0)\,s} = 0.80\,kN$
(to the east).

Newton's first law of motion

A body at rest remains at rest, and a moving body continues moving in a straight line at constant speed, unless acted upon by a resultant external force.

Example: a parachutist who has reached terminal velocity when the air resistance has become equal (and opposite) to the weight.

The first law is just a special case of the second, since

if $F_{res} = 0$, then $\dfrac{\Delta p}{\Delta t} = 0$, so the body's momentum doesn't change!

Key Term

Newton's first law = see main text.

① A ball of mass 0.057 kg is thrown at a wall. Its velocities just before hitting, and just after leaving, are 17 m s^{-1} east and 13 m s^{-1} west. Find:

- its change in momentum.

- the mean force of the ball on the wall if they are in contact for 0.15 s.

② A piece of timber is hauled across level ground by a rope which exerts a horizontal force of 280 N. In the first 8.0 s of hauling, the timber acquires 1200 N s of momentum. Find the mean frictional force acting.

③ Use the word 'velocity' to state Newton's first law with fewer words.

Newton's third law = see main text.

Principle (law) of conservation of momentum = see main text.

》 Pointer

Note the handling of momentum as a vector in the 'spheres' example:

- The initial momentum of the 5.0 kg sphere is 5.0×1.8 Ns to the left, so equivalent to -5.0×1.8 Ns to the right.

- The question asked for a velocity, so you mustn't forget to give the direction! Again, the minus sign matters!

Bodies exerting forces on each other

Newton's third law of motion

When a body A exerts a force on a body B, B exerts an equal and opposite force on A.

Example: two positive ions, A and B.

F_A and F_B are vectors and $F_A = -F_B$.

Using Newton's second law, and assuming no forces except the mutual forces, F_A and F_B,

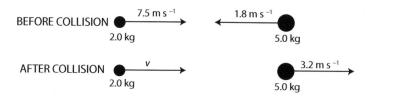

$$\frac{\Delta p_A}{\Delta t} = -\frac{\Delta p_B}{\Delta t} \qquad \text{so} \qquad \Delta p_A = -\Delta p_B$$

In other words, A's *change* in momentum over any interval is equal and opposite to B's, so the *vector sum* of A's momentum and B's momentum never changes. This applies to a 'system' of any number of bodies.

The principle (or law) of conservation of momentum

The vector sum of the momenta of the bodies in a system is constant, provided there is no resultant force from outside the system.

The law is especially applicable to collisions, because the forces from outside the system (such as friction) are usually very small compared with the collision forces between the bodies themselves. The law has been confirmed in a vast number of sub-atomic particle collisions.

Applying the law: an example

Find the velocity of the 2.0 kg sphere after the collision.

BEFORE COLLISION ● $\xrightarrow{7.5 \text{ m s}^{-1}}$ $\xleftarrow{1.8 \text{ m s}^{-1}}$ ●
      2.0 kg   5.0 kg

AFTER COLLISION ● $\xrightarrow{v}$ ● $\xrightarrow{3.2 \text{ m s}^{-1}}$
      2.0 kg   5.0 kg

Omitting units and considering momentum to the right:

Vector sum of initial momenta = Vector sum of final momenta

So $\qquad 2.0 \times 7.5 - 5.0 \times 1.8 = 2.0 \times v + 5.0 \times 3.2$

So $\qquad\qquad 15 - 9.0 = 2.0 \, v + 16$

So $\qquad\qquad v = -5.0 \text{ m s}^{-1}$

We conclude that, after the collision, the 2.0 kg sphere has a velocity of 5.0 m s^{-1} to the left.

④ A 3 000 kg wagon moving west at 11.0 m s^{-1} collides with a 5 000 kg wagon moving east at 8.0 m s^{-1}, which then moves west, at 4.0 m s^{-1}. What is the new velocity of the 3 000 kg wagon? [Hint: put data on a diagram!]

Elastic and inelastic collisions

*An **elastic collision** is one in which no kinetic energy is lost or gained.*

At 'ordinary' temperatures, collisions between atoms of inert gases (such as helium) are elastic. But objects made of many atoms – that includes all objects we can see – collide **inelastically**: some of their KE is transferred to additional random thermal vibration energy of their atoms.

Key Terms

Elastic collision = one in which no kinetic energy is lost or gained.

Inelastic collision = one in which kinetic energy is lost.

Using speeds to calculate lost kinetic energy

We simply calculate the sum of the kinetic energies, $\frac{1}{2}m_1v_1^2 + \frac{1}{2}m_2v_2^2 \dots$, before and after. Kinetic energy is a scalar, so directions don't matter.

Example: Two skaters approach each other as shown, and keep hold of each other when they collide. Calculate the kinetic energy change.

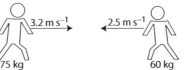

First we use momentum conservation to find v, the skaters' speed after the collision. Omitting units and considering momentum to the right:

$$75 \times 3.2 - 60 \times 2.5 = 135\,v \qquad \text{so} \qquad v = 0.67 \text{ m s}^{-1} \text{ (to the right)}$$

So   initial KE $= \frac{1}{2} \times 75 \times 3.2^2 + \frac{1}{2} \times 60 \times 2.5^2 = 572$ J;

and   final KE $= \frac{1}{2} \times 135 \times 0.67^2 = 30$ J; change $= -542$ J

The collision between the skaters is therefore extremely inelastic! (If they pushed each other away, colliding skaters *could* actually *gain* kinetic energy – transferred in their muscles from chemical energy.)

» Pointer

Two colliding hard spheres may retain more than 90% of their KE.

» Pointer

Conservation of momentum applies to collisions, elastic or inelastic, as long as there are no forces from outside.

Momentum of a photon

Photons can be absorbed and emitted and can take part in collisions. The principle of conservation of momentum applies every time. A special formula is needed, though, for a photon's momentum p_{phot}:

$$p_{\text{phot}} = \frac{h}{\lambda}$$

in which h is the Planck constant and λ is the photon wavelength.

Example: A photon of wavelength 9.52×10^{-8} m is absorbed by a hydrogen atom of mass 1.67×10^{-27} kg that is initially stationary. Calculate the speed the atom acquires. (Its mass change is negligible.)

So $\dfrac{h}{\lambda} + 0 = mv$ so $v = \dfrac{1}{m}\dfrac{h}{\lambda} = \dfrac{1}{1.67 \times 10^{-27}\text{kg}} \times \dfrac{6.63 \times 10^{-34}\text{ J s}}{9.52 \times 10^{-8}\text{m}} = 4.2 \text{ m s}^{-1}$

⑤ Calculate the KE lost in the collision between spheres in the example on the last page.

⑥ The excited nucleus of a $^{24}_{11}$Na atom emits a γ ray photon of wavelength 4.50×10^{-13} m. Calculate:

   (a) The photon's momentum.

   (b) The recoil speed of the atom (mass $= 3.98 \times 10^{-26}$ kg).

⊙ᐸᐸᐸ quickfire

⑦ It is proposed to levitate (that is prevent from falling) a leaf of mass 0.70×10^{-6} kg, by shining light from a laser on to its underside. Calculate:

(a) The number of photons of wavelength 630 nm which must hit per second in order to do this. (Assume perfect reflection.)

(b) The power of the laser beam.

⚑ Grade boost

In the example, note how working in symbols as long as possible saved calculation, writing – and *time*.
In this case we also gain insight. λ turns out to be irrelevant. For a given light intensity a larger λ would give photons of less momentum but more of them. We didn't even *need* to assume the light to be monochromatic.

Calculating the force of light on a body

The atom in the last example acquires the photon's momentum, and experiences a force as the absorption takes place.

If a stream of photons is absorbed by a body, there will be a succession of such hits. We can calculate the *mean* force on the body while the photons are striking using:

$$\text{mean force} = \frac{\text{photon momentum absorbed}}{\text{time taken}}$$
$$= \frac{\text{number of photon absorbed} \times \text{momentum per photon}}{\text{time taken}}$$

If the photons bounce back, or as many are re-emitted 'backwards' as absorbed, there's twice the momentum change – and twice the mean force.

Example: A perfectly reflective 'solar sail' attached to a spacecraft has an area of 25 m². Calculate the force exerted on it by sunshine of intensity 1.2 kW m^{-2} falling normally on it. You may assume that the light behaves as if it were monochromatic, of wavelength 550 nm.

$$\text{Energy of photon} = \frac{hc}{\lambda} = \frac{6.63 \times 10^{-34} \text{ J s} \times 3.00 \times 10^8 \text{ m s}^{-1}}{550 \times 10^{-9} \text{ m}} = 3.62 \times 10^{-19} \text{ J}$$

$$\text{So number of photons per second} = \frac{1200 \text{ W m}^{-2} \times 25 \text{ m}^2}{3.62 \times 10^{-19} \text{ J}} = 8.29 \times 10^{22} \text{ s}^{-1}$$

$$\text{But momentum of photon} = \frac{h}{\lambda} = \frac{6.63 \times 10^{-34} \text{ J s}}{550 \times 10^{-9} \text{ m}} = 1.21 \times 10^{-27} \text{ N s}$$

$$\text{So mean force} = 2 \times 8.29 \times 10^{22} \text{ s}^{-1} \times 1.21 \times 10^{-27} \text{ N s} = 0.20 \text{ mN}$$

Here's the same thing again, but working in symbols up to the last moment. (I = light intensity, A = surface area.)

$$\text{Energy of photon} = \frac{hc}{\lambda}$$

$$\text{So number of photons per second} = IA \div \frac{hc}{\lambda} = \frac{IA\lambda}{hc}$$

$$\text{But momentum of photon} = \frac{h}{\lambda}$$

$$\text{So mean force} = 2 \times \frac{IA\lambda}{hc} \times \frac{h}{\lambda} = \frac{2IA}{c} = \frac{2 \times 1200 \text{ W m}^{-2} \times 25 \text{ m}^2}{3.00 \times 10^8 \text{ m s}^{-1}} = 0.20 \text{ mN}$$

Given a few years, that spacecraft could reach quite a speed!

Circular motion

Measuring angles in radians

The idea is to draw an arc of a circle, of any radius, r, centred on O, (where the 'arms', OA and OB, of the angle meet). See diagram.

Then **the angle θ in radians** is given by:

$$\theta = \frac{arc\ length}{radius} \quad that\ is \quad \theta = \frac{s}{r}$$

If $s = r$, then $\theta = 1$ radian.

For a complete revolution, $s = 2\pi r$ so $\theta = \frac{2\pi r}{r} = 2\pi$

Thus, 2π rad $= 360°$, π rad $= 180°$, 1 rad $= \frac{180°}{\pi} = 57.3°$, $1° = \frac{\pi}{180}$ rad.

Example: What is $60°$ in radians?

$$60° = 60 \times 1° = 60 \times \frac{\pi}{180}\,rad = \frac{\pi}{3}\,rad = 1.05\,rad.$$

The unit 'rad' is often omitted when there's no ambiguity. For example, you may write $\theta = \frac{\pi}{3}$, meaning $\theta = \frac{\pi}{3}$ rad, but don't write $\theta = 1.05$. In some of the formulae below, involving angular velocity, 'rad' is omitted.

Angular velocity

*The **angular velocity**, ω, of a point moving at a constant rate in a circular path with its centre at point O is defined as*

$$\omega = \frac{angle\ swept\ out\ (about\ O)}{time\ taken}, \quad that\ is \quad \omega = \frac{\theta}{t}.$$

UNIT: rad s^{-1}

For one whole revolution, $\theta = 2\pi$, and $t = T$, this being the time for one revolution (one cycle).

Thus, $\omega = \frac{2\pi}{T}$ that is $\omega = 2\pi \times \frac{1}{T}$ so $\omega = 2\pi f.$

in which f is the **frequency of rotation**: *the number of revolutions, or cycles, per unit time.*

Example: Calculate the angular velocity of the seconds hand of a clock.

$$\omega = \frac{2\pi}{T} = \frac{2\pi}{60\,s} = 0.105\,rad\,s^{-1}$$

>> *Pointer*

The degree is an *arbitrary* unit, because there's no *fundamental* reason for choosing 360 degrees in one turn. By contrast, the radian is a *natural* unit. Its use simplifies several angle-related formulae.

>> *Pointer*

You'll never have to *measure* an arc length to determine an angle in radians. (Use a protractor, then convert from degrees to radians.)

⑧ Express in radians, leaving in the π, $180°$, $90°$, $45°$, $30°$.

⑨ A wheel rotates at 3000 turns per minute. Find its angular velocity.

Speed and angular velocity

Suppose a body moves round a circular path at speed v. It traverses an arc of length $s = vt$ in a time t. But $s = r\theta$,

so $r\theta = vt$, that is $\dfrac{\theta}{t} = \dfrac{v}{r}$. So $\omega = \dfrac{v}{r}$ and $v = r\omega$.

$s = vt$
$= r\theta$

>> **Pointer**

Check that the units of $\dfrac{v^2}{r}$ are those of acceleration.

Centripetal acceleration

A body moving at constant speed around a circular path is accelerating, because its velocity is always changing (in direction).

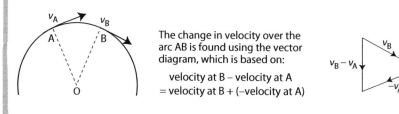

The change in velocity over the arc AB is found using the vector diagram, which is based on:

velocity at B – velocity at A
= velocity at B + (–velocity at A)

>> **Pointer**

You should show, using $v = r\omega$, that the two equations given for centripetal acceleration really are equivalent.

As the vector diagram suggests, the change in velocity, and hence the acceleration, is **centripetal:** *always directed towards the circle centre.*

For a body moving at speed v (and angular velocity ω) in a circle of radius r, the magnitude of the acceleration is:

$$a = \frac{v^2}{r} \quad \text{or, equivalently,} \quad a = r\omega^2$$

Example: The *London Eye* is a giant wheel rotating at a constant angular velocity. Each revolution takes 30 minutes. Calculate the acceleration of a point on the wheel 60 m from its centre.

$$\omega = \frac{2\pi}{T} = \frac{2\pi}{30 \times 60 \text{ s}}; \quad a = r\omega^2 = 60\text{m} \times \left(\frac{2\pi}{30 \times 60 \text{ s}}\right)^2 = 7.3 \times 10^{-4} \text{ m s}^{-2}.$$

⑩ A train is travelling at 18.0 m s^{-1} on a curved section of track. The curve is an arc of a circle of radius 120 m. Find the train's centripetal acceleration.

Centripetal force

A body can't move in a circle at constant speed without having a resultant force acting on it towards the centre of the circle, to give it the centripetal acceleration. Using Newton's second law,

$$F_{res} = ma \quad \text{so in this case} \quad F_{res} = m\frac{v^2}{r} \quad \text{and} \quad F_{res} = mr\omega^2$$

Example: A conker, of mass 0.0060 kg, is attached to a string of length 0.50 m and whirled in a horizontal circle at a rate of 3.0 revolutions per second. Calculate the horizontal force of the string on the conker.

$$F = mr\omega^2 = mr(2\pi f)^2 = 0.060 \text{ kg} \times 0.50 \text{ m} \times (2\pi \times 3.0 \text{ s}^{-1})^2 = 1.1\text{N}$$

quickfire

⑪ A carriage of the train in Quickfire 10 has a mass of 36000 kg. Find the centripetal force it is experiencing.

What external 'object' exerts this force on the carriage?

Oscillations

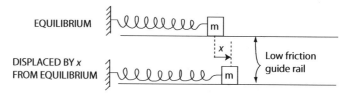

Simple harmonic motion

Systems that can oscillate

One of the simplest systems that can oscillate is a body attached to a spring that is fixed at its other end. When the body is displaced from its equilibrium position and released, it oscillates back and forth.

When the body's displacement is x, the spring's extension is x, and, according to Hooke's law, the spring exerts on the block, a force proportional to x given by:

$$F = -kx.$$

- The minus sign is needed because the force is in the opposite direction to x.
- k is the **spring constant:** the force exerted by the spring per unit extension.

Assuming resistive forces are negligible, the body's acceleration is:

$$a = \frac{F}{m} \quad \text{so} \quad a = -\frac{k}{m}x \quad \text{which is often written as} \quad a = -\omega^2 x.$$

ω^2 is a constant given by $\omega^2 = \dfrac{k}{m}.$

Oscillations in which $a = -$ constant $\times x$ are called **simple harmonic motion** (SHM). In words:

A body performs **SHM** *if its acceleration is proportional to its displacement from a fixed point, but is in the opposite direction to its displacement.*

(We deal only with cases where the displacements are along a straight line.)

The relationship is shown in the sketch-graph. A is the **amplitude:** *the maximum value of the displacement.*

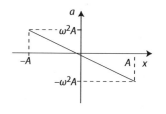

Key Terms

Spring constant = the force exerted by the spring per unit extension.

Simple harmonic motion = see main text.

Amplitude = the maximum value of the displacement.

≫ Pointer

A body *hanging* from a spring, displaced vertically from equilibrium and released, is an easier system to set up, and obeys the same equation: $a = -(k/m)x$. Here, x is displacement from equilibrium (but this is not equal to spring extension).

≫ Pointer

It isn't just mass-spring systems, for which $a = -\omega^2 x$. For example, a simple pendulum (a small body on a light string) does SHM when pulled aside a *small* distance from its rest position, and released.

quickfire

⑫ How, briefly, is ω^2 found from the graph alongside?

Variation of displacement with time for a body in SHM

Key Terms

Phase = see main text.

Periodic time = the time for one cycle of oscillation.

Phase constant = see main text.

As we'll see later, a body will have acceleration given by $a = -\omega^2 x$ if (and only if) its displacement varies with time according to:

$$x = A \sin(\omega t + \varepsilon) \qquad (\omega, A \text{ and } \varepsilon \text{ are constants.})$$

This motion is closely related to that of a point, P, moving with angular velocity ω round and round a circle of radius A. In fact, x is the vertical *component* of P's displacement from the circle centre (see diagram), and ωt and ε are the angles shown. $(\omega t + \varepsilon)$ is called the **phase**.

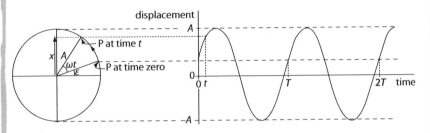

» Pointer

Note how the value of the constant, ω, is fixed by the system itself (by k and m for a mass-spring system).

But A and ε are determined by how the system is set in motion and timed.

A is the amplitude of the SHM: the maximum displacement. For the physical system (such as a body on a spring) it is determined by how the body is set in motion, for example by how far we pull the body from its equilibrium position, before letting go.

The **periodic time**, T, the time for one cycle of oscillation, is – see diagram – the time for one revolution of P.

So $\quad T = \dfrac{2\pi}{\omega} \quad$ and $\quad$ frequency, $f = \dfrac{1}{T} \quad$ so $\quad f = \dfrac{\omega}{2\pi}$

Example
A block of mass 0.16 kg hangs from a spring of spring constant 40 N m^{-1}.
Calculate the periodic time of its oscillations when displaced vertically and released.

$$\omega^2 = \frac{k}{m} \quad \text{so} \quad \omega = \sqrt{\frac{k}{m}} = \sqrt{\frac{40\,\text{Nm}^{-1}}{0.16\,\text{kg}}} = 15.8\,\text{s}^{-1}.$$

$$T = \frac{2\pi}{\omega} = \frac{2\pi}{15.8\,\text{s}^{-1}} = 0.40\,\text{s.} \left(\text{More directly: } T = \frac{2\pi}{\omega}, \text{ so } T = 2\pi\sqrt{\frac{m}{k}} = \dots \right)$$

ε is called the **phase constant.** It allows us to choose zero time to be at any point in the body's cycle.

The commonest values to choose are:

$\varepsilon = 0 \quad$ so $\quad x = A \sin(\omega t)$

$\varepsilon = \dfrac{\pi}{2} \quad$ so $\quad x = A \sin\left(\omega t + \dfrac{\pi}{2}\right)$

which is the same as $x = A \cos(\omega t)$

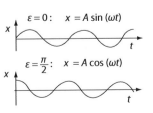

quickfire

⑬ A metal ball of mass 0.12 kg hanging from a spring is displaced vertically and released. It performs 43 cycles of oscillation in a *minute*. Calculate the spring constant.

QF 14–16 concern a metal ball hanging from a long thread, to form a pendulum. The ball is pulled aside horizontally by 0.040 m in the +x direction from its rest position and released. It performs SHM of period 2.0 s.

⑭ Calculate the displacement of the ball 1.2 s after release.

⑮ What is the displacement 1.5 s after release? [Easy by sketch-graph!]

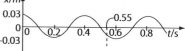

⑯ Calculate the times from release at which the displacement is −0.020 m:

(a) For the first time.

(b) For the next time.

Examples of using $x = A \sin (\omega t + \varepsilon)$

Example 1 A body of mass 0.16 kg hangs from a spring of spring constant 40 N m^{-1}. Calculate the displacement of the body 0.55 s after it has been released from rest with an initial displacement of +0.030 m.

$A = 0.030$ m, because the displacement will oscillate between ±0.30 m.

$\omega = 15.8$ s^{-1}, as worked out in the example on the previous page.

$\varepsilon = \dfrac{\pi}{2}$ if we call the release time (from maximum displacement) $t = 0$.

So $x = A \cos (\omega t) = 0.030$ m × cos(15.8 × 0.55 rad) = −0.022 m.

- to evaluate cos(15.8 × 0.55 rad) directly, your calculator needs to be in *radian* mode (not degree mode).
- Use a sketch-graph to check that the answer is sensible. Recall that in this case, $T = 0.40$ s.

Example 2 A piston in an engine is moving with SHM, of amplitude 0.040 m, and frequency 35 Hz. At one point in its cycle its upward displacement from its mid position is 0.024 m, and is increasing.

(a) Find how long it takes to reach this point from its mid position.

Choose $\varepsilon = 0$, to make $t = 0$ when piston passes through its mid position, going up. (We'll call upwards the +x direction.)

Then $x = A \sin (\omega t)$, so $\sin (\omega t) = \dfrac{x}{A} = \dfrac{0.024 \ m}{0.040 \ m} = 0.600$

So $\omega t = \sin^{-1}(0.600) = 0.644$ rad (Remember: calculator in radian mode!)

So $t = \dfrac{0.644}{2\pi \times 35 \ s^{-1}} = 2.93$ ms To 2 s.f., $t = 2.9$ ms.

A check: $\dfrac{T}{4} = \dfrac{1}{4} \times \dfrac{1}{f} = \dfrac{1}{4} \times \dfrac{1}{35}$ s $= 7.14$ ms.

Reassuringly, 2.93 ms < 7.14 ms.

(b) How much longer will it be before this displacement occurs again?

The 'inverse sine' (sin^{-1}) function on a calculator gives you only the angle (with the given sine) in the range $-\dfrac{\pi}{2}$ to $+\dfrac{\pi}{2}$.

To find any more times, *after* 2.9 ms, you use a circle diagram or – as here – a sketch-graph.

The extra time elapsing is seen to be 8.4 ms. Note use of $T/4 = 7.14$ ms.

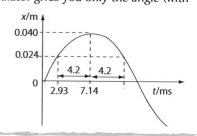

Velocity of a body in SHM

A displacement–time (x–t) graph is sketched (top graph) for a body moving according to

$$x = A \sin(\omega t + \varepsilon).$$

For simplicity the graph is drawn for the case $\varepsilon = 0$.

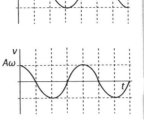

The gradient of the tangent to the x–t graph at any time gives the velocity at that time. Hence the shape of the velocity–time (v–t) graph. In fact v varies with t according to

$$v = A\omega \cos(\omega t + \varepsilon).$$

The largest value a cosine (or a sine) can have is 1. For example, when $(\omega t + \varepsilon) = 0$, $\cos(\omega t + \varepsilon) = 1$.

So $\quad v_{max} = A\omega.$

Example 1 A metal ball of mass 0.10 kg hangs from a spring of spring constant 3.6 N m^{-1}. What amplitude of oscillation will give the ball a maximum speed of 0.21 m s^{-1}?

$$v_{max} = A\omega = A\sqrt{\frac{k}{m}} \quad \text{So} \quad A = v_{max}\sqrt{\frac{m}{k}} = 0.21\sqrt{\frac{0.10}{3.6}}\ \text{m} = 0.035\ \text{m}.$$

Example 2 At what displacement from the equilibrium position will the ball have half its maximum speed?

$$v = A\omega \cos(\omega t) = v_{max}\cos(\omega t) \quad \text{so} \quad \cos(\omega t) = \frac{v}{v_{max}} = \frac{1}{2} \quad \text{so} \quad \omega t = \frac{\pi}{3}.$$

$$x = A\sin(\omega t) = 0.035\ \text{m}\ \sin\left(\frac{\pi}{3}\right) = 0.030\ \text{m}.$$

A sketch-graph shows that *whenever $x = \pm0.30$ m*, the ball will have half its maximum speed.

Acceleration of a body in SHM

The gradient of the tangent to the v–t graph at any time gives the acceleration at that time. Hence the shape of the acceleration–time (a–t) graph. In fact a varies with t according to:

$$a = -A\omega^2 \sin(\omega t + \varepsilon).$$

But $\qquad x = A\sin(\omega t + \varepsilon).$ $\qquad$ So $\qquad a = -\omega^2 x.$

This backs up our earlier claim that SHM, as defined by $a = -\omega^2 x.$ (with constant ω), implies that $x = A\sin(\omega t + \varepsilon).$

Grade boost

Make sure that you can sketch the E_k–t and E_p–t graphs.

» Pointer

The equation for E_p, in terms of m and ω, applies even if E_p is not just *elastic*. For a body hanging from a spring and oscillating up and down, E_p is a sum of elastic and gravitational PEs.

» Pointer

Putting $E_p = 0$ at $x = 0$ is just a conventional choice for an oscillating system.

» Pointer

Energies can also be plotted against x. Check that these graphs make sense to you.

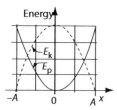

» Pointer

Study how energy is transferred from kinetic to potential and vice versa twice per cycle as the system (for example, pendulum) oscillates – a classic illustration of the conservation of energy.

⊙◀◀◀◀ quickfire

⑱ Calculate E_p and E_k for a system in SHM when $x =$ 0.030 m, if $m = 0.120$ kg, $f = 2.5$ Hz and $A = 0.060$ m.

Energy interchange in SHM

For simplicity, in the diagrams we've chosen $\varepsilon = 0$.

Kinetic energy, E_k

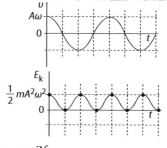

The body has KE given by $E_k = \frac{1}{2}mv^2$. So:

- $E_k = 0$ whenever $v = 0$,
- E_k is never negative,
- $E_k = \frac{1}{2}mA^2\omega^2$ when $v = v_{max} = A\omega$

Hence the points plotted on the E_k–t graph.

Its shape is sinusoidal, but raised up, and of frequency $2f$.

E_k and t are related by: $E_k = \frac{1}{2}mA^2\omega^2\cos^2(\omega t + \varepsilon)$

Potential energy, E_p

Consider our original case: a body attached to a horizontal spring and displaced by x from its equilibrium position. The spring stores elastic PE (equal to the area under the force–extension graph), given by

$E_p = \frac{1}{2}kx^2$ which, because $\omega^2 = \dfrac{k}{m}$, can be written $E_p = \frac{1}{2}m\omega^2 x^2$.

- $E_p = 0$ whenever $x = 0$. [See second Pointer.]
- E_p is never negative.
- $E_p = \frac{1}{2}mA^2\omega^2$ when $x = A$.

Hence the points on the E_p–t graph.

E_p and t are related by:

$E_p = \frac{1}{2}mA^2\omega^2\sin^2(\omega t + \varepsilon)$

The graph is just like the E_k–t graph, but shifted along, so that E_p is high when E_k is low and vice versa.

Indeed we can show that

$$E_k + E_p = \frac{1}{2}mA^2\omega^2,$$

so the *total* energy of the system never changes (see bottom graph).

Damped oscillations

Natural oscillations *occur when a body on a spring, a pendulum – or any other system with a mass and a force pulling it towards an equilibrium point – is displaced from equilibrium and released.*

Real natural oscillations are **damped**: *their amplitude decreases with time.* This is due to resistive forces like air resistance, which act on the oscillating body in the opposite direction to its velocity. (SHM is an *ideal* case: amplitude is constant because we ignore resistive forces.)

Work done by the body against resistive forces transfers energy from the system into the random energy of the particles of the body and – in the case of air resistance – the surrounding air. The air and the body both get slightly warmer; for the oscillating system $E_k + E_p$ decreases.

Here is an *x–t* graph for damped oscillations:

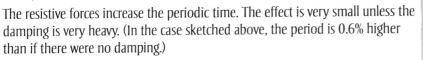

- The periodic time stays the same throughout the motion.

- *The amplitude* **falls exponentially** *with time: each cycle it falls by the same fraction (if resistive force is proportional to speed).*

The resistive forces increase the periodic time. The effect is very small unless the damping is very heavy. (In the case sketched above, the period is 0.6% higher than if there were no damping.)

If damping is increased (maybe by giving the body a larger and larger surface area) we will reach so-called **critical damping**: *the body doesn't oscillate if displaced and released from rest, but returns to equilibrium without overshoot – in a shorter time than if the damping is more than critical.*

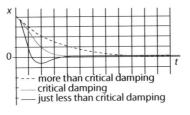

--- more than critical damping
····· critical damping
— just less than critical damping

Car suspensions use springs that compress when wheels hit a ramp in the road. The car would then oscillate like an upside-down mass on a spring, but damping devices ('shock absorbers') provide (almost) critical damping, so the car returns to equilibrium height above ground quickly and without overshoot.

>> **Pointer**
Transfer of energy to random energy of particles is sometimes called energy *dissipation*.

Grade boost
Before sketching damped oscillations, mark time scale at equal intervals, and draw in exponential guidelines.

quickfire

⑲ For the top graph, what fraction of:

(a) the amplitude, (b) the total energy, at the start of a cycle remains at the end?

>> **Pointer**
Some door-closer mechanisms use critical damping.

Key Terms

Forced oscillations = see main text.

Resonance = see main text.

quickfire

(20) What is the *natural* frequency of the mass-spring system shown in the diagram?

Grade boost

Make sure you can sketch a resonance curve. Note that however low the forcing frequency, the system will still oscillate, so there will be a finite amplitude.

» Pointer

Resonance can be a nuisance. Rattles or buzzing can occur when rotating machinery, speeding up or slowing down, touches on the natural frequency of an item that can oscillate. Old buses may exhibit such resonances. More modern vehicles contain more damping material.

Forced oscillations

Forced oscillations occur when a system capable of natural oscillations is subjected to a periodically varying *driving force*.

The system soon settles down to oscillating at the frequency of the driving force.

Forced oscillations can be investigated with the apparatus shown. The periodically varying force is applied to the mass–spring system by the (constant amplitude) vibrating pin, powered by a signal generator. From this we select various frequencies of driving force, and measure the steady-state amplitude of the mass's oscillations.

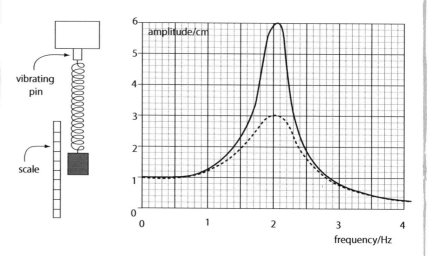

The graph (full line) of amplitude against driving force frequency is at a maximum when this frequency is (nearly) equal to the *natural* frequency of the mass-spring system. This peaking is called **resonance**. The curve is called a 'resonance curve' or a 'response curve'.

Increasing the damping reduces the amplitude of the forced oscillations, but reduces it by a smaller and smaller fraction the further away we go from resonance. So the curve (broken line) is not as *sharp*. The peak occurs at a slightly lower frequency of driving force.

The reason for increased damping not having much effect on the response curve far from resonance is that the mass's mean speed is low, so the resistive forces are low.

A use of resonance

Certain electrical circuits have natural frequencies of oscillation of current through them. When you select (or 'tune in') a particular radio station, you are adjusting the natural frequency of one of these circuits to that of the radio waves from the station, so its waves force a much larger current through the circuit than other stations' waves.

Gases

Molecules

Gases consist of particles called **molecules**. In so-called **monatomic** gases (such as helium and neon) the molecules are single atoms. In hydrogen, oxygen, nitrogen and many other gases, each molecule consists of more than one atom 'bonded' together.

The pressure of a gas, and how it depends on volume and temperature, can be explained in terms of the motion of its molecules.

Moles

A mole (abbreviates to 'mol') of molecules is a batch of 6.02×10^{23} molecules. *The number of molecules per mole is called the* **Avogadro constant**, N_A.

Thus $\qquad N_A = 6.02 \times 10^{23} \, \text{mol}^{-1}$.

It follows that, if we have N molecules, the *amount*, n of gas, in moles, is:

$$n = \frac{N}{N_A} \quad \text{so} \quad N = nN_A$$

>> *Pointer*

In PH4 you won't have to use the formula for rmm in terms of the mass of the $^{12}_{6}$C atom.

Relative molecular mass (rmm) and molar mass

The relative molecular mass (rmm), M_r, of a molecule is defined as

$$M_r = \frac{\text{mass of molecule}}{\frac{1}{12} \text{mass of } ^{12}_{6}\text{C atom}}.$$

Examples of rmms: hydrogen: 2.01, helium: 4.00, oxygen: 32.0, nitrogen: 28.0. (You don't have to remember these!)

There is an easy relationship between the rmm of a molecule and **molar mass** *(the mass per mole of the molecules)*

$$\text{molar mass} = \frac{M_r}{1000} \, \text{kg mol}^{-1}$$

Example: How many molecules are there in 5.0 kg of oxygen gas?

$$\text{molar mass} = \frac{M_r}{1000} \text{kg mol}^{-1} = \frac{32.0}{1000} \text{kg mol}^{-1} = 0.032 \, \text{kg mol}^{-1}$$

So, amount in moles, $n = \dfrac{\text{mass of gas}}{\text{mass per mole}} = \dfrac{5.0 \, \text{kg}}{0.032 \, \text{kg mol}^{-1}} = 156 \, \text{mol}$

and number of molecules, $N = nN_A = 156 \, \text{mol} \times 6.02 \times 10^{23} \text{mol}^{-1} = 9.41 \times 10^{25}$.

>> *Pointer*

The Avogadro number is not arbitrary, but is defined so as to give the simple equation:

$$\text{molar mass} = \frac{\text{rmm}}{1000} \text{kg mol}^{-1}.$$

㉑ Calculate the mass (in kg) of an oxygen molecule (rmm = 32.0)

㉒ What is the mass of 1.00×10^{25} helium molecules?

Squeezing a gas: what we find

A sample of gas can be squeezed into a (much) smaller volume. The smaller the volume, V, the larger the pressure, p, the gas exerts (at same temperature).

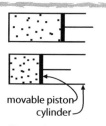

movable piston
cylinder

Boyle's law

For a fixed mass of gas at constant temperature, the pressure (p) exerted is inversely proportional to the volume (V) occupied.

This means that if we halve V, then p doubles; if we treble V then p decreases by a factor of 3, and so on. (Check either graph!) This is equivalent to

$$pV = \text{constant}$$

provided that temperature and mass of gas don't change.

Boyle's law is an experimental law. It applies quite well to gases at 'ordinary' densities, but with greater and greater accuracy as the gas density approaches zero (when the mean separation of the molecules is very large). We say that the gas is approaching **ideal gas** behaviour.

quickfire

㉓ For the sample of gas for which the graphs are drawn, calculate the pressure at 300 K when the volume is 0.090×10^{-3} m³. (Use $pV = $ constant.)

⟫ Pointer

The kelvin (K) is the SI unit of temperature. Note the plain 'K'. Contrast with °C for degree Celsius.

Temperature

The higher the temperature, the larger the value of pV for a sample of gas. In fact, for an ideal gas, pV is *proportional* to temperature, T, measured on the so-called Kelvin scale. This is not just luck: T is *defined* to be proportional to pV for a sample of gas as its density approaches zero!

Temperature, so defined, is an **absolute temperature**: it has its zero at **absolute zero**: the temperature at which an ideal gas would have zero pV. This is the lowest temperature possible, the temperature at which the particles of matter have their least possible random energy. The details (beyond A-Level!) of the definition of the Kelvin scale imply that the freezing point and boiling point of water (at a pressure of 101.3 kPa) are, to 4 significant figures, 273.2 K and 373.2 K.

Temperatures in degree Celsius are now *defined* as:

$$\theta/°C = T/K - 273.15, \quad \text{that is} \quad T/K = \theta/°C + 273.15.$$

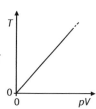

quickfire

㉔ The full line and the broken line on the p–V graphs are both for the same sample of gas. At what kelvin temperature is the gas when the broken line applies?

The ideal gas equation

Boyle's law and the dependency of pV on kelvin temperature, T, are both included in the *ideal gas equation*

$$pV = nRT \qquad \text{or, equivalently} \qquad pV = NkT$$

n is the amount of gas in moles.
R is the molar gas constant.
$R = 8.31 \text{ J mol}^{-1} \text{ K}^{-1}$.

N is the number of molecules.
k is the Boltzmann constant.
$k = 1.38 \times 10^{-23} \text{ J K}^{-1}$

By comparison $\quad Nk = nR \quad$ so $\quad Nk = \dfrac{N}{N_A}R \quad$ so $\quad k = \dfrac{R}{N_A}$

Note how the ideal gas equation implies Boyle's law: the right-hand side – and hence pV – are constant when n (or, equivalently, N) and T are constant.

Example: a car tyre contains 0.0140 m^3 of nitrogen at a pressure of 320 kPa and a temperature of 290 K. Calculate the number of nitrogen molecules and the mass of nitrogen:

$$N = \frac{PV}{kT} = \frac{320 \times 10^3 \times 0.014 \text{ J}}{1.38 \times 10^{-23} \text{ J K}^{-1} \times 290 \text{ K}} = 1.12 \times 10^{24}$$

$$n = \frac{N}{N_A} = \frac{1.12 \times 10^{24}}{6.02 \times 10^{23} \text{mol}^{-1}} = 1.86 \text{ mol}; \quad \text{molar mass of nitrogen} = \frac{28.0}{1000} \text{kg mol}^{-1}$$

$$\text{So mass of nitrogen} = 1.86 \text{mol} \times \frac{28.0}{1000} \text{kg mol}^{-1} = 0.052 \text{ kg}$$

The kinetic theory of gases

A gas consists of particles (called molecules) in rapid random motion in space which is otherwise empty. The molecules continually collide with each other and with the walls of the container. We assume that:

- collisions between molecules are elastic (at least on average),
- the molecules themselves occupy a negligible fraction of the container volume,
- the molecules exert negligible forces on each other, except when colliding.

These become more and more realistic the lower the density of a gas.

Individual molecules moving in a gas cannot be seen, even with special microscopes, but the theory's success lies in what it can explain. Start with the basic property that a gas can be squeezed into a smaller volume: according to the kinetic theory we are simply reducing empty space between molecules!

Mean square speed = see main text.

rms speed = see main text.

Grade boost

Make sure you know what m and N stand for in $pV = \frac{1}{3}Nm\overline{c^2}$.

» Pointer

Check that the units are the same on both sides of the equations $pV = \frac{1}{3}Nm\overline{c^2}$ and $p = \frac{1}{3}\rho\overline{c^2}$.

» Pointer

c_{rms} is greater than the ordinary mean, $\overline{c}$ (except if all the molecules have the same speed!).

quickfire

㉗ Calculate c_{rms} for molecules with speeds 200 m s^{-1}, 400 m s^{-1} and 600 m s^{-1}.

Gas pressure according to kinetic theory

Gas pressure is caused by the random bombardment of the container walls by molecules. Because of the randomness, the pressure will be the same on any 'patch' of the container wall, and is given by

$$\text{pressure} = \frac{\text{mean force on wall}}{\text{area of wall}}$$

The force due to the random hits is equal and opposite to the mean rate of change of the molecules' momenta as they collide with the wall and bounce back. Here we are using Newton's second and third laws. Working out the consequences mathematically leads to the equation:

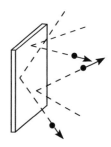

$pV = \frac{1}{3}Nm\overline{c^2}$ or its alternative form, $p = \frac{1}{3}\rho\overline{c^2}$.

In these equations, p and V are gas pressure and container volume.

N is the number of molecules in the container.

m is the mass of one molecule.

ρ is the gas density. Because Nm is the total mass of all the molecules in volume V, then $\rho = Nm/V$, hence the alternative form of the kinetic theory equation.

$\overline{c^2}$ is the **mean square speed** of the molecules, defined by:

$$\overline{c^2} = \frac{c_1^2 + c_2^2 .... + c_N^2}{N}$$

in which $c_1, c_2, ... c_N$ are the speeds of the individual molecules.

There will be a wide range of speeds, as some molecules will have acquired high speeds in 'lucky' collisions, others much lower.

We define the **root mean square (rms) speed, c_{rms}**, by

$$c_{rms} = \sqrt{\overline{c^2}} = \sqrt{\frac{c_1^2 + c_2^2 .... + c_N^2}{N}}$$

Example: for 3 molecules with speeds 357 m s^{-1}, 401 m s^{-1}, 532 m s^{-1},

$$\overline{c^2} = \frac{357^2 + 401^2 + 532^2}{3} = 1.90 \times 10^5 \text{m}^2\text{ s}^{-2}; \qquad c_{rms} = \sqrt{\overline{c^2}} = 436\text{ ms}^{-1}.$$

The significance of c_{rms} is that if all the molecules had this one speed, the gas pressure would be the same as for the actual speeds ($c_1, c_2, ... c_N$).

Finding the rms speed of molecules

The equation $p = \frac{1}{3}\rho \overline{c^2}$ enables us to find the rms speed of the (unobservable) molecules from easily measurable 'everyday' quantities.

Example: At room temperature and a pressure of 101 kPa, 1.00×10^{-3} m^3 of nitrogen is found to have a mass of 1.17×10^{-3} kg. Find c_{rms}.

$$\rho = \frac{\text{mass}}{\text{volume}} = \frac{1.17 \times 10^{-3} \, \text{kg}}{1.00 \times 10^{-3} \, \text{m}^3} = 1.17 \, \text{kg m}^{-3}$$

$$c_{rms} = \sqrt{\overline{c^2}} = \sqrt{\frac{3p}{\rho}} = \sqrt{\frac{3 \times 101 \times 10^3 \, \text{N m}^{-2}}{1.17 \, \text{kg m}^{-3}}} = 509 \, \text{m s}^{-1}$$

Grade boost

To find c_{rms} it's usually much easier to use $p = \frac{1}{3}\rho \overline{c^2}$ than $pV = \frac{1}{3}Nm\overline{c^2}$. Sometimes (as in part (b) of the example at the bottom of the page) you may not have the data to use either. But at least in that example, (a) gave a hint!

The mean kinetic energy of molecules

We have equations for pV in terms of molecular quantities, and in terms of temperature:

$$pV = \frac{1}{3}Nm\overline{c^2} \quad \text{and} \quad pV = NkT$$

Equating the two right-hand expressions for pV...

$$\frac{1}{3}Nm\overline{c^2} = NkT \quad \text{so} \quad \frac{1}{3}m\overline{c^2} = kT$$

$$KE = \frac{1}{2}m\overline{c^2}$$

so, finally

$$\frac{1}{2}m\overline{c^2} = \frac{3}{2}kT$$

$\frac{1}{2}m\overline{c^2}$ is the mean *translational* kinetic energy of a gas molecule, that is the KE of its moving around (as opposed to KE of rotation, which some molecules also have). As we see, it is proportional to T. So kelvin temperature is a measure of the mean translational KE of a gas molecule.

According to the equation, at any particular temperature, the molecules of all gases have the same mean translational kinetic energy. An oxygen molecule, with 16 times the mass of a hydrogen atom, will have a quarter of the rms speed of a hydrogen molecule, at the same temperature. Check!

Example: Calculate (a) the mean translational kinetic energy (b) the rms speed of a nitrogen molecule (rmm = 28.0), at 300 K.

(a) $\frac{1}{2}m\overline{c^2} = \frac{3}{2}kT = 1.50 \times 1.38 \times 10^{-23} \, \text{J K}^{-1} \times 300 \, \text{K} = 6.21 \times 10^{-21} \, \text{J}$

(b) $m = \dfrac{\text{molar mass}}{N_A} = \dfrac{0.028 \, \text{kg mol}^{-1}}{6.02 \times 10^{23} \, \text{mol}^{-1}} = 4.65 \times 10^{-26} \, \text{kg}$

So $c_{rms} = \sqrt{\overline{c^2}} = \sqrt{\dfrac{\frac{1}{2}m\overline{c^2}}{\frac{1}{2}m}} = \sqrt{\dfrac{6.21 \times 10^{-21} \, \text{J}}{\frac{1}{2} 4.65 \times 10^{-26} \, \text{kg}}} = 517 \, \text{m s}^{-1}$

quickfire

㉘ A cylinder of volume 0.025 m^3 contains 6.1 mol of oxygen (rmm = 32.0) at a pressure of 600 kPa. Calculate:

(a) the mass of the oxygen,

(b) the density of the oxygen,

(c) the rms speed of the molecules,

(d) the temperature,

(e) the mean translational KE of the molecules,

(f) the mass of an oxygen molecule.

Thermodynamics

In thermodynamics we study the **internal energy** of a system, and transfers of energy as work and heat into and out of the system. The laws of thermodynamics apply to systems ranging from rubber bands to stars. The favourite system at A-level is a sample of ideal gas.

Internal energy

The internal energy, U, of a system is the sum of the random kinetic energies of its particles and the potential energies of interactions between them.

quickfire

㉙ Use $pV = nRT$ to find T_A and T_B, the temperatures of the gas at A and B, in the pV diagram below (for 0.080 mol of an ideal monatomic gas).

Internal energy of an ideal monatomic gas

An ideal gas has negligible forces between its molecules (except during collisions) so the potential energy of interactions can be taken as zero.

So $\qquad U$ = sum of kinetic energies of N molecules

$\qquad\qquad = N \times$ mean kinetic energy of molecule $= N \times \frac{1}{2} m \overline{c^2}$

But $\qquad\qquad\qquad\qquad \frac{1}{2} m \overline{c^2} = \frac{3}{2} kT$

So $U = \frac{3}{2} NkT \qquad\qquad$ or, since $Nk = nR$, $\qquad\qquad U = \frac{3}{2} nRT$.

This equation applies to monatomic gases such as helium, whose molecules have only translational kinetic energy. For other gases the $\frac{3}{2}$ has to be replaced by a larger factor; but, for *all* gases behaving ideally, U depends only on T.

》 Pointer
Knowing T_A and T_B, we can find the change in internal energy for AB ...

$\Delta U = U_B - U_A$

$\quad = \frac{3}{2} nRT_B - \frac{3}{2} nRT_A$

$\quad = \frac{3}{2} nR(T_B - T_A)$

$\quad = 75\ \text{J}$

(Shortcut: write U as $U = \frac{3}{2} pV$ and use values of p and V straight from the graph!)

p–V diagrams for a gas

We shall be studying *changes* to a system consisting of some gas in a cylinder with a piston that can be moved or held still. The temperature can be altered. The *p–V* diagram shows three kinds of change:

- AB: *change at constant volume:*
  T must be increased, for p to increase.
- CD: *change at constant pressure:*
  T must increase, for V to increase.
- EF: *change at constant temperature* **(isothermal change)**.

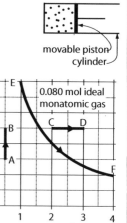

quickfire

㉚ Calculate ΔU for CD. And (easy!) for EF.

Energy flows into and out of a system

We classify these flows into just two kinds: *work* and *heat*.

Work

A system does work $F \Delta x$ when it exerts a force F that moves a distance Δx in the same direction as the force.

Work done by system, $W = F \Delta x$.

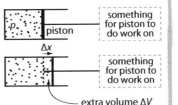

The system we're most concerned with is a gas at pressure p in a cylinder. The work done by the gas when its volume expands by ΔV can be written – see Pointer – as

$$W = p \, \Delta V$$

Unless ΔV is very small, p may change greatly during the expansion. We must sum all the bits of work, $p \, \Delta V$, that is the areas of all the narrow strips under the p–V graph, from initial volume V_1 to final volume, V_2. So:

Work done by gas, W = Area under p–V graph.

Note: If the gas volume contracts, so the graph line has a right-to-left trend, work is done *on* the gas, so W is negative.

Examples of work calculations:

AB: *change at constant volume:*

$$\Delta V = 0 \qquad \text{so} \qquad W = 0$$

CD: *change at constant pressure:*

$$W = p \Delta V$$

$$= 250 \times 10^3 \times (3 - 2) \times 10^{-3} \, \text{J} = 250 \, \text{J}$$

EF: *isothermal change.*

We need to find the area under the curve EF. One way to do so is to draw a straight line (the broken line) *by eye* so that the area under it is equal to that under the curve. The area under the broken line is that of a triangle sitting on a rectangle.

area $= \frac{1}{2}$ triangle base $\times$ triangle ht + rectangle base $\times$ rectangle ht

$$= \frac{1}{2} (4 - 1) \times 10^{-3} \times (310 - 60) \times 10^3 \, \text{J} + (4 - 1) \times 10^{-3} \times 60 \times 10^3 \, \text{J}$$

$$= 375 \, \text{J} + 180 \, \text{J}, \text{ so work done by gas over EF} = 555 \, \text{J}.$$

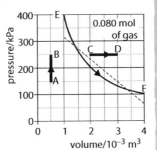

≫ Pointer

The gas in the cylinder will exert a force pA on a piston of area A. If the piston moves out a distance Δx, the gas volume will rise by $\Delta V = A \, \Delta x$. So:

$$F \Delta x = pA \frac{\Delta V}{A} = p \Delta V.$$

⌃ Grade boost

If you're asked to find the work done during a particular change, you must state whether the work is done *on* or *by* the gas.

⊙⟫⟫⟫ quickfire

(31) Calculate the work done in the following changes:

(a) A gas contracts from a volume of $0.35 \times 10^{-3} \, \text{m}^3$ to $0.50 \times 10^{-3} \, \text{m}^3$ at a constant pressure of $70 \times 10^3 \, \text{Pa}$.

(b) The isothermal expansion of the gas along EF, as in the graph, but over just the part from $2.0 \times 10^{-3} \, \text{m}^3$ to $4.0 \times 10^{-3} \, \text{m}^3$.

Key Terms

Heat = see main text.

First law of thermodynamics = see main text.

Grade boost

Don't confuse *heat* and *temperature*! It would be like confusing electric charge and electric potential.

Grade boost

Systems don't *store* or *possess* heat. They possess *internal energy*. Remember: heat, like work, is energy *in transit*.

Heat

Heat *is energy flowing from a region of higher temperature to a region of lower temperature, because of the temperature difference.*

Compare with the flow of *charge* due to a potential difference . . .

It takes time for a given amount of heat to flow (though the greater the temperature gradient, $(T_1 - T_2)/L$, the greater the rate of flow).

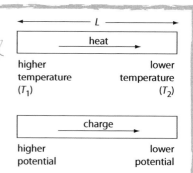

When *no* heat flows between two bodies or two regions, assuming they aren't thermally insulated from each other, they must be at the same temperature. We say that they are in thermal equilibrium.

For a *system* at a lower temperature than its surroundings, energy will flow in through the system's boundary. This energy flow is *heat*, Q. For example, heat will enter a cool gas through the walls of its container if we put a flame underneath! Conversely, heat will *leave* the system if its surroundings are cooler.

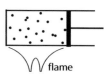

quickfire

③② 0.050 mol of ideal monatomic gas $\left(\text{for which } U = \frac{3}{2}nRT\right)$ expands at a constant pressure of 100 kPa from a volume of $1.25 \times 10^{-3}\,\text{m}^3$ to $1.50 \times 10^{-3}\,\text{m}^3$. Calculate:

(a) The change in temperature.

(b) The change in internal energy.

(c) The work done.

(d) The heat flow.

The first law of thermodynamics

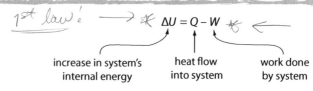

$$\Delta U = Q - W$$

increase in system's internal energy   heat flow into system   work done by system

- This is a case of the principle of conservation of energy.

- ΔU is a change in a *property* of the system: its internal energy, U.

  Q and W are *not* properties, nor changes in properties, of the system. They are both energy *in transit* between the system and the outside world.

- If heat flows *out* of the system, Q is negative. If work is done *on* the system W is negative.

Example: During some process a system has 600 J of work done on it, and its internal energy falls by 900 J. Calculate the heat flow.

$$Q = \Delta U + W = (-900\,\text{J}) + (-600\,\text{J}) = -1500\,\text{J}$$

Therefore 1500 J of heat flows *out* of the system.

Applying the first law of thermodynamics

Rapid expansion of an ideal gas

The significance of a *rapid* change is that it doesn't allow time for much heat to flow. $Q = 0$ (almost), so, using the *first law*:

$$\Delta U = -W.$$

Since the gas does work, W is positive, so U falls, and with it, the temperature. We can feel the cooling of air squashed into a plastic syringe, when we let the piston move out quickly, doing work against one's hand (not just letting go).

Note that the p–V graph does *not* obey pV = constant. Check this!

Rapid *compression* of a gas produces a temperature *rise*. In a diesel engine the temperature rise produced by rapid compression of air is great enough to ignite injected fuel (without the need for a spark).

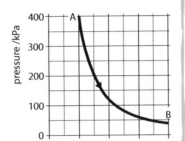

Slow (isothermal) expansion of an ideal gas

This time heat *will* have time to flow in. (It helps if the cylinder walls conduct heat well.) The gas temperature will not be able to fall more than slightly below that of its surroundings. Thus the expansion is essentially *isothermal*: constant temperature, so for an ideal gas, $\Delta U = 0$. Using the *first law*:

$$0 = Q - W \qquad \text{that is} \qquad Q = W.$$

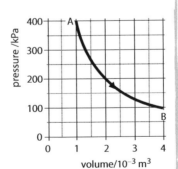

- In this case, heat flowing into a system doesn't make it hotter!
- Until the gas pressure falls too low, the isothermal expansion allows us to turn heat into work, which can, in principle, be used to lift weights, generate electricity, propel a vehicle and so on. For this transfer of energy not to be just a 'one-off', we need to take the gas over and over again through a *cycle* of changes.

③③ This question refers to the p–V graph for the rapid expansion. Calculate:

(a) The temperature at B. It is 300 K at A.

(b) The change in internal energy, assuming

$$U = \tfrac{3}{2}nRT.$$

(c) Hence the work done by the gas.

≫ Pointer

Using the 'area' method you should do a rough check of your last answer.

③④ How, briefly, would you determine the heat flow into the gas, given the p–V graph for the isothermal case?

Cycles of changes

ABCDA represents one particular clockwise cycle of changes for a gas, with the extremes of volume at A and C.

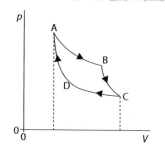

- Over a cycle the gas returns to its original p, V and (therefore) T.

So $\Delta U = 0$.

It follows from the *first law* that

$$0 = Q - W \qquad \text{that is} \qquad Q = W.$$

So the effect of the cycle is that a net quantity, Q, of heat enters the gas, and an equal net quantity of work is done by the gas.

- The net work done by the gas over the cycle ABCDA is

W = work done *by* gas over ABC − work done *on* gas over CDA

= area under ABC − area under ADC

So W = area inside 'loop' ABCDA

Example: Calculate the net heat taken in over the 'square' cycle shown.

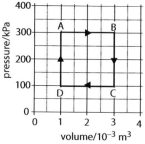

Heat in = Work out

= Area inside loop

= $2.0 \times 10^{-3} \times 200 \times 10^{3}$ J

= 400 J

Note that this is the resultant of heat taken in over AB and DA and (rather less) heat given out over BC and CD.

Solids and liquids

Solids and liquids change their volumes very little (compared with gases), and therefore the amount of work, W, that they do against external pressures is usually negligible, and

$$\Delta U = Q.$$

The heat input needed to raise the temperature of mass m of a solid or liquid by ΔT is given by

$$Q = mc\Delta T$$

In which c is a constant for the particular substance, called its **specific heat capacity (SHC)**. *Unit*: $J\,kg^{-1}\,K^{-1}$

Example: Calculate the temperature rise expected when 1.2 kg of water (SHC: 4180 $J\,kg^{-1}\,K^{-1}$) is heated in a 3.0 kW kettle for 60 seconds.

$$\Delta T = \frac{Q}{mc} = \frac{3000\,W \times 60\,s}{1.2\,kg \times 4180\,J\,kg^{-1}\,K^{-1}} = 36\,K \ (=36°C)$$

In fact the temperature rise will be a little less, owing to heat losses.

Key Term

Specific heat capacity (SHC) = see main text.

》Pointer

The K and the °C are the same size, so temperature *changes* are the same in both units.

Electric fields

Electric field strength

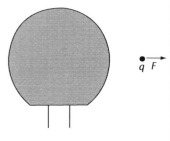

>> *Pointer*
You'll soon see the sense in using V m^{-1} as a unit for E, but, for now, note that
V m^{-1} = J C^{-1} m^{-1} = N m C^{-1} m^{-1} = N C^{-1}

We can test for the presence of an electric field using a positive charge, q. We shall call this a 'test-charge'.

If q experiences a force proportional to its charge, q, we say it is in an electric field. For example, the test-charge will reveal an electric field near a working Van de Graaff generator (See diagram).

The **electric field strength** or **electric intensity**, **E**, at a point is defined as

$$E = \frac{force\ on\ (positive)\ test\ charge}{test\ charge} \quad that\ is \quad E = \frac{F}{q}$$

- *units*: N C^{-1} (= V m^{-1}) See Pointer.
- Electric field strength is a vector (because force is a vector).
- We define E as F/q because twice the test charge will feel twice the force, so F/q doesn't depend on q, but only on the field that q is in.

We often need the equation re-arranged as

$$F = qE$$

Example: A test charge of 5.0 nC experiences a force of 0.40 mN at a point near a Van de Graaff sphere. Calculate the electric field strength at that point.

$$E = \frac{F}{q} = \frac{0.4 \times 10^{-3}\ N}{5.0 \times 10^{-9}\ C} = 80\ kN\ C^{-1} \quad (that\ is\ 80\ kV\ m^{-1})$$

Example: Calculate the acceleration of a positive ion of mass 4.65×10^{-26} kg and charge 3.20×10^{-19} C placed at the same point. (Assume forces other than from the electric field are negligible.)

$$Force\ on\ ion = mass \times acceleration$$

So $\quad qE = ma$

So $\quad a = \dfrac{qE}{m} = \dfrac{3.20 \times 10^{-19} C \times 80 \times 10^3\ N C^{-1}}{4.65 \times 10^{-26}\ kg} = 5.5 \times 10^{11}\ m\ s^{-2}$

◉≪≪≪ **quickƒire**

㊱ Typically there is a naturally arising downward electric field of strength 120 Vm^{-1}, just above the Earth's surface. Find the force experienced by a +2.0 nC charge placed there.

Coulomb's law

Two 'point charges' (compact charges), Q_1 and Q_2, separated by a distance r, in a vacuum (or air) exert forces on each other as shown. Experimentally, we find:

$$F = \frac{1}{4\pi\varepsilon_0}\frac{Q_1 Q_2}{r^2}.$$

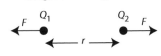

Charges of same sign

Charges of opposite sign

The dependency on $1/r^2$ makes this a so-called 'inverse square law'.

ε_0 is a constant, unfortunately called **the permittivity of free space**.

$\varepsilon_0 = 8.85 \times 10^{-12}\, C^2\, m^{-2}\, N^{-1}$ sometimes written as $\varepsilon_0 = 8.85 \times 10^{-12}\, F\, m^{-1}$
(The 'F' stands for 'farad', the unit of capacitance – a PH5 topic!)

Example: Two equal compact charges, 0.30 m apart in air, repel each other with forces of 7.8 μN. Calculate the charges.

If the charge of each is Q, then $F = \frac{1}{4\pi\varepsilon_0}\frac{Q^2}{r^2}$. Re-arranging:

$$Q = \sqrt{4\pi\varepsilon_0 r^2 F} = \sqrt{4\pi \times 8.85 \times 10^{-12}\, C^2\, m^{-2}\, N^{-1} \times (0.30\,m)^2 \times 7.8 \times 10^{-6}\, N}.$$

$Q = 8.8$ nC Both charges are positive or both are negative.

» Pointer

$\dfrac{1}{4\pi\varepsilon_0} = 8.99 \times 10^9\, N\, m^2\, C^{-2}$

Feel free to memorise this and use it. If we called it 'K', Coulomb's law would look simpler, but we retain the ε_0 version, as ε_0 has wider significance.

» Pointer

Note that the presence of the electric field due to Q doesn't depend on q being in place to test for it!

E due to a point charge

In Coulomb's law we can choose to put $Q_1 = Q$ and to regard this charge as the source of an electric field. Q_2 can be regarded as a test charge, q.

So $F = \dfrac{1}{4\pi\varepsilon_0}\dfrac{Qq}{r^2}$, that is $\dfrac{F}{q} = \dfrac{1}{4\pi\varepsilon_0}\dfrac{Q}{r^2}$

So E at distance r from Q is $E = \dfrac{1}{4\pi\varepsilon_0}\dfrac{Q}{r^2}$.

The direction of the field near Q is radially outwards (as shown) if Q is positive, radially inwards if Q is negative.

Example: An E–r graph (full line) is plotted for point source, Q. Find Q.

Using the graph point at $r = 0.10$ m:

$Q = 4\pi\varepsilon_0 \times r^2 E$

$= 4\pi \times 8.85 \times 10^{-12}\, C^2\, m^{-2}\, N^{-1}$

$\times (010\,m)^2 \times 4000\, N\, C^{-1}$

$= 4.45$ nC

quickfire

(37) Note the inverse square law as displayed in the graph. What happens to E each time r is doubled?

quickfire

(38) Calculate E at 0.30 m from a charge of 4.45 nC.

Key Terms

Electric potential = see main text.

Electrical potential energy = see main text.

Potential difference = see main text.

Electric potential and electrical potential energy

The **electric potential** of a point P in an electric field is defined by:

$$V = \frac{\left(\begin{array}{c}\text{work done by the field on a charge } q \\ \text{as } q \text{ goes from P to infinity}\end{array}\right)}{q}$$

$\underbrace{\qquad}_{} = EPE(q)$

Scalar. *Unit*: JC^{-1} = volt (V)

- 'Infinity' means very far from the charges that cause the field.
- The definition observes the convention that that V is zero at infinity.
- The top line of the definition – the work done on q as q goes from P to infinity – is what we mean by q's **electric potential energy** at P.

So V is the electrical potential energy per unit test charge, just as E is the *force* per unit test charge,

and   Electrical PE of $q = qV$

quickfire

㊴ An electric field has an almost constant value of 30 kN C^{-1} to the east over a region of space. Calculate the electrical pd between a point A and a point B which is 0.20 m east of A.

Which point is at higher potential?

quickfire

㊵ A charge of −0.90 nC is taken from A to B in the same set-up. Calculate the change in its electrical PE.

» Pointer

To see why the area under the E–x graph gives the pd, divide the area into very thin vertical strips. Over any one of these, E hardly changes, so its area really is $E\Delta x$.

Field strength and potential difference

Consider just a small distance, Δx, moved by q in the direction of E. q loses electrical potential energy:

$$\text{Change in PE} = - \text{ work done on } q \text{ by field}$$

So $q\Delta V = - (\text{force on } q) \times \Delta x$

So $q\Delta V = - qE \times \Delta x$

So $\Delta V = - E\Delta x$

ΔV is called the **potential difference (pd)**.

Suppose we know how E varies with x. To find the potential difference between points x_1 and x_2, some distance apart, we can't usually apply $\Delta V = -E\Delta x$ in one go, because E will change as we go between x_1 and x_2. In this case we use:

$$\Delta V = -\text{area under } E - x \text{ graph between } x_1 \text{ and } x_2.$$

Example: Using the graph on the previous page, estimate the difference in potential between points at 0.10 m and 0.40 m from a charge of 4.45 nC.

By eye, the (triangular) area under the broken line is *roughly* the same as that under the curve.

So $\Delta V = -\frac{1}{2}\text{base} \times \text{height} = -\frac{1}{2} \times (0.40\,\text{m} - 0.10\,\text{m}) \times 2000\,\text{V m}^{-1} = -300\,\text{V}.$

The point at 0.10 m will be at the higher potential (as the field will do work on a positive test charge going from 0.10 m to 0.40 m).

Electric potential due to a point charge, Q

The *potential* at distance r from a point charge Q is equal to the area under the E–r graph from r to infinity. Using mathematics (integration), this is found to be:

$$V = \frac{Q}{4\pi\varepsilon_0 r}$$

(The V–r graph is sketched for a charge, Q, of 4.45 nC.)

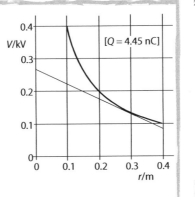

[Q = 4.45 nC]

Example:

An ion of charge $+3.20 \times 10^{-19}$ C and mass 4.65×10^{-26} kg is released from rest at a point A, 0.10 m from a charge, Q, of $+10$ nC. It moves further and further from Q. Calculate:

(a) the ion's electrical potential energy (PE) at A

(b) the ion's electrical PE at a point B, 0.30 m from Q.

(c) the ion's speed at B.

(a) Potential at $A = V_A = \dfrac{1}{4\pi\varepsilon_0}\dfrac{Q}{r_A} = 8.99\times10^9 \times \dfrac{10\times10^{-9}}{0.10}\,V = 899\,V$

  PE of ion at $A = q \times V_A = 3.2\times10^{-19}\,C \times 899\,V = 2.88\times10^{-16}\,J$

(b) Potential due to Q is inversely proportional to distance from Q, so

  PE of ion at $B = \tfrac{1}{3} 2.88\times10^{-16}\,J = 0.96\times10^{-16}\,J$

(c) $(KE + PE)$ of ion at $A = (KE + PE)$ of ion at B

  So $\ 0 + 2.88\times10^{-16}\,J = \tfrac{1}{2}mv^2 + 0.96\times10^{-16}\,J$

  So $\ v = \sqrt{\dfrac{2\times(2.88-0.96)\times10^{-16}\,J}{m}} = \sqrt{\dfrac{2\times1.92\times10^{-16}\,J}{4.65\times10^{-26}\,kg}} = 9.1\times10^4\ m\,s^{-1}$

> **Pointer**
> The relationship between V and r in
> $$V = \frac{Q}{4\pi\varepsilon_0 r}$$
> is one of inverse proportionality. Compare the shape of the graph with that of the earlier E–r graph, also drawn for a charge Q of 4.45 nC (on a similar grid).

> **Pointer**
> As $r \to \infty$,
> $$V = \frac{Q}{4\pi\varepsilon_0 r} \to 0,$$
> according with the convention that V is zero at infinity.

> **Pointer**
> Generalising from the example, the PE of a charge q, sitting in the field of a charge Q, is given by
> $$PE = qV = \frac{qQ}{4\pi\varepsilon_0 r}$$
> (The PE really belongs to the *system* of Q and q, rather than specifically to q.)

Potential gradient

We can write the relationship $\Delta V = -E\Delta x\ $ as $\ E = -\dfrac{\Delta V}{\Delta x}$

$\Delta V/\Delta x$ is called the potential gradient. Its units are V m^{-1}.

The equation implies that the gradient of the tangent to an E–x graph (or, for a radial field, an E–r graph) at a point gives the electric field strength at that point.

Example: Find E at a distance of 0.30 m from a charge of 4.45 nC, using the V–r graph on this page.

Having drawn the tangent shown,

$$E = -\frac{\Delta V}{\Delta x} = -\frac{(0.09 - 0.27)\,kV}{(0.40 - 0)\,m} = -(-0.045\,kV\,m^{-1}) = 0.045\,kV\,m^{-1}.$$

E is positive, so the field is in r direction: radially outwards.

④① Calculate the *highest* speed reached by the ion in the example.

④② Find E at 0.20 m from a charge of 4.45 nC by using a tangent to the V–r graph above. Check using the earlier E–r graph.

43 Calculate the electric field strength at a distance of 0.070 m from a compact charge of 0.80 nC.

quickfire

44 Charges of +0.80 nC are placed at two of the vertices (corners), A and B, of an equilateral triangle of side length 0.070 m. Calculate the electric field strength at the third vertex, C. Give its direction as well as magnitude.

quickfire

45 Repeat the last Quickfire, but with the charge at A being +0.80 nC, and the charge at B being −0.80 nC.

quickfire

46 Calculate the potential at C in Quickfire 44.

quickfire

47 Calculate the potential at C in Quickfire 45.

Electric field strength due to a number of charges

We find the electric field strength at a point, P, due to a number of nearby point charges, using vector addition. Consider the set-up shown below left.

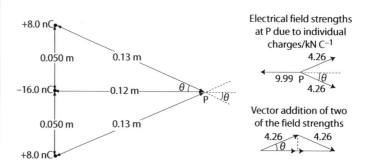

First calculate the magnitudes of E at P due to the individual charges.

For the +8.0 nC, $E = \dfrac{1}{4\pi\varepsilon_0}\dfrac{Q}{r^2} = 8.99\times10^9\,\text{N m}^2\,\text{C}^{-2}\times\dfrac{8.0\times10^{-9}\,\text{C}}{(0.13\ \text{m})^2}$

$= 4.26\ \text{kN C}^{-1}$.

Similarly, for the −16.0 nC, $E = 9.99\ \text{kN C}^{-1}$.

The *directions* of these fields at point P are shown above.

We now add together the fields due to the 8.0 nC charges. This is done in the vector diagram, noting, from the main diagram, that

$$\cos\theta = \dfrac{0.12}{0.13}.$$

Equivalently, we see that vertical components of the fields cancel, leaving just the horizontal components. So the total field at P, now including that due to the −16.0 nC charge, is

$$E = (2\times4.26\times\cos\theta - 9.99)\ \text{kN C}^{-1}\ \text{to the right}$$
$$= -2.1\ \text{kN C}^{-1}\ \text{to the right} = 2.1\ \text{kN C}^{-1}\ \text{to the left}$$

Electric potential due to a number of charges

This is much easier to calculate than E, because potential is a scalar quantity! We'll now find the potential at point P in the set-up above.

First calculate the potentials at P due to each of the individual charges.

For each +8.0 nC, $V = \dfrac{1}{4\pi\varepsilon_0}\dfrac{Q}{r} = 8.99\times10^9\,\text{N m}^2\,\text{C}^{-2}\times\dfrac{8.0\times10^{-9}\,\text{C}}{0.13\ \text{m}} = 0.55\ \text{kV}$.

Similarly, for the −16.0 nC, $V = -1.20\ \text{kV}$.

So total potential at P $= 2\times0.55\ \text{kV} - 1.20\ \text{kV} = -0.10\ \text{kV}$

Electric field lines

These are the full lines with arrowheads on them, in the diagrams below. *Their direction, at each point along them, gives the direction of the electric field at that point.* (The broken lines are explained later.)

So for 'isolated' charges, the field lines are radial:

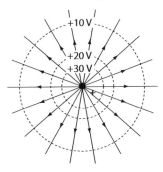 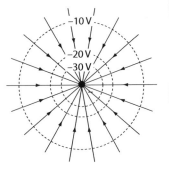

- The lines start on positive charges and end on negative charges (even though the diagrams above show only one end of each line).

- The lines have the 'bonus' property of indicating the field *strength*: the closer they come together the stronger the field.

- **Electric field lines** never intersect. Suppose, for example, we move the two 'isolated' charges together. At each point there won't be two separate fields, but a single resultant field – found by vector addition of the fields due to the individual charges.

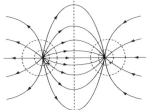

Equipotentials

These are surfaces all points on which are at the same potential.

In the diagrams above they are shown (in section) as broken lines. They are therefore very much like contour lines on a map, joining points of equal height (and therefore equal *gravitational* potential).

- **Equipotentials** and electric field lines cross at right angles.

- In the diagrams above, the equipotentials are drawn with roughly equal differences of potential between them. This means that the closer the equipotentials the stronger the field – because the greater the potential gradient!

>> *Pointer*
You won't be expected to draw from memory the curvy field pattern (for the two charges together).

Grade boost

To build your confidence, choose an off-centre point in the third diagram, consider the magnitudes and directions of the field strengths due to the individual charges, and sketch a rough vector addition diagram. Does the direction of the resultant field agree roughly with that of the field line?

>> *Pointer*
It should be clear that the potential of the middle equipotential in the third diagram is zero.

Gravitation: fields and potentials

Gravitational field strength = see main text.

Newton's law of gravitation = see main text.

Gravitational forces between particles obey an inverse square law – as do forces between charges – our last topic! We can make use of many of the same ideas.

Gravitational field strength

» Pointer

Equivalence check on units for g:
$N\,kg^{-1} = kg\,m\,s^{-2}\,kg^{-1} = m\,s^{-2}$.

A gravitational field is a region where a mass (a so-called *test-mass*), m, experiences a force proportional to m.

The **gravitational field strength**, g, at a point is defined as

$$g = \frac{\text{force on } m}{m} \qquad \text{that is} \qquad g = \frac{F}{m}.$$

- g is a vector quantity. Its units are $N\,kg^{-1}$ (or – see Pointer – $m\,s^{-2}$).
- If a test mass is released in a gravitational field, and other forces on it are negligible, then, using $F = ma$, its acceleration is:

$$a = \frac{F}{m} = \frac{mg}{m} = g.$$

» Pointer

When a test mass of 4.0 kg is hung from a force-meter on the Moon's surface, the reading is 6.50 N.

Hence $g = \dfrac{F}{m} = \dfrac{6.50\,N}{4.00\,kg} = 1.63\,N\,kg^{-1}$

And free-fall acceleration = $1.63\,m\,s^{-2}$.

So, whatever the mass m of the test mass, its free-fall acceleration is equal to the gravitational field strength! For an example see second pointer.

Newton's law of gravitation

» Pointer

Newton's law of gravitation doesn't apply accurately in regions of very high g (such as inside, or close to, stars).

The gravitational force between two particles is an attractive force proportional to the product of their masses, m_1 and m_2, and inversely proportional to the square of their separation, r.

Mathematically, $\qquad\qquad F = G\dfrac{m_1 m_2}{r^2}.$

(48) Two electrons are 1.00 mm apart. Calculate:

(a) The electric repulsive force between them.

(b) The gravitational force between them.
($e = 1.60 \times 10^{-19}$ C, $m_e = 9.11 \times 10^{-31}$ kg).

G is called **Newton's gravitational constant** (or 'big G'). By experiment, $G = 6.67 \times 10^{-11}\,N\,kg^{-2}\,m^2$ ($= 6.67 \times 10^{-11}\,kg^{-1}\,m^3\,s^{-2}$).

- m_1 and m_2 are always positive. The force is always attractive; this is sometimes shown with a minus sign, by writing $F = -Gm_1 m_2 / r^2$.
- The law applies to particles ('point masses'). Stars and planets aren't particles, but they *are* nearly *spherically symmetric*: spherical, with mass distributed evenly all round. When Newton added 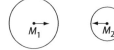 together the forces that each particle of one of these bodies exerts on each particle of another, he found a very neat result: *the bodies behave as if all their mass were concentrated at their centres.*

» Pointer

The last Quickfire should convince you of why gravity is said to be a very weak force.

g due to a point, or spherically symmetric mass

In Newton's law we can choose to put $m_1 = M$, and to regard M as the source of a gravitational field. m_2 can be regarded as a test mass, m.

So $\quad F = G\dfrac{Mm}{r^2} \quad$ that is $\quad \dfrac{F}{m} = G\dfrac{M}{r^2} \quad$ so $\quad g = \dfrac{GM}{r^2}$.

This is the field strength outside a spherically symmetric object of mass M, at distance r from its centre. g is directed *towards* the centre of M; as sometimes shown with a minus sign: $g = -GM/r^2$

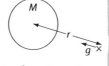

Example: The moon's radius is 1.74×10^6 m and $g = 1.62$ N kg^{-1} on its surface. Calculate its mass.

$$M = \frac{r^2 g}{G} = \frac{(1.74 \times 10^6 \text{m})^2 \times 1.62 \text{ N kg}^{-1}}{6.67 \times 10^{-11} \text{ N kg}^{-2} \text{ m}^2} = 7.4 \times 10^{22} \text{ kg}$$

quickfire

(49) The mean radius of the Earth is 6.37×10^6 m and $g = 9.81$ N kg^{-1}. Calculate the mass of the Earth.

quickfire

(50) Hence calculate the mean density of the Earth.

Gravitational potential and gravitational potential energy

The **gravitational potential** at a point P in a g-field is defined by:

$$V = \frac{\left(\begin{array}{c}\text{work done by the field on a mass } m \\ \text{if } m \text{ is taken from P to infinity}\end{array}\right)}{m} \quad \text{Scalar.} \quad \textit{unit}: \text{J kg}^{-1} = \text{m}^2\text{s}^{-2}$$

- 'Infinity' means very far from the bodies that cause the field.
- The definition keeps to the convention that V is zero at infinity.
- Except at infinity, V will always be negative, as force on m due to the field is in the opposite direction (at least roughly) to m's journey from P to infinity. This is because gravitational forces are *attractive*.
- The top line of the definition – the work done by the field on mass m if m is taken from P to infinity – is m's **gravitational potential energy** at P (and is negative).

So V is the gravitational potential energy per unit test mass, just as g is the *force* per unit test mass,

and $\quad$ Gravitational PE of $m = mV$

➤ Pointer

Note how close the definitions and equations are to those for electric fields. But beware the minus sign in
$$V = -\frac{GM}{r} \text{ (see next page).}$$
So for the system of M and m: PE $= mV = -\dfrac{GmM}{r}$.

Gravitational potential outside a spherically symmetric body

> **Pointer**
>
> In the g–r graph, we are using $g = -GM/r^2$. The minus sign shows that g is in the $-r$ direction.

⊙≪≪≪ quickfire

(51) Using data from the graphs, calculate:

(a) the field strength,

(b) the potential, at 8.0×10^{11} m from a star of mass 6.00×10^{30} kg.

This is given by
$$V = -\frac{GM}{r}$$
[minus sign essential]

g–r and V–r graphs are shown below for a star of mass 6.00×10^{30} kg.

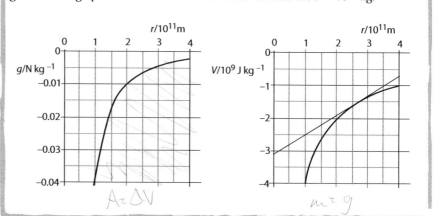

g and gravitational potential difference

The change in gravitational potential, ΔV, taking place over a distance Δx in the direction of g, is:

$$\Delta V = -g\,\Delta x \qquad \text{so} \qquad g = -\frac{\Delta V}{\Delta x}$$

Changes in gravitational potential are represented by areas under the g–x (or g–r) graph, and g at a point is the gradient of the V–x (or V–r) graph at that point (the 'gravitational potential gradient').

Example:

Use the V–r graph above to find the gravitational field strength at 2.5×10^{11} m from the centre of a star of mass 6.00×10^{30} kg.

Using the tangent drawn,

$$g = -\frac{\Delta V}{\Delta r} = -\frac{[-0.7 - (-3.1)] \times 10^9 \text{ J kg}^{-1}}{[4.0 - 0] \times 10^{11} \text{ m}} = -6.0 \times 10^{-3} \text{ N kg}^{-1}$$

This agrees with the value read from the E–r graph.

> **Pointer**
>
> See the Electric fields section for more detail on the equations corresponding to $\Delta V = -g\Delta x$, $g = -\Delta V/\Delta x$.

> **Pointer**
>
> The equation PE = mgh is based on $\Delta V = -g\Delta x$. It applies only if $h \ll r_{\text{earth}}$, so g is constant over h. It takes the zero of PE to be at the bottom of h, rather than infinity. PE = mgh won't usually be the right equation to use in questions on gravitation!

Conservation of energy in a grav'l field

When unpowered spacecraft, satellites and planets move in gravitational fields we can apply the principle of conservation of energy in the form:

$$(\text{gravitational PE} + \text{KE})_1 = (\text{gravitational PE} + \text{KE})_2$$

in which the subscripts refer to any points in the journey.

Example: The moon's mass is 7.35×10^{22} kg and its radius is 1.74×10^6 m. Calculate how far a rocket will rise if launched vertically from the moon's surface at a speed of 2000 m s^{-1}.

The furthest point reached, at r_2, let us say, from the centre of the moon, will be when the rocket has run out of KE.

But   (PE + KE) just after launch = (PE + KE) at furthest point

So

$$-m\frac{GM}{r_1} + \tfrac{1}{2}mv_1^2 = -m\frac{GM}{r_2} + 0$$

Dividing through by the rocket mass, m, and putting in figures, omitting units:

$$-\frac{6.67 \times 10^{-11} \times 7.35 \times 10^{22}}{1.74 \times 10^6} + \tfrac{1}{2}2000^2 = -\frac{6.67 \times 10^{-11} \times 7.35 \times 10^{22}}{r_2} + 0$$

So

$$-2.82 \times 10^6 + 2.00 \times 10^6 = -\frac{4.90 \times 10^{12}}{r_2}$$

So

$$r_2 = 6.0 \times 10^6 \text{ m}$$

And now the final step – easily forgotten. The distance the rocket rises *from the moon's surface* is $r_2 - r_1 = (6.0 - 1.7) \times 10^6$ m $= 4.3 \times 10^6$ m.

⑤② What other form of energy (apart from kinetic and gravitational potential) should (ideally) be taken into account for bodies travelling through the Earth's atmosphere?

Escape speed (or escape velocity)

The **escape speed** is the minimum speed needed for a body to escape as far as we please ('to infinity') from the surface of a star, planet or satellite.
'Minimum speed' implies that the body doesn't have any KE left at infinity. The PE will also be zero at infinity, according to convention.

Example: Calculate the escape speed for a body on the Earth, given that the Earth's mass is 5.97×10^{24} kg and its mean radius is 6.37×10^6 m.

We have   (PE + KE) just after launch = (PE + KE) at infinity

So

$$-m\frac{GM}{r_1} + \tfrac{1}{2}mv_\text{esc}^2 = 0 + 0 \quad \rightarrow \tfrac{1}{2}mv_\text{esc}^2 = m\frac{GM}{r_1}$$

So $v_\text{esc} = \sqrt{\dfrac{2GM}{r_1}} = \sqrt{\dfrac{2 \times 6.67 \times 10^{-11}\,\text{N kg}^{-2}\,\text{m}^2 \times 5.97 \times 10^{24}\,\text{kg}}{6.37 \times 10^6\,\text{m}}} = 11.2 \text{ km s}^{-1}$

⑤③ Calculate the escape speed for a body on the Moon (mass: 7.35×10^{22} kg, radius: 1.74×10^6 m).

Field strengths and potentials due to more than one body

An example of scalar addition of potentials: finding the potential at point P in the example...

$$V = -\frac{GM_E}{x} + \left(-\frac{GM_M}{y}\right)$$

Substituting figures for M_E, M_M, x, y, G, we find that $V = -1.29$ MJ kg^{-1}

(54) Calculate the potentials at two positions either side of P, along the line EM:

(a) 3.14×10^8 m from E

(b) 3.64×10^8 m from E

These answers should support the claim that V has a maximum at P.

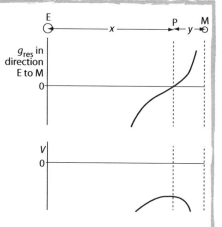

The resultant field strength at a point is the *vector* sum of field strengths due to each body. The resultant potential is the *scalar* sum of potentials due to each body.

Example: Comment on the sketch-graphs of field strength and potential along the line joining Earth (E) and Moon (M), and locate point P. (*Data*: mass of Earth = 5.97×10^{24} kg, mass of Moon = 7.35×10^{22} kg, distance from E to M = 3.82×10^8 m)

Between E and P, the Earth's field (towards E) predominates, but, between P and M, the Moon's predominates. P is where the vector sum of the fields is zero,

So $\quad \dfrac{GM_M}{y^2} - \dfrac{GM_E}{x^2} = 0 \quad$ that is $\quad \dfrac{M_M}{y^2} = \dfrac{M_E}{x^2}$

So $\quad \dfrac{x}{y} = \sqrt{\dfrac{M_E}{M_M}} = \sqrt{\dfrac{5.97 \times 10^{24} \text{ kg}}{7.35 \times 10^{22} \text{ kg}}} = 9.01 \quad$ that is $\quad x = 9.01y$.

But $x + y = 3.82 \times 10^8$ m $\quad$ so $\quad 10.01\, y = 3.82 \times 10^8$ m

So $\quad y = 0.38 \times 10^8$ m $\quad$ and $\quad x = 9.01\, y \quad$ so $\quad x = 3.44 \times 10^8$ m

As for the gravitational potential, we know it is always negative and that it will be most negative near E and M. The maximum value will be at P because $g = 0$ here, so $\Delta V/\Delta r$, the rate of change of potential with distance along EM, will be zero here. See sketch-graph of V.

Orbits in gravitational fields

Key Term
Kepler's laws = see main text.

Kepler's laws of planetary motion

1. Each planet moves in an ellipse, with the Sun at one focus.
2. The line joining the Sun to a planet sweeps out equal areas in equal times. This implies that, in its orbit, the closer a planet is to the Sun, the faster it moves.
3. For the different planets in the solar system:

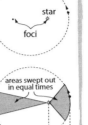

T^2 is proportional to r^3, that is $\dfrac{T^2}{r^3}$ = a constant

in which T is the planet's period (or planet's year) and r is the semi-length of ellipse's 'major axis'.

In the diagram $r = \dfrac{r_{max} + r_{min}}{2}$

The laws were discovered by *observation*. Later, Newton showed that the planets would move thus if pulled by the Sun with an inverse square law force.

Circular orbits

These are a special case, for which $r_{min} = r_{max}$, of elliptical orbits.

The diagram shows a body of mass m orbiting a body of mass M. We assume $M \gg m$, so M remains stationary.

M's gravitational pull provides m with its centripetal acceleration. We apply $F = ma$ to find an equation for T, in two equivalent ways.

$\dfrac{GMm}{r^2} = mr\omega^2$ so $\dfrac{GM}{r^2} = r\omega^2$ or,

$\dfrac{GMm}{r^2} = m\dfrac{v^2}{r}$ so $\dfrac{GM}{r^2} = \dfrac{v^2}{r}$

But $\omega = \dfrac{2\pi}{T}$ so $\dfrac{GM}{r^2} = r\dfrac{4\pi^2}{T^2}$

Re-arranging: $v^2 = \dfrac{GM}{r}$

Re-arranging: $T^2 = \dfrac{4\pi^2}{GM}r^3$

But $v = \dfrac{2\pi r}{T}$ so $T = \dfrac{2\pi r}{v}$

So $T^2 = \dfrac{4\pi^2 r^2}{v^2} = \dfrac{4\pi^2}{GM}r^3$

So, at least in the case of circular orbits, we have shown that Kepler's third law follows from the law of gravitation.

Grade boost
Before studying orbits you need to know the Circular motion section.

» Pointer
Most planets' orbits are not very 'eccentric': they're quite close to circular – as is the Moon's orbit, and those of man-made satellites.

55 If a planet were discovered in a circular orbit of 9 times the radius of the Earth's orbit, what would be its orbital period in earth-years?

» Pointer
The left-hand derivation is clearly the shorter if all we want is the $T-r$ relationship.
The right-hand derivation goes via $v^2 = \dfrac{GM}{r}$, which is important in its own right. You should know both.

» Pointer
By square-rooting both sides, the $T-r$ relationship can also be written as
$T = \dfrac{2\pi}{\sqrt{GM}} r^{3/2}$

Using orbit theory for satellites and planets

quickfire

56. The moon's orbital radius is 3.84×10^8 m and its orbital period is 27.3 days, Calculate a figure for the mass of the Earth.

quickfire

57. Taking the Earth to move in a circular orbit of radius 1.5×10^{11} m, calculate a figure for the mass of the Sun.

» Pointer

Signals can be beamed to a geostationary satellite from a transmitter on the ground, and received (boosted) from the satellite by 'dishes' over a wide area of the Earth's surface, without any need to 'track' the satellite across the sky.

Example 1: A geostationary satellite is a man-made satellite with a circular orbit in the plane of the equator and of period 24 hours, so that it is always above one point on the equator. Starting from Newton's law of gravitation, determine the height of the satellite above the Earth's surface. [Mass of Earth = 5.97×10^{24} kg, radius of Earth = 6.37×10^6 m]

section through plane of equator

Earth's gravitational pull supplies centripetal force on satellite,

so $\dfrac{GMm}{r^2} = mr\omega^2$ that is $GM = r^3\omega^2$

But $\omega = \dfrac{2\pi}{T}$ so $GM = r^3\dfrac{4\pi^2}{T^2}$ that is $r^3 = \dfrac{GMT^2}{4\pi^2}$

So $r = \sqrt[3]{\dfrac{GMT^2}{4\pi^2}} = \left(\dfrac{6.67 \times 10^{-11} \times 5.97 \times 10^{24} \times (24 \times 3600)^2}{4\pi^2}\right)^{\frac{1}{3}} = 42.2 \times 10^6$ m

(raising to the power of $\frac{1}{3}$ means cube-rooting.)

And, finally: height above Earth = 42.2×10^6 m $- 6.37 \times 10^6$ m $= 36 \times 10^6$ m.

Example 2: The distances of the Earth and Jupiter from the Sun are 1.50×10^{11} m and 7.78×10^{11} m. Calculate Jupiter's year in earth-years.

We use Kepler's third law. There is no need to evaluate the constant, nor to convert years to seconds – if we do some algebra first.

$$\dfrac{T^2}{r^3} = \text{constant} \quad \text{so} \quad \dfrac{T_J^2}{r_J^3} = \dfrac{T_E^2}{r_E^3} \quad \text{so} \quad \dfrac{T_J^2}{T_E^2} = \dfrac{r_J^3}{r_E^3} = \left(\dfrac{r_J}{r_E}\right)^3$$

Thus $T_J = T_E\left(\dfrac{r_J}{r_E}\right)^{\frac{3}{2}} = 1.00 \text{ year} \times \left(\dfrac{7.78 \times 10^{11}\text{m}}{1.50 \times 10^{11}\text{m}}\right)^{\frac{3}{2}} = 11.8 \text{ years}$

Rotation of galaxies, and dark matter

A spiral galaxy is a huge collection of stars, together with gas and dust, distributed roughly in disc formation and rotating about its centre.

We can use Newton's law of gravitation to predict the rotation speed of a particle of mass m at distance r from the centre of the galaxy.

$$\frac{GMm}{r^2} = m\frac{v^2}{r} \quad \text{that is} \quad v^2 = \frac{GM}{r} \quad \text{and} \quad v = \sqrt{\frac{GM}{r}}$$

M is the mass of galactic material between the particle and the centre of the galaxy. A crude assumption of spherical symmetry is being made.

We can estimate the observable, so-called 'baryonic' mass, M_B, of the galaxy from the electromagnetic (e-m) radiation it gives out, and from the e-m radiation absorbed by gas clouds. Most of this mass is concentrated in the 'central bulge' of the galaxy.

This means that *outside* the central bulge, we'd expect M to change little and to be roughly equal to M_B. Hence the theoretical graph (dotted), which, outside the central bulge, is drawn to follow $v = \sqrt{GM/r}$ with a constant value for M.

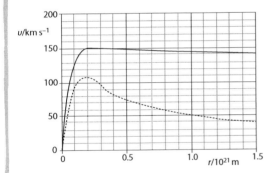

We can easily estimate the value of M on which this graph is based. Selecting the point at $r = 0.5 \times 10^{21}$ m:

$$M = \frac{rv^2}{G} = \frac{0.50 \times 10^{21}\,\text{m} \times (74 \times 10^3\,\text{m s}^{-1})^2}{6.67 \times 10^{-11}\,\text{N kg}^{-2}\text{m}^2} = 4.1 \times 10^{40}\ \text{kg}$$

For some galaxies we can *measure* v at various distances, r, using a technique based on *Doppler shift*. (See later section.) The full line on the graph is typical of the *measured* v plotted against r. We conclude that:

- The mass in the galaxy extends far beyond the central bulge (as v does not fall off with r in the expected way).
- The overall mass of the galaxy is much greater than M_B by something like a factor of 10.

These discrepancies are too large to be accounted for by errors of *measurement*. Instead, the most favoured theory is that galaxies contain **dark matter**, which, unlike baryonic matter, doesn't interact with electromagnetic radiation. Its nature is not known.

Key Term

Dark matter = see main text.

≫ Pointer

The equation $v = \sqrt{GM/r}$ for the rotation speed of a particle, m, in the galaxy assumes a spherically symmetric distribution of mass between m and the galactic centre. This is not quite right, because the galaxy, though bulgy near the middle, is flatter than spherical.

quickfire

⑤⑧ Why do the v–r graphs rise from zero to their maximum values?

quickfire

⑤⑨ What can be said about rv^2 for the dotted (theoretical) graph beyond about 0.3×10^{21} m?

quickfire

⑥⓪ Evaluate the ratio
$$\left(\frac{v_{\text{full line}}}{v_{\text{broken line}}}\right)^2 \text{ at}$$
1.5×10^{21} m and state the significance of this ratio (making the crude assumption of spherical symmetry).

≫ **Pointer**

If $M_1 \gg M_2$, C may be inside M_1.

≫ **Pointer**

The speeds of the bodies are in the same ratio as their orbital radii, since $\dfrac{v_1}{v_2} = \dfrac{r_1\omega}{r_2\omega} = \dfrac{r_1}{r_2}$.

≫ **Pointer**

Applying $F = ma$ to M_1 in the system, and dividing both sides by M_1, gives $\dfrac{GM_2}{d^2} = r_1\omega^2$.

By expressing r_1 in terms of d you can reach the equation

$$T = 2\pi\sqrt{\dfrac{d^3}{G(M_1 + M_2)}}.$$

◉≪≪≪ **quickfire**

⑥ Two stars, each with the same mass as the Sun, form a binary system (circular orbits) of period one earth-year. Calculate d_{SS}/d_{SE} in which d_{SS} is the separation of the centres of the stars, and d_{SE} is the Earth's orbital radius. [Hint: Use Kepler 3 equations for the new system and for the Earth.]

Binary systems

Our system will consist of two bodies, of masses M_1 and M_2 (for example, two stars or a star and a large planet) in which each mass is large enough to affect the other's motion detectably.

Both M_1 and M_2 will orbit the same point, C, called the system's centre of mass, with the same angular velocity. We shall assume *circular* orbits. The position of C is given (see diagram) by

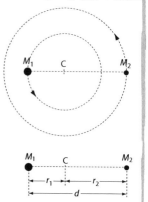

$$r_1 = \dfrac{M_2}{M_1 + M_2}d \quad \text{and} \quad r_2 = \dfrac{M_1}{M_1 + M_2}d$$

Quick checks to make on these equations

- $r_1 + r_2 = d$.
- $M_1 r_1 = M_2 r_2$ which is equivalent to $M_1 r_1 \omega^2 = M_2 r_2 \omega^2$.

(This simply equates the magnitudes of mass × acceleration for M_1 and M_2 – since they exert equal and opposite forces on each other.)

Kepler's third law for binary systems

Both bodies have a periodic time of $T = 2\pi\sqrt{\dfrac{d^3}{G(M_1 + M_2)}}$.

Example:

A double star (Delta Capricorni A and B) has an orbital period of 8.83×10^4 s (just over a day). The orbital speeds of A and B are 9.25×10^4 m s^{-1} and 20.6×10^4 m s^{-1}. Calculate the masses of A and B.

First we'll work out r_A, and r_B, using the speeds and the period.

$$v_A = \dfrac{2\pi r_A}{T}, \text{ so } r_A = \dfrac{v_A T}{2\pi} = \dfrac{9.25 \times 10^4\,\text{ms}^{-1} \times 8.83 \times 10^4\,\text{s}}{2\pi} = 1.30 \times 10^9\,\text{m}$$

and

$$r_B = \dfrac{20.6 \times 10^4\,\text{ms}^{-1} \times 8.83 \times 10^4\,\text{s}}{2\pi} = 2.89 \times 10^9\,\text{m}$$

Now we'll find $M_A + M_B$ by re-arranging the 'Kepler 3' equation.

$$M_A + M_B = \dfrac{4\pi^2 d^3}{T^2 G} = \dfrac{4\pi^2 (1.30 \times 10^9\,\text{m} + 2.89 \times 10^9\,\text{m})^3}{(8.83 \times 10^4\,\text{s})^2 \times 6.67 \times 10^{-11}\,\text{N kg}^{-2}\,\text{m}^2} = 5.58 \times 10^{30}\,\text{kg}$$

But $r_A = \dfrac{M_B}{M_A + M_B}d$ so $M_B = (M_A + M_B)\dfrac{r_A}{d} = 5.58 \times 10^{30}\,\text{kg}\,\dfrac{1.30 \times 10^9\,\text{m}}{4.19 \times 10^9\,\text{m}}$

Thus $M_B = 1.73 \times 10^{30}$ kg and $M_A = (5.58 - 1.73) \times 10^{30}$ kg $= 3.85 \times 10^{30}$ kg

Measurements of velocity by Doppler shift

This has been the key technique in recent discoveries of planets outside the solar system, black holes and extra mass in galaxies.

Key Term

Radial velocity of a star = the component along our line of sight of its velocity relative to us.

The Doppler effect for light

If a source of light and an observer are moving further apart, the observed wave frequency is lowered (as each successive wave 'peak' has further to travel). Since $\lambda = c/f$, the observed wavelength is increased; we say there is a 'Doppler shift to the red'. If source and observer are *moving closer* there is a 'shift to the blue'.

The change, $\Delta\lambda$, in wavelength of a spectral line is given by

$$\frac{\Delta\lambda}{\lambda} = \frac{v_{rad}}{c}$$

in which λ is the unshifted wavelength and v_{rad} is the **radial velocity**: the component along our line-of-sight of the star's (or other source's) velocity relative to us. A source approaching us is given a negative value of v_{rad}, so $\Delta\lambda$ correctly comes out negative. (The equation is approximate, but when $v \ll c$, as in the cases below, it is almost exact.)

» Pointer

Move away Don't forget to give the values of v_{min} and v_{max} their correct signs.

Red-shift = $\cdot \uparrow\lambda$, $\cdot \downarrow f$, $\cdot \oplus v$

Blue-shift = $\downarrow\lambda$, $\uparrow f$, $\ominus v$
↑ Move closer

Doppler determination of a star's orbital velocity

Our example will be the star 51 Pegasi. Lines in its spectrum were found to have a regularly changing Doppler shift. For one absorption line, identified as a hydrogen line of 656 nm, the extreme shifts are -1.04×10^{-13} m and $+1.45 \times 10^{-13}$ m. So the extreme radial velocities are:

$$v_{min} = c\frac{\Delta\lambda}{\lambda} = 3.00\times10^8 \text{ m s}^{-1} \times \frac{-1.04\times10^{-13} \text{ m}}{656\times10^{-9} \text{ m}} = -47.6 \text{ m s}^{-1}$$

$$v_{max} = c\frac{\Delta\lambda}{\lambda} = 3.00\times10^8 \text{ m s}^{-1} \times \frac{+1.45\times10^{-13} \text{ m}}{656\times10^{-9} \text{ m}} = +66.3 \text{ m s}^{-1}$$

In fact, the radial velocity, plotted against time varies as on the left:

The sinusoidal variation in v_{rad} is just what we'd find if the star were in circular orbit. For orbital speed v, assuming that the orbit is being viewed edge-on (right hand diagram), $v_{max} = v$ and $v_{min} = -v$, so $v_{max} - v_{min} = v - (-v) = 2v$. The sinusoid on the graph is lifted up, showing that, in addition to the orbital motion, there is a steady velocity component away from us. But it will still be true that $v_{max} - v_{min} = 2v$.

Thus orbital speed, $v = \frac{1}{2}(v_{max} - v_{min}) = \frac{1}{2}[66.3 - (-47.6)] \text{ m s}^{-1} = 57.0 \text{ m s}^{-1}$.

⑥② The star's mean radial velocity is $\frac{1}{2}(v_{max} + v_{min})$. Hence calculate the steady radial velocity superimposed on the oscillatory part of 51 Pegasi's radial velocity arising from its orbiting.

quickfire

⑥③ Light of wavelength 510 nm from the star Tau Boötes is found to exhibit a varying Doppler shift between -291.5×10^{-13} m and -275.5×10^{-13} m, with a period of 3.31 days. Calculate the star's orbital speed and orbital radius.

⊚ ⫸⫸⫸ quickfire

64 In 2008 the star GJ 1046 $(7.29 \times 10^{29}$ kg) was found to have a wobble. Its orbital speed is 1830 m s^{-1} and its period is 169 days. Calculate:

(a) The star's orbital radius.

(b) The separation of star (S) and 'planet' (P) (with the approximation $M_S + M_P = M_S$).

(c) P's orbital radius.

(d) P's mass. This is so large (>13 times Jupiter's mass) as to make P a 'brown dwarf', rather than a planet.

(e) P's orbital speed.

⊚ ⫸⫸⫸ quickfire

65 What assumptions did you make about the orbit in Quickfire 64?

⧈ Grade boost

Checks to make on your working: $M_s > M_p$ but $r_s < r_p$. Candidates often submit a planet's mass that is much greater than the star's!

⧈ Grade boost

Note the approximations applicable in the usual case, when $M_s \gg M_p$:
- $(M_s + M_p) = M_s$ in the Kepler 3 equation,
- $r_p = d$ in $M_p r_p = M_s r_s$.

Determining a binary system from one body's orbit

If we know, from Doppler measurements, a star's orbital velocity, v, and period, T, we can find its orbital radius, r_S, because $v = 2\pi r/T$.

Using the data ($v = 57.0$ m s^{-1}, $T = 4.23$ day) for 51 Pegasi,

$$r_S = \frac{vT}{2\pi} = \frac{57.0 \text{ m s}^{-1} \times 4.23 \times 24 \times 3600 \text{ s}}{2\pi} = 3.32 \times 10^6 \text{ m.}$$

This is about half the Earth's radius. Such a small stellar orbit, often called a 'wobble', indicates the presence of a companion, making up a binary system. The companion of 55 Pegasi is invisible and (judging by its small effect on the star) of very much smaller mass than the star – presumably a planet.

We can now find the separation, d, of star (S) and planet (P), using

$$T = 2\pi \sqrt{\frac{d^3}{G(M_S + M_P)}} \quad \text{so} \quad d = \left[\frac{T^2 G(M_S + M_P)}{4\pi^2} \right]^{\frac{1}{3}}.$$

From its spectrum and luminosity, 51 Pegasi is estimated to be a Sun-like star of mass $M_S = 2.1 \times 10^{30}$ kg. It is likely that $M_P < 0.01\, M_S$, so putting M_S instead of $M_S + M_P$ will make hardly any difference.

$$\text{Thus } d = \left[\frac{T^2 G M_S}{4\pi^2} \right]^{\frac{1}{3}} = \left[\frac{(4.23 \times 24 \times 3600)^2 \times 6.67 \times 10^{-11} \times 2.1 \times 10^{30} \text{m}^3}{4\pi^2} \right]^{\frac{1}{3}}$$

So $d = 7.8 \times 10^9$ m. But $r_s = 3.32 \times 10^6$ m, so $r_p = d - r_s = 7.8 \times 10^9$ m.

So, to 2 s.f., r_p is indistinguishable from d (and would be even with 3 s.f.).

We can now find the planet's mass, M_P, using $M_p r_p = M_S r_S$:

$$M_P = M_S \frac{r_S}{r_P} = 2.1 \times 10^{30} \text{ kg} \times \frac{3.32 \times 10^6 \text{ m}}{7.8 \times 10^9 \text{ m}} = 8.9 \times 10^{26} \text{ kg.}$$

This is about half the mass of Jupiter. (The real figure will be larger if we are not, in fact, viewing the system nearly edge on.) The orbital radius, r_P, is about a seventh that of Mercury – so the planet will be roasting! This was the first discovery (1995) of a planet belonging to a star similar to the Sun.

Summary: PH4 Oscillations and Fields

Momentum

- Definition and vector nature of momentum.
- Newton's second law of motion stated in terms of momentum. Application to a body of constant mass. Newton's first law.
- Newton's third law.
- The principle of conservation of momentum and its use in 1-dimenional collisions.
- Elastic and inelastic collisions.
- Momentum of a photon given by h/λ.
- Radiation pressure due to absorbed or reflected photons.

Circular motion

- The radian measure of angle.
- Angular velocity, rotation period, frequency.
  $$\omega = 2\pi f = \frac{2\pi}{T}, \ \omega = \frac{v}{r}.$$
- Centripetal acceleration
  $$a = \frac{v^2}{r} = r\omega^2.$$

Oscillations

- Definition of simple harmonic motion (SHM) based on $a = -\omega^2 x$.
- Interpretation and use of $x = A \sin(\omega t + \varepsilon)$ in which
  $$\omega = 2\pi f = \frac{2\pi}{T}.$$

- Interpretation and use of
  $$T = 2\pi\sqrt{\frac{m}{k}}.$$
- $v = A\omega \cos(\omega t + \varepsilon)$.
- x–t, v–t, a–t and a–x graphs.
- KE and PE interchange during SHM. Graphs: E_k–t, E_p–t, E_k–x and E_p–x. Calculations.
- Damped oscillations. x–t graph.
  Critical damping and its use in vehicle suspensions.
- Forced oscillations. Practical example. Graph of amplitude against driving frequency, and effect of increased damping on the curve.
  Resonance. Sometimes useful and sometimes to be avoided. Examples.

Gases

- Molecules, moles, the Avogadro constant, relative molecular mass (M_r), molar mass.
  Meaning and use of $n = \dfrac{N}{N_A}$.
  Molar mass/kg $= \dfrac{M_r}{1000}$.
- Boyle's law.
- The Kelvin temperature scale.
- The ideal gas equation of state $PV = nRT$, or $PV = NkT$.
- R is molar gas constant, k is Boltzmann constant. $k = R/N_A$.
- Assumptions of the kinetic theory of gases.

- $pV = \frac{1}{3}Nm\overline{c^2}$ and its equivalent, $p = \frac{1}{3}\rho\overline{c^2}$. Meaning and use.
- $c_{rms} = \sqrt{\overline{c^2}}$ Meaning and use.
- Mean translational kinetic energy of a gas molecule is $\frac{3}{2}kT$. Derivation from $PV = nRT$ and $pV = \frac{1}{3}Nm\overline{c^2}$. Translational kinetic energy per mole $= \frac{3}{2}RT$.

Thermodynamics

- The internal energy, U, of a system.
- For an ideal monatomic gas, $U = \frac{3}{2}nRT$.
- Work done by gas, $W = p\Delta V$. $W =$ area under p–V graph even if p varies.
  Heat as energy in transit from a higher to a lower temperature region.
- Meaning and use of $\Delta U = Q - W$.
- Understanding that Q and W are energies *in transit* and not properties, nor changes in properties, of the system.
- Solids and liquids: $Q = \Delta U$ because W is usually negligible and $Q = mc\Delta T$ or $Q = mc\Delta\theta$ in which c is specific heat capacity.

Electric fields

- Definition of an electric field strength: $E = \dfrac{F}{q}$.

- Coulomb's law: $F = \dfrac{1}{4\pi\varepsilon_0} \dfrac{Q_1 Q_2}{r^2}$.

  The electric field strength due to a point charge: $E = \dfrac{1}{4\pi\varepsilon_0} \dfrac{Q}{r^2}$.

- Electric potential V. Electrical potential *energy* of $q = qV$.

- Potential difference, $\Delta V = -E\Delta x$. $\Delta V =$ area under E–x graph even if E varies.

- Electric potential due to a point charge: $V = \dfrac{1}{4\pi\varepsilon_0} \dfrac{Q}{r}$.

- Field strength = potential gradient = slope of V–x graph: $E = -\dfrac{\Delta V}{\Delta x}$.

- Vector addition of field strengths due to a number of charges.

- Scalar addition of potentials due to a number of charges.

- Electric field lines and equipotentials: properties and simple cases.

Gravitation: field strength and potential

- Gravitational field strength: $g = \dfrac{F}{m}$.

- Newton's law of gravitation: $F = G\dfrac{m_1 m_2}{r^2}$.

- g due to a point, or spherically symmetric, body of mass M: $g = G\dfrac{M}{r^2}$.

- Gravitational potential V. Gravitational potential *energy* of $m = mV$.

- Gravitational potential outside a spherically symmetric body: $V = -G\dfrac{M}{r}$.

- Gravitational potential difference, $\Delta V = -g\Delta x$. $\Delta V =$ area under g–x graph.

- Field strength = potential gradient = slope of V–x graph: $g = -\dfrac{\Delta V}{\Delta x}$.

- Conservation of energy for bodies moving in a gravitational field.

- Escape speed.

- Vector addition of field strengths due to a number of spherically symmetric bodies.

- Scalar addition of potentials due to a number of spherically symmetric bodies.

Orbits in gravitational fields

- Kepler's laws of planetary motion.

- Circular orbits and derivation of $T^2 = \dfrac{4\pi^2}{GM} r^3$.

- Planets and satellites in circular orbits.

- Rotating galaxies and dark matter.

- Binary systems: bodies rotate about centre of mass of system.

  Orbital radii: $r_1 = \dfrac{M_2}{M_1 + M_2} d$

  and $r_2 = \dfrac{M_1}{M_1 + M_2} d$ consistent with $M_1 r_1 = M_2 r_2$.

- Kepler's third law for binary systems: $T = 2\pi \sqrt{\dfrac{d^3}{G(M_1 + M_2)}}$.

- Finding radial velocities of stars by Doppler shift: $\dfrac{\Delta\lambda}{\lambda} = \dfrac{v}{c}$.

- Orbital speed $= \frac{1}{2}(v_{max} - v_{min})$.

- Determining a binary system from one body's orbit.

Knowledge and Understanding

PH5 Magnetism, Nuclei and Options

Essentially, this module explores applications of electric and magnetic fields while introducing radioactivity and nuclear energy. The capacitor is the first important device to be considered – its electric field, ability to store charge and energy are delved into, leading to the exponential discharge through a resistor. Magnetic fields start with the foundation of the force on a current carrying wire in a B-field before progressing to moving charges in B-fields and this leads to the theory of circular motion of particles in B-fields. Two sources of B-fields are then studied (long wire and solenoid). Particle accelerators and the Hall Effect are used as synoptic and difficult applications of magnetic fields giving some modern realism to this tricky topic.

Magnetism would not be complete without a study of electromagnetic induction. Faraday's and Lenz's laws are introduced along with applications of induced currents including explanations of a rotating coil generator. Inducing alternating EMFs is a natural precursor to the relationship between rms and peak values and their importance in calculating mean output powers in simple ac circuits. Some details of measuring alternating pd's and their frequencies with an oscilloscope are also provided. In contrast, the module finishes with radioactivity and nuclear energy. The three types of nuclear radiation, their properties and uses are discussed and a good grounding in the mathematical theory of radiation is provided. Nuclear energy is a natural progression to radioactivity where the mass energy equivalence is introduced. This advances to calculating energies released in nuclear reactions and binding energies per nucleon, which in turn leads to the binding energy per nucleon graph and its explanations of nuclear stability. The conclusion of the module is the increasingly important nuclear fission reactor along with some details of its operation and problems.

Revision checklist

Tick column 1 when you have completed brief revision notes.

Tick column 2 when you think you have a good grasp of the topic.

Tick column 3 during final revision when you feel you have mastered the topic.

			1	2	3	Notes
p57	**5.1**	**Capacitance**				
p57		Capacitors and charge				
p58		Define capacitance				
p58		E-field, energy and capacitance equations				
p60		Combining capacitors				
p62		Discharging a capacitor through a resistor				

			1	2	3	Notes
p65	**5.2**	**B-fields**				
p65		Force on a wire carrying current				
p66		Fleming's left-hand rule (FLHR)				
p66		Force on a charge moving in a magnetic field				
p68		The Hall probe				
p70		Magnetic fields				
p71		Force between two wires carrying a current				
p73		Ion beams and accelerators				
p77	**5.3**	**Electromagnetic induction**				
p77		Magnetic flux				
p78		Flux linkage				
p79		Faraday's law				
p82		Lenz's law				
p84		Rotating coil in a magnetic field				
p85		Alternating current and rms				
p87		The oscilloscope				
p90	**5.4**	**Radioactivity and radioisotopes**				
p90		Properties of α, β, and γ radiation				
p92		Differentiating between α, β, and γ radiation				
p93		Background radiation				
p93		Theory of radioactivity				
p95		Uses of radioisotopes				
p97	**5.5**	**Nuclear energy**				
p97		Mass–energy equivalence $E = mc^2$				
p98		Stability of nuclei				
p100		Binding energy/nucleon graph				
p101		Nuclear fission/fission reactors				

Capacitance

Capacitors and charge

Capacitors are simple devices that store charge. They are made of two parallel metal plates separated by an insulator. For A-level calculations, you will always have air or vacuum between the plates. In practice, capacitors will have other insulators (called **dielectrics**) between the plates. Dielectrics increase **capacitance** and some can increase capacitance by a factor of thousands.

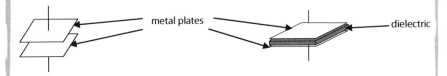

metal plates — dielectric

When a pd is applied to a capacitor, charge is transferred from the power supply to the plates. The plates then carry an equal and opposite charge (the net charge being zero in agreement with conservation of charge from PH1).

$+Q$ $-Q$

The amount of charge Q on each plate depends on the pd applied and the size of the capacitor, in fact it's proportional to both of them:

$$Q = CV$$

However, in the WJEC data sheet you'll see $C = \dfrac{Q}{V}$ and this is used as a definition of capacitance (see Key term).

There is a misconception that a capacitor is similar to a cell. This is not true. This misconception arises from poor use of terms regarding a 'charged' and 'discharged' cell – the person who decided to call cells or batteries 'charged' was either an idiot or a non-physicist. You should consider a cell to be a 'pump' that can provide a flow of charge until it has run out of chemical energy. A capacitor, on the other hand, really does require charging using a pd.

Key Terms

Capacitance =
$\dfrac{\text{charge on either plate}}{\text{pd between plates}}$
Unit: F (farad) [= C V^{-1}]

Dielectric = insulator between the plates of a capacitor, also serving to make the capacitance larger than if there were just empty space.

>> *Pointer*
You can also define capacitance by giving the equation $C = \dfrac{Q}{V}$ and defining the terms, i.e. C = capacitance, Q = charge held, V = pd across plates.

▲ **Grade boost**
The simplest way to increase the capacitance of a capacitor is to add a dielectric – this has been the answer to questions in the past.

Capacitance

This is the equation that you'll need to use in order to calculate the capacitance of actual metal plate capacitors:

$$C = \frac{\varepsilon_0 A}{d}$$

where A is the area of the plates, d is the distance between the plates and ε_0 is the permittivity of free space that you encountered in PH4. Three things to note here:

1. Capacitance is proportional to the plate area.
2. Capacitance is inversely proportional to separation of the plates.
3. You will only ever need to do calculations based on capacitors with air or vacuum between the plates so that you can use ε_0 (8.85×10^{-12} F m^{-1} which you'll see on the front of the WJEC data sheet).

Here's a typical easy starter question on capacitors:

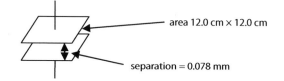

area 12.0 cm × 12.0 cm

separation = 0.078 mm

Calculate:

(i) The capacitance of the capacitor.

(ii) The charge stored on the capacitor when charged by a 14.3 V cell.

Answer

(i) $C = \dfrac{\varepsilon_0 A}{d} = \dfrac{8.85 \times 10^{-12} \times 0.12 \times 0.12}{0.078 \times 10^{-3}} = 1.63 \times 10^{-9}$ F (or 1.63 nF)

(ii) $Q = CV = 1.63 \times 10^{-9} \times 14.3 = 2.33 \times 10^{-8}$ C (or 23.3 nC)

The most difficult thing about these types of question is getting the unit conversions and the powers of 10 correct.

quickfire

①

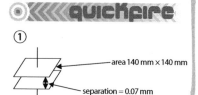

area 140 mm × 140 mm

separation = 0.07 mm

Calculate:

(i) The capacitance.

(ii) The pd required to store a charge of 211 nC.

quickfire

②

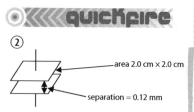

area 2.0 cm × 2.0 cm

separation = 0.12 mm

Calculate the charge held by the capacitor when charged by a cell of EMF 1.6 V.

E-field, energy and capacitance equations

The energy stored by a capacitor (or its internal energy U) is given by the equation:

$$U = \tfrac{1}{2}QV$$

This is the equation that appears on the WJEC data sheet but it can be combined with $Q = CV$ to provide another two equations:

$$U = \tfrac{1}{2}QV = \tfrac{1}{2}CV^2 = \frac{Q^2}{2C}$$

Here's a quick demonstration of the charge and energy that a capacitor can store. First, charge a large capacitor (~1000 µF) using a 9 V cell. Then disconnect the cell. Note that the charge held by the capacitor must remain after it has been disconnected because it has nowhere to go. Then touch the two legs of the capacitor to discharge it (short circuit). You should see a tiny little spark due to the large discharge current. How much charge and energy were stored by the 1000 µF capacitor?

$+Q$ $-Q$

$$Q = CV = 1000 \times 10^{-6} \times 9 = 0.009 \text{ C} \qquad \text{or} \qquad 9.0 \text{ mC}$$

and
$$U = \tfrac{1}{2}CV^2$$

$$U = \tfrac{1}{2} \times 1000 \times 10^{-6} \times 9^2 = 0.0405 \text{ J}$$

These are not very large numbers even though 1000 µF (1 mF) is a large capacitor for electronics. However, the current is a different matter altogether. When the legs of the capacitor are 'shorted' there is no resistance in the circuit – not even an internal resistance of a cell (see PH1). The only resistance present is the resistance of a few centimetres of tinned wire coming from the capacitor which will be ~0.01 Ω. With an initial pd of 9V, this gives an initial current of $I = \dfrac{V}{R} = \dfrac{9}{0.01} = 900$ A.

Another tricky concept that reappears from PH4 is the electric field (E-field). The E-field is uniform between capacitor plates and is given by the equation $E = \dfrac{V}{d}$.

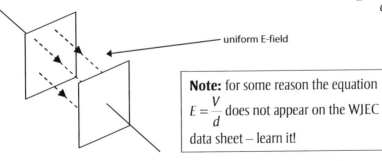
uniform E-field

Note: for some reason the equation $E = \dfrac{V}{d}$ does not appear on the WJEC data sheet – learn it!

There aren't many questions that an examiner can ask regarding the electric field in a capacitor but here's one that will set off some more sparks.

When air is subjected to an electric field greater than 3×10^6 V m^{-1} the air itself is said to 'break down' and a spark will jump across the gap of the field (this is what also happens in lightning). A parallel plate capacitor has square-shaped plates with air between them. The pd is increased across its plates until a spark discharge occurs when the pd is 540 V. The charge stored by the capacitor just before the spark appears is 8.7 µC. What are the dimensions of the capacitor?

quickpire

③

area 3.8 cm × 3.8 cm

The capacitor is charged by a 12 V power supply and stores a charge of 84 nC. Calculate the separation of the plates.

quickpire

④ A 470 µF capacitor is charged using a cell of EMF 9.52 V and is then discharged through a resistor of 0.24 Ω. Calculate:

  (i) The charge stored by the charged capacitor.

  (ii) The energy stored by the charged capacitor.

  (iii) The initial current when the capacitor starts to discharge.

quickpire

⑤ Calculate the separation of the plates of a capacitor given that a spark jumps across the plates when $V = 1650$ V (remember $E = 3 \times 10^6$ V m^{-1}).

⊙ ❰❰❰ quickfire

⑥ The energy stored in the capacitor in Quickfire 5 just before sparking was 4.2 J. Calculate the capacitance and the area of the plates. Is the separation and area of these plates achievable in your lab using tin foil?

⤊ Grade boost

The equations for combining capacitances are the same as combining resistances **but the parallel and series equations are switched**.

Answer

First, find the separation of the plates using the equation for the field:

$$E = \frac{V}{d} \quad \rightarrow \quad d = \frac{V}{E} = \frac{540}{3 \times 10^6} = 1.8 \times 10^{-4} \text{ m (0.18 mm)}$$

You can also calculate the capacitance:

$$C = \frac{Q}{V} = \frac{8.7 \times 10^{-6}}{540} = 1.61 \times 10^{-8} \text{ F (16.1 nF)}$$

Now you can calculate the area of the plates:

$$C = \frac{\varepsilon_0 A}{d} \quad \rightarrow \quad A = \frac{Cd}{\varepsilon_0} = \frac{1.61 \times 10^{-8} \times 1.8 \times 10^{-4}}{8.85 \times 10^{-12}} = 0.327 \text{ m}^2$$

because the question stated that the plates were square, length of sides of plates = $\sqrt{.0327} = 0.572$ m (or 57.2 cm)

Finally, the dimensions of the capacitor are (572 × 572 × 0.18) in mm.

Plates + gap on between.

Combining capacitors

Similar to resistors, capacitors can be combined either in parallel or in series. Although the formulae for combining capacitors are the same, the equations for the parallel and series cases are swapped.

Capacitors in series

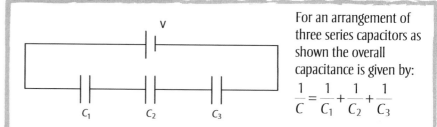

For an arrangement of three series capacitors as shown the overall capacitance is given by:

$$\frac{1}{C} = \frac{1}{C_1} + \frac{1}{C_2} + \frac{1}{C_3}$$

similar to the equation for resistors in parallel. This means that the overall capacitance is always less than the smallest capacitor, i.e. in a series combination you can't store as much charge – you can think of it as 'increasing' the separation of the plates and decreasing the overall capacitance.

Capacitors in parallel

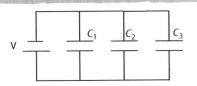

For an arrangement of three parallel capacitors as shown the overall capacitance is given by:

$$C = C_1 + C_2 + C_3$$

Exactly the same as for resistors in series, you simply add the capacitances to obtain the overall capacitance. A good way of looking at this is that your parallel capacitors are, effectively, one big capacitor with a bigger area. Hence, the capacitance increases and you can store more charge.

Examples

Calculate the overall capacitance of the following two combinations:

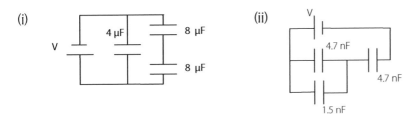

(i)

(ii)

Grade boost

In the last example of parallel capacitors it was easier to use nF and remember that the final answer must be in nF.

⑦ Calculate the overall capacitance:

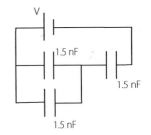

Answers

(i) The 8 µF in series with the other 8 µF gives 4 µF (no need for a calculator you should see that it's the same as two equal resistors in parallel). You now have two 4 µF capacitors in parallel which gives 8 µF (it would have been far more sensible just to have the one 8 µF capacitor in the first place).

(ii) First, the 4.7 nF in parallel with the 1.5 nF is easy, you add them and get an overall capacitance of 6.2 nF. Then you need to calculate the overall capacitance of 6.2 nF in series with 4.7 nF.

$$\frac{1}{C} = \frac{1}{C_1} + \frac{1}{C_2} = \frac{1}{6.2} + \frac{1}{4.7} = 0.374 \quad \rightarrow \quad C = \frac{1}{0.374} = 2.7 \text{ nF}$$

⑧ Calculate the overall capacitance:

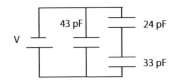

Discharging a capacitor through a resistor

The standard circuit for charging and discharging a capacitor is shown on the right. When the switch is up, the capacitor charges. When the switch is down, the capacitor discharges through the resistor.

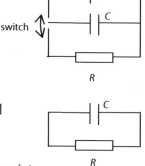

>> *Pointer*

You don't have to understand the origin of $Q = Q_0 e^{-t/RC}$ but you have to be able to use it.

Grade boost

Practise using the equation $Q = Q_0 e^{-t/RC}$ the maths is essential for PH6 also.

When the capacitor is discharging, you effectively have this circuit. The charged capacitor provides a pd across the resistor which gives a current.

The current through the resistor is $\dfrac{\Delta Q}{\Delta t}$ and from the point of view of the capacitor, this is the rate at which the capacitor is **losing** charge. For the capacitor you can write:

$$\frac{\Delta Q}{\Delta t} = -\text{current} = -\frac{V}{R} = -\frac{Q/C}{R} = -\frac{Q}{CR}$$

If you're doing A-level maths you should be able to integrate the above equation but from a physics point of view it's better to understand what the equation means and why the final answer makes sense.

The equation $\dfrac{\Delta Q}{\Delta t} = -\dfrac{Q}{CR}$ tells you that the capacitor is losing charge at a rate that is proportional to the charge on the capacitor $\left(\dfrac{\Delta Q}{\Delta t} \propto -Q\right)$. So, when the capacitor is fully charged, it loses charge quickly. As the charge decreases, the capacitor then loses charge at a slower rate.

If you plot a graph of charge on the capacitor against time, the charge must go from a certain value (Q_0 say) to zero. But you also know that the gradient of the line $\left(\dfrac{\Delta Q}{\Delta t}\right)$ is always decreasing (because $\dfrac{\Delta Q}{\Delta t} \propto -Q$). You can probably guess the shape of the graph – it's an exponential decay. This is always true when you have a variable that is decreasing at a rate proportional to the variable itself. In this case, the charge is decreasing at a rate proportional to the amount of charge held. A similar case (to a good approximation) is the flow of water out of a burette – the rate of decrease of height of water is proportional to the height of the water. Similarly, in radioactive decay, the rate of decrease of radioactive nuclei is proportional to the number of radioactive nuclei present. All these examples give exponential decays.

The equation for the discharging capacitor and its graph are shown.

$$Q = Q_0 e^{-t/RC}$$

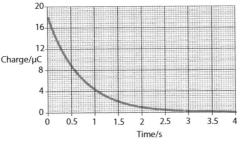

Example

In the discharge graph given, the pd used to charge the capacitor was 12.0 V. Use values from the graph to calculate:

  (i)   The value of the capacitor C.

  (ii) The value of the resistor R.

  (iii) **The time constant** (RC).

Answers

  (i) You need to notice (from the graph) that the initial charge on the capacitor is 18 μC then use the equation:

$$C = \frac{Q}{V} = \frac{18 \times 10^{-6}}{12} = 1.5 \times 10^{-6}\,\text{F} \qquad \text{(or 1.5 μF)}$$

  (ii) First rearrange a little

$$Q = Q_0 e^{-t/RC} \quad \rightarrow \quad \frac{Q}{Q_0} = e^{-t/RC}$$

now take logs

$$\ln\left(\frac{Q}{Q_0}\right) = \ln\left(e^{-t/RC}\right) = -\frac{t}{RC}$$

a bit more rearranging gives:

$$R = \frac{-t}{\ln\left(\dfrac{Q}{Q_0}\right)C}$$

Now all you need to do is plug in some numbers. First, $Q_0 = 18$ μC, then you need Q and t from the graph. There's no obvious choice to use but $t = 1.0$ s and $Q = 4.4$ μC seem quite sensible. This finally gives an answer:

$$R = \frac{-1}{\ln\left(\dfrac{4.4}{18}\right) \times 1.5 \times 10^{-6}} = 4.73 \times 10^5\,\Omega\ \text{(or 470 kΩ)}$$

≫ Pointer

Remember the circuit for charging and discharging a capacitor, it's useful and has been known to turn up on PH6.

≫ Pointer

You don't have to know the theory or the maths for the exponential decay but understanding the principles will be useful especially for later physics (i.e. $\dfrac{\Delta Q}{\Delta t} \propto -Q$ leading to exponential decay).

Grade boost

Get used to using the exponential equation; it comes up many times in A2 (discharging, radioactivity, biological measurement and in PH6). You'll also have to be able to take logs of the exponential equation to calculate times.

⑨ Do part (ii) of the example by calculating 37% of 18 μC then reading the time constant (RC) off the graph. Equate this value to RC to find a value for R.

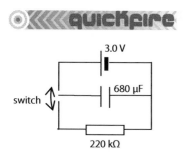

⑩ (i) In the circuit, how do you charge then discharge the capacitor?

(ii) Calculate the time constant.

(iii) Calculate the initial charge on the capacitor.

(iv) Calculate the time the capacitor takes to lose half its charge.

(v) What percentage of the energy of the capacitor remains when it has lost half its charge?

That was a lot of algebra just to find the resistance but don't worry, this type of manipulation is the most difficult that you'll ever come across at A-level.

(iii) This is a lot easier!

time constant = $RC = 4.73 \times 10^5 \times 1.5 \times 10^{-6} = 0.71$ s

You can do a quick check that the time constant is correct because after 1 time constant the capacitor should be 63% discharged (this is something that all electronics people memorise).

If you read the graph carefully you'll see that the charge is around 6.5 μC after 0.71 s. This 6.5 μC as a percentage of 18 μC is:

$$\frac{6.5}{18} \times 100 = 36\%$$

i.e. the capacitor is (100 – 36 =) 64% discharged which is close enough to 63% considering the size of the graph. Had you known this fact about the time constant before doing part (ii), you could have saved a lot of time and effort.

B-fields

The force on a wire carrying current in a magnetic field

Have a look at the wire shown between the poles of a strong magnet. Wires carrying a current at an angle to a magnetic field will experience a force. The force is given by the equation:

$$F = BI\ell \sin \theta$$

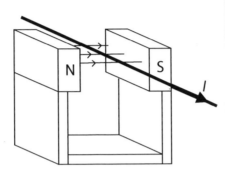

where B is the magnetic flux density (or B-field), I is the current, ℓ is the length of the wire in the B-field and θ is the angle between the wire and the magnetic field.

To obtain the maximum force (for a given field, wire and current) you need $\sin \theta = 1$. The angle θ should be 90°, i.e. the wire should be at right angles to the magnetic field (B-field). In the 3D diagram shown, the wire passes through the B-field perpendicular to the field lines so you can simplify the equation (in this case) to:

$$F = BI\ell$$

Now, let's calculate the greatest force you can exert on a wire in a typical lab. The maximum strength magnet you're likely to have in your lab will have $B = 0.2$ T (roughly) with a length between the poles of around 5 cm. The maximum current you're likely to get out of your most expensive power supply will be around 10 A. This gives a maximum force (using the above set-up) of:

$$F = 0.2 \times 10 \times 0.05 = 0.1 \text{ N}$$

Not very impressive really. Nonetheless, this is the effect that makes all electric motors work; from the motor in your Blu-ray player to the starter motor that starts your car every morning.

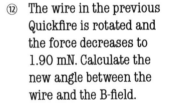

quickfire

⑪ Calculate the force acting on a wire of length 2.50 cm in a uniform magnetic flux density (B-field) of 0.144 T when the wire carries a current of 760 mA at an angle of 78.0° to the magnetic field.

quickfire

⑫ The wire in the previous Quickfire is rotated and the force decreases to 1.90 mN. Calculate the new angle between the wire and the B-field.

≫ Pointer

Questions on $F = BI\ell \sin \theta$ tend to be straightforward, the difficulty comes later with Fleming's left hand rule and $F = Bqv \sin \theta$.

» Pointer

Practise Fleming's left-hand rule, it comes up regularly.

» Pointer

Note that the force is always at right angles to both the field and the current.

⑬ State the direction of the forces on the wire

(i)

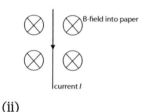

(ii)

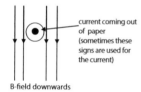

Fleming's left-hand rule (FLHR)

What about the direction of the force? This is one of the trickiest things to do at A-level because you have to think in 3D. You need to use Fleming's left-hand rule (or FLHR for short). Here's a picture of a hand to demonstrate the rule.

You need to align your **F**irst finger along the direction of the **F**ield (B-field) and your se**C**ond finger along the direction of the **C**urrent. Your thu**M**b will then point out the direction of **M**otion.

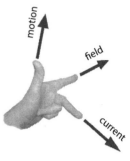

If you apply this rule to the initial set-up above, you'll find you don't have to move your left hand much from that in the diagram on the right to find that your thumb is pointing upwards indicating that the force on the wire is up. In exam papers, the set-up won't be quite so simple and you may have to contort your left hand into a strange position to find the correct direction.

Sometimes the magnetic field will not be represented by field lines but rather by arrow heads or arrow tails:

⊙ Signifies a field coming out of the paper

⊗ Signifies a field going into the paper

Examples

Using FLHR, you should be able to find that the force on the above wire is up.

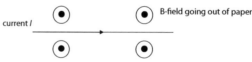

Now, if you turn your left hand upside down and point your first finger towards your face you should find that the force on the wire in the second example is down.

Force on a charge moving in a magnetic field

This theory is very similar to the force on a wire in a magnetic field and you'll need to use FLHR again to predict the direction of the force. The equation you'll be using is:

$$F = Bqv \sin \theta$$

where *B*, once again is the magnetic flux density (or B-field), *q* is the size of the moving charge, *v* is the velocity of the moving charge and *θ* is the angle between the velocity and the B-field. You can actually derive the equation $F = BI\ell \sin \theta$ using $F = Bqv \sin \theta$ and $I = nAve$

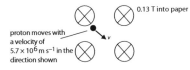

Example

A proton moves in a magnetic field as shown. Calculate the magnitude and direction of the force on the proton.

Answer

Perhaps this might be difficult to picture at first (you need to think in 3D) but the proton is moving at right angles to the B-field. Hence *θ* = 90°, and

$$F = Bqv \sin 90 = Bqv = 0.13 \times 1.6 \times 10^{-19} \times 5.7 \times 10^6 = 1.2 \times 10^{-13} \text{ N}$$

To find the direction, you use FLHR and use the direction of the proton velocity as the direction of the current. After pointing your first finger into the paper and rotating you should find that the direction of the force is as shown. Note that the force is at right angles to the velocity (and to the B-field).

Interestingly, if you consider a proton with the same speed but a slightly different direction (see diagram), the force will be the same magnitude but with a slightly different direction. With a net force at right angles to the motion you should see that this set-up will give circular motion. What is the radius of motion of the proton?

You should remember from circular motion in PH4:

$F = \dfrac{mv^2}{r}$ and you can equate this to the magnetic force $F = Bqv$

so $\dfrac{mv^2}{r} = Bqv \rightarrow \dfrac{mv}{r} = Bq \rightarrow r = \dfrac{mv}{Bq}$

putting in the actual numbers $r = \dfrac{1.67 \times 10^{-27} \times 5.7 \times 10^6}{0.13 \times 1.6 \times 10^{-19}} = 0.46$ m (or 46 cm)

The fact that charged particles tend to perform circular motion in magnetic fields is extremely useful and led to the development of the TV, the discovery of the mass of the electron as well as being used in particle accelerators and mass spectrometers.

Example

The diagram shows an electron moving in a circular path in a B-field that is coming out of the paper as shown. Place an arrow on the path to show the direction of motion of the electron.

Grade boost

Remember how to derive $r = \dfrac{mv}{Bq}$ using $\dfrac{mv^2}{r} = Bqv$. There are often questions on circular motion due to charged particles in B-fields.

⑭ Derive the equation $F = BI\ell \sin \theta$ from considering a force of $F = Bqv \sin \theta$ on electrons in a wire of cross-sectional area *A* and length ℓ in a uniform field *B*.

⑮ Calculate the force on an electron travelling at a velocity of 25×10^6 m s⁻¹ at an angle of 35° to a uniform B-field of 3.4×10^{-3} T

⑯ By equating the other expression for the centripetal force ($m\omega^2 r$) to the force on a charged particle (Bqv), derive the expression $\omega = \dfrac{Bq}{m}$ (which is the equation that led to the design of the cyclotron).

Answer

You need to apply FLHR to some point on the electron's path and remember that the force (thumb) is towards the centre of the circle (it's a centripetal force). Your second finger will then give you the current. Unfortunately, the charge on an electron is negative, so you have to reverse the direction of the current to get the direction of motion of the electron. You should eventually arrive at the answer that the electron is going anticlockwise along the circular path.

The Hall probe

Grade boost

Know your Hall probe well. It's a favourite question worth around 10 marks. You'll often have to apply FLHR, use $Bev = Ee$, $E = \dfrac{V}{d}$ and even calculate n (giving its unit as m^{-3}).

This is a particularly important device for measuring B-fields but it is also used continuously in research and high-tech. facilities to measure electron properties in semiconductor chips. Here's how it works:

Hall probe

current

B-field into Hall probe

If you apply FLHR to the set-up you should find that the force is upwards on the free electrons that are providing the current. This means that the free electrons will move toward the top face of the Hall probe making the top of the Hall probe negatively charged. This cannot carry on forever because the electrons will be repelled by the negative charge on the top surface. Very soon, an equilibrium will be reached when the magnetic force (Bqv or Bev) is balanced by the electric repulsion force. But what is this electric repulsion force? You should remember that the force is the electric field multiplied by the charge (Eq or Ee from PH4). Now for a little bit of algebra:

Magnetic force = electric force

$$Bev = Ee \quad \rightarrow \quad Bv = E$$

but the electric field can be related to the pd between the bottom and top plate using the equation $E = \dfrac{V}{d}$ (same as for a capacitor). Hence,

$$Bv = E = \frac{V}{d} \quad \rightarrow \quad V = Bvd \quad {***}$$

and it's this pd across the Hall probe that you can actually measure using a simple voltmeter. This pd is usually called the Hall voltage (V_H). You get an idea of how this Hall voltage is useful when you realise that v is the drift velocity of the electrons. So you can measure the drift velocity if you know the dimensions of the Hall probe (in this case d) and the B-field (V_H you can measure with your voltmeter).

$$v = \frac{V_H}{Bd}$$

but you can go even further if you've got an ammeter and know the equation $I = nAve$.

⑰ Show how you'd connect a voltmeter to the Hall probe to measure the Hall voltage.

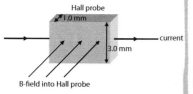

Hall probe
1.0 mm
current
3.0 mm
B-field into Hall probe

⑱ The Hall voltage in Quickfire 17 is 3.6×10^{-6} V. Calculate the electric field associated with this Hall voltage.

rearranging for v gives $v = \dfrac{I}{nAe}$ then substitute in $v = \dfrac{V_H}{Bd}$

$$\frac{I}{nAe} = \frac{V_H}{Bd} \quad \rightarrow \quad n = \frac{IBd}{V_H Ae}$$

You can simplify this expression for n further when you realise that the cross-sectional area (A) of the probe is $A = t \times d$:

$$n = \frac{IBd}{V_H t \times de} = \frac{IB}{V_H te}$$

Quite incredible when you think about it. You can actually measure the drift velocity and number of free electrons per m³ just by using a cheap little ammeter and voltmeter (although you do need to know your B-field and d and t for your probe).

Tricky Hall probe example

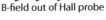 $\star$ Arrows = conventional / real ?? $\star$

(i) Connect a voltmeter correctly to the probe to show how you would measure the Hall voltage.

(ii) Explain which face of the probe will become positive (the current is due to free electrons).

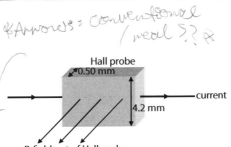

Hall probe
0.50 mm
4.2 mm
current
B-field out of Hall probe

(iii) The Hall voltage is 820 nV and the B-field is 0.14 T. Calculate the drift velocity of the free electrons.

(iv) The current is 0.47 mA. Calculate the number of free electrons per unit volume.

Answers

(i) Attach the voltmeter (right) to the top and bottom face of the above Hall probe.

(ii) The force is down (using FLHR) so the bottom face becomes negative and the top face becomes positive (due to a deficiency of electrons).

(iii) From $Bev = Ee \rightarrow Bv = E \rightarrow Bv = \dfrac{V_H}{d} \rightarrow v = \dfrac{V_H}{Bd}$

so $v = \dfrac{V_H}{Bd} = \dfrac{820 \times 10^{-9}}{0.14 \times 4.2 \times 10^{-3}} = 1.39 \times 10^{-3}$ m s⁻¹ (or 1.39 mm s⁻¹)

(iv) The equation has been derived earlier but here it is again:

$$\frac{I}{nAe} = \frac{V_H}{Bd} \rightarrow n = \frac{IBd}{V_H Ae} = \frac{IB}{V_H te} = \frac{0.47 \times 10^{-3} \times 0.14}{820 \times 10^{-9} \times 0.50 \times 10^{-3} \times 1.6 \times 10^{-19}}$$

$$n = 1.00 \times 10^{24} \text{ m}^{-3}$$

⟫ **Pointer**

You can rearrange

$$n = \frac{IB}{V_H te} \text{ to get } V_H = \frac{BI}{nte},$$

i.e. the Hall voltage is proportional to the B-field. This is why Hall probes are often used to measure B.

⚑ **Grade boost**

If you're a B–A* candidate, you should be comfortable in deriving all the Hall Effect equations – just remember the principles and the equations will come naturally. If you're not comfortable deriving the equations, memorise them – some weaker candidates earn extra marks with this tactic.

Hall probe for Quickfires 19–22

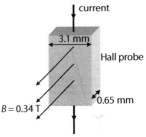

current
3.1 mm
Hall probe
0.65 mm
$B = 0.34$ T

⊙⦻⦅⦅⦅ **quickfire**

⑲ Show how you would connect a voltmeter to the Hall probe to measure the Hall voltage.

⊙⦻⦅⦅⦅ **quickfire**

⑳ The charge carriers are free electrons. Explain why the right face of the probe becomes positive.

⊙⦻⦅⦅⦅ **quickfire**

㉑ The Hall voltage is 1.35 μV. Calculate: (i) the Hall field (E) and (ii) the drift velocity of electrons.

⊙ ⫷⫷⫷⫷ **quickpire**

② The current is 870 μA. Calculate *n* and give its unit.

Using a Hall probe to measure a B-field

This is the last thing you need to know about the Hall probe.

When measuring a B-field with a Hall probe you simply need to:

(i) place the probe in the field and

(ii) orientate it so that its front face is at right angles to the B-field (alternatively you can just twiddle it around until you get a maximum reading).

Magnetic fields

Here are two magnetic fields that you should be able to sketch:

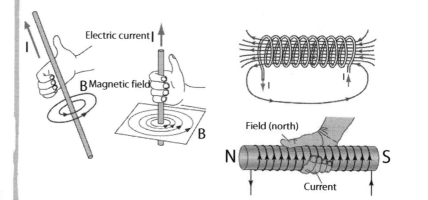

》 *Pointer*

You need to learn these sketches of field lines but you may remember them from GCSE.

⊙ ⫷⫷⫷⫷ **quickpire**

② Sketch the field lines

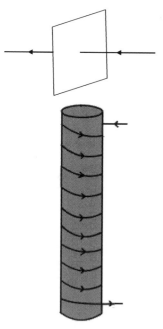

The two diagrams on the left show the magnetic field lines due to a long wire, and the two diagrams on the right show the magnetic field due to a long solenoid (cylindrical coil of wire). You'll need to know the directions of the field also but the good news is that the right-hand grip rule works for both (see diagrams). For the straight wire, place your thumb in the direction of the current and your grip follows the direction of the field lines. For the solenoid, let your grip follow the route of the current and your thumb will point in the direction of the B-field *inside* the solenoid.

You'll also need to do calculations based on the magnetic field of a long wire and the magnetic field of a long solenoid (both equations are on the data sheet).

For a long wire, the magnetic flux density (B-field) is given by:

$$B = \frac{\mu_0 I}{2\pi a}$$

where μ_0 is the permeability of free space, I is the current in the wire and a is the shortest distance to the wire.

Inside a long solenoid, the magnetic flux density is given by:

$$B = \mu_0 n I$$

where μ_0 is still the permeability of free space, I is the current in the solenoid and n is the number of turns per unit length of the solenoid.

Examples

(i) Calculate the magnetic flux density at a distance of 2.7 mm from a long wire carrying a current of 5.2 A.

(ii) A solenoid of length 145 cm has 26 500 turns and carries a current of 358 mA. Calculate the magnetic flux density inside the solenoid.

Answers

(i) $B = \dfrac{\mu_0 I}{2\pi a} = \dfrac{4\pi \times 10^{-7} \times 5.2}{2\pi \times 2.7 \times 10^{-3}} = 0.39$ mT

(ii) $n = \dfrac{26500}{1.45} = 18300$ turns per metre

$B = 4\pi \times 10^{-7} \times 18300 \times 0.358 = 8.23$ mT

One final thing that you need to know about solenoids is this. An iron core inside a solenoid increases hugely the magnetic field strength. From the equation $B = \mu_0 n I$ you should see that doubling the current will double the magnetic flux density and likewise the number of turns per unit length. However, putting a nearly pure iron core will increase the B-field by a factor of many thousands (even up to 200 000 times for pure iron).

Force between two wires carrying a current

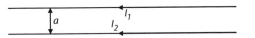

When two wires carry a current they will exert forces on one another. The reason for this is as follows:

1 The top wire has a magnetic field.
2 The bottom wire is in this field.
3 The bottom wire 'feels' a force due to $F = BI\ell \sin\theta$.

Of course, the reverse argument is absolutely valid:

1 The bottom wire has a magnetic field.
2 The top wire is in this field.
3 The top wire 'feels' a force due to $F = BI\ell \sin\theta$.

How large is the force and what's its direction?

To answer this you need the formula:

$$B = \frac{\mu_0 I}{2\pi a} = \frac{\mu_0 I_1}{2\pi a}$$

For the field due to the top wire in the position of the bottom wire: you should recall the shape of the circular field lines around the wire and realise that the

㉔ A solenoid has a B-field inside it of 1.75 mT while carrying a current of 0.240 A. Calculate the number of turns per metre of the solenoid.

㉕ A long wire carries a large constant current of 214 A. When does the magnetic flux density become greater than 1 mT?

㉖ Use FLHR and the right-hand grip rule to show that the magnetic force acting between the two parallel wires is repulsive.

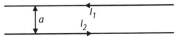

quickfire

㉗ Calculate the force per unit length acting on the long wires shown.

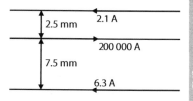

quickfire

㉘ Show that the force acting on the middle wire is zero (hint: the middle wire is in the field due to the other two wires, so you only need to consider the field due to the top and bottom wires).

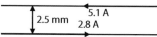

B-field (due to the top wire) will be coming out of the paper at the position of the bottom wire. This is at right angles to the direction of the current in the wire, so $\sin \theta = 1$.

Now using $F = BI\ell \sin \theta$ for the bottom wire.

$$F = BI\ell \sin \theta = \frac{\mu_0 I_1}{2\pi a} \times I_2 \times \ell \sin \theta = \frac{\mu_0 I_1 I_2 \ell}{2\pi a}$$

For the direction you'll need FLHR. The field is coming out of the paper so point your first finger towards your face and you should find that the force on the bottom wire is upward. By Newton's 3rd law, the force on the top wire must be of equal size and downward (i.e., two parallel wires carrying a current in the same direction experience an attractive force).

Let's see if it's possible to get a big force between wires in a lab. You might be able to get your hands on the 10 A power supply again and have two 5 m long wires maybe 1 mm apart. This gives a force of:

$$F = \frac{\mu_0 I_1 I_2 \ell}{2\pi a} = \frac{4\pi \times 10^{-7} \times 10 \times 10 \times 5}{2\pi \times 0.001} = 0.1 \text{ N} \quad \text{(again, not a large force)}$$

Although this force is not exactly impressive, it is, in fact, used for the definition of the **ampere**. The actual definition is this:

The ampere is the current that flows through two infinite, thin, parallel wires, one metre apart in vacuum, producing a force between the wires of exactly 2×10^{-7} N per metre of length. **Unit: A**.

Let's check to see if this is definition makes sense:

$$F = \frac{\mu_0 I_1 I_2 \ell}{2\pi a} \quad \rightarrow \quad \frac{F}{\ell} = \frac{\mu_0 I_1 I_2}{2\pi a}$$

but the definition says that both currents = 1A. This gives a force per unit length $\left(\frac{F}{\ell}\right)$ of

$$\frac{F}{\ell} = \frac{4\pi \times 10^{-7} \times 1 \times 1}{2\pi \times 1} = 2 \times 10^{-7} \text{ N m}^{-1}$$

which is exactly what it said in the definition – it makes sense.

Ion beams and accelerators

In PH5 you also need to know a little about the effect of magnetic and electric fields on ion beams and this leads naturally to particle accelerators. You don't have to memorise the details of the particle accelerators but you need to be able to apply the physics you already know to them.

Let's start with the very first particle accelerator that was invented in the 1850s. This was just an empty glass tube with a cathode and anode to accelerate electrons.

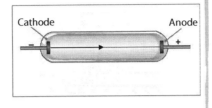

Similar to a capacitor, there's a uniform electric field between the cathode and the anode. This is what accelerates the electrons and you can calculate the acceleration using the following equation (not in the data sheet):

$$F = Eq$$

but you can combine the above equation with $E = \dfrac{V}{d}$ and $F = ma$ to give

$$a = \frac{Vq}{md}$$

If the distance between the cathode and the anode is 10 cm and you apply a pd of 100 V. You get rather a large acceleration:

$$a = \frac{Vq}{md} = \frac{100 \times 1.6 \times 10^{-19}}{9.11 \times 10^{-31} \times 0.1} = 1.8 \times 10^{14}\ \mathrm{m\,s^{-2}}$$

How much energy has the electron gained just before it reaches the anode? using $W = q\Delta V_E$ (from PH4)
$$= 1.6 \times 10^{-19} \times 100 = 1.6 \times 10^{-17}\ \mathrm{J}$$

This is where a new unit of energy is defined – the **electron-volt** (eV). It's the energy gained by an electron when accelerated through a pd of 1 V, i.e. the energy gained by the electron above was 100 eV because it was accelerated through 100 V.

The particle accelerator on the right is slightly more complicated. It also has a vertical electric field to deflect the electrons. Obviously the electrons will be attracted to the positively charged plates.

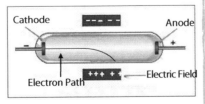

This means that they are accelerated from left to right but are also deflected downwards as shown. The upper and lower plates will behave like a capacitor and there will be a uniform field between them. The electrons will therefore experience a constant force downwards of $E_{\mathrm{vertical}}q$.

≫ Pointer

The constant acceleration of the electrons means that you can apply the constant acceleration equations to the electron motion (see q3, PH5 2010).

 **quickfire**

㉙ Use $F = Eq$, $E = \dfrac{V}{d}$ and $F = ma$ to derive $a = \dfrac{Vq}{md}$

 **quickfire**

㉚ Equate the 100 eV of energy to $\frac{1}{2}mv^2$ for an electron to calculate the speed of an electron after it has been accelerated through 100 V.

 **quickfire**

㉛ An electron is accelerated through a pd of 5.78 V. Calculate its final KE in:

(i) eV.

(ii) J.

Linear accelerator (Linac)

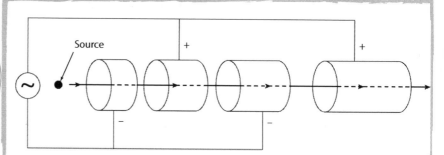

㉜ A proton has a KE of 5.7 keV and it was accelerated from rest using an electric field.

  (i) What was the pd between which the proton was accelerated?

  (ii) Calculate the KE of the proton in J.

》 Pointer

The electric field always increases the speed of the charged particles while the magnetic field keeps their paths circular.

This is a series of tubes that are charged either +ve or –ve depending on the alternating pd sent to them. First, let's say that a proton is accelerated to the right towards the –ve tube. When the proton arrives inside the tube there is no force acting on it and this is when the direction of the pd changes. When the proton is in the next gap between the tubes, the second tube is now –ve and the electric field accelerates it to the right again. The important thing is to ensure that the pd is synchronised so that the proton is inside a tube as the pd changes direction. This is achieved by keeping the frequency constant but increasing the lengths of the tubes and the gaps between them (because the proton is travelling a greater and greater distance in the same time).

㉝ Calculate the frequency of a cyclotron if it's accelerating electrons in a field of 0.115 T.

㉞ The alternating pd of a Linac is 125 kV. Through how many tubes must a proton pass before it has 750 keV of energy?

Cyclotron

Again the acceleration (or speed increase) is provided by an electric field. As a proton (say) is in the gap between the two Dees (semi-circular plates) it's accelerated across the gap by an electric field. The magnetic field shown keeps the proton in a circular motion,

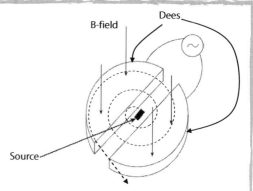

but as the speed of the proton increases so does the radius of its circle. Hence the proton spirals out and eventually leaves the cyclotron.

㉟ In Quickfire 34 how would your answer change for:

  (i) an electron?

  (ii) a helium nucleus (hint: with charge +2e)?

This is where the previous Quickfire 16 is handy. You can calculate the frequency of the pd from the theory:

$m\omega^2 r = Bqv$ but from circular motion $v = \omega r$

$m\omega^2 \cancel{r} = Bq\omega \cancel{r}$

$$m\omega = Bq \rightarrow \omega = \frac{Bq}{m} \quad \text{but} \quad \omega = 2\pi f \rightarrow f = \frac{Bq}{2\pi m}$$

Note that the frequency is a constant because the B-field is uniform and q and m are both constants. This is the beauty of the cyclotron – the frequency stays the same even as the velocity of the charged particle is increasing.

Example

Calculate the frequency of the pd supply for a cyclotron accelerating protons in a uniform magnetic flux density of 4.22 T, ($m_p = 1.67 \times 10^{-27}$ kg).

Answer

$$f = \frac{4.22 \times 1.60 \times 10^{-19}}{2\pi \times 1.67 \times 10^{-27}} = 64.3 \times 10^6 \text{ Hz (or 64.3 MHz)}$$

Synchrotron ✗ Controlled cyclotron !✗

The diagram on the right is a simplified synchrotron but it shows the fundamental principles of its operation. The speed increase is again provided by the alternating pd and, again, the charged particles will be performing circular motion due to the B-field. The acceleration now occurs 4 times per 'orbit' when the particles

✗ Uniform field all across ✗

B-field out of paper

Source

are crossing between the differently charged tubes. In contrast to the cyclotron, however, the path remains constant (same radius) so the B-field must increase in strength as the particles move quicker. Also, the frequency of the ac supply must increase as the particles' speed increases.

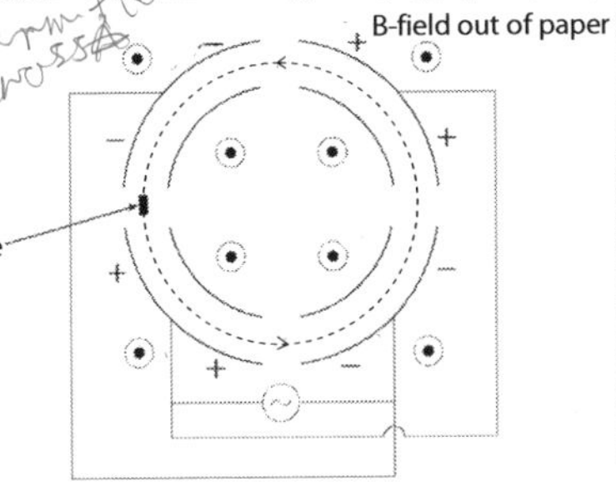

Example

A synchrotron operates with a pd of 30 kV. What is the increase of KE of a helium nucleus after it has completed 8 cycles of the synchrotron?

Answer

A helium nucleus has a charge of $+2e$, therefore each time it crosses a gap it gains 60 keV of energy. Each cycle means being accelerated 4 times, hence the increased KE will be:

$$60 \text{ keV} \times 4 \times 8 = 1920 \text{ keV} (= 1.92 \text{ MeV})$$

Example

Calculate the speed of a helium nucleus with a KE of 1.92 MeV.

Answer

First the conversion

$$1.92 \text{ MeV} = 1.92 \times 10^6 \times 1.6 \times 10^{-19} \text{ J}$$

then you need $\qquad KE = \frac{1}{2}mv^2$

rearranged gives $\qquad v = \sqrt{\dfrac{2 \times KE}{m}}$

---

quickfire

(36) Why can't particle accelerators accelerate neutrons?

quickfire

(37) In the diagram of the synchrotron, use FLHR to work out whether the particle being accelerated is +ve or −ve.

Grade boost

Always, for circular motion (including gravitational orbits PH4)
$\dfrac{mv^2}{r}$ = Net force or
$m\omega^2 r$ = Net force

Grade boost

In general, if you're given or need to calculate a velocity use $\dfrac{mv^2}{r}$ = Net force but if it's period, frequency or angular velocity use $m\omega^2 r$ = Net force

>> Pointer

You often have to work out speeds of particles with a particular KE, $v = \sqrt{\dfrac{2 \times KE}{m}}$ is quite a useful equation to remember.

quickfire

㊳ The speed of an electron being accelerated in a synchrotron is doubled. What is the change in:

(i) the frequency of the ac voltage?

(ii) the B-field?

(iii) the KE of the electron?

a mass of 4u is good enough for this calculation but this would be given in an exam question:

$$v = \sqrt{\frac{2 \times 1.92 \times 10^6 \times 1.6 \times 10^{-19}}{4 \times 1.66 \times 10^{-27}}} = 9.62 \times 10^6 \ \text{m s}^{-1}$$

Example

The radius of a synchrotron is 4.80 m. Calculate the (instantaneous) magnetic flux density (B) and frequency of the pd when the particles being accelerated are helium nuclei with a speed of $9.62 \times 10^6 \ \text{m s}^{-1}$.

Answer

Using $\dfrac{mv^2}{r} = Bqv \quad \rightarrow \quad B = \dfrac{mv}{qr} = \dfrac{4 \times 1.66 \times 10^{-27} \times 9.62 \times 10^6}{2 \times 1.6 \times 10^{-19} \times 4.80} = 0.0416 \ \text{T}$

(see earlier)

and using $m\omega^2 r = Bq\omega r \quad \rightarrow \quad f = \dfrac{Bq}{2\pi m} = \dfrac{0.0416 \times 2 \times 1.6 \times 10^{-19}}{2\pi \times 4 \times 1.66 \times 10^{-27}} = 320 \ \text{kHz}$

(see earlier)

However, this is the frequency of performing circles, the frequency of the ac supply will be twice this (because in one period of the alternating supply the particle is accelerated twice and the particle is accelerated 4 times in one orbit of the synchrotron):

$$\text{Frequency of the ac supply} = 640 \ \text{kHz}$$

Electromagnetic induction

This is the effect responsible for producing electricity and could well be the single most valuable discovery leading to our high standards of living in the 21st century. The bad news is that the concept of electromagnetic induction is quite difficult to understand and usually challenges students when they face it in the exam. Moving wires and coils in magnetic fields (or stationary coils and wires in changing magnetic fields) all seem a little invisible and mysterious but it nearly all comes down to understanding one simple law which you'll come across later – Faraday's law.

Magnetic flux

Here's a quick definition that will give you an idea of why the B-field is often given the strange-sounding name of *magnetic flux density*. Take a look at the diagram of a surface of area A in a uniform B-field.

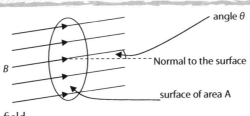

In this set up, the **magnetic flux** of the surface is defined as:

$\Phi = AB$ cos θ.

You also need to remember the unit of magnetic flux – the weber, Wb. If you can't remember this in an exam, use a bit of common sense and write the unit as Tm^2 and save yourself the possible deduction of a mark (see Pointer).

In many respects, the difficulty has already started because you have to imagine an area and an invisible magnetic field. However, the area will nearly always be the area of some sort of a loop of wire and won't be related to an imaginary surface.

By rearranging the equation and taking θ = zero (which it will be for nearly all A-level questions):

$$B = \frac{\Phi}{A}$$

so that the B-field is the magnetic flux divided by the area or, in other words, the *magnetic flux density* (and hence the strange name).

》 Pointer
You can often obtain an alternative unit using an equation, e.g. the unit of magnetic flux (Wb) is $m^2 \times T$ from $\Phi = AB$ cos θ, (remember that cos θ is a ratio and dimensionless).

》 Pointer
Magnetic flux may seem strange, abstract and useless but it'll be essential when you get to Faraday's law later.

Example

The magnetic flux through a coil of area $32\ cm^2$ is 8.7 µWb. The B-field through the coil is uniform and always at right angles to the area enclosed by the coil. Calculate B, the magnetic flux density.

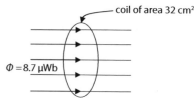

coil of area 32 cm²

$\Phi = 8.7$ µWb

Answer

First, $\theta = 0$ and you can use the rearranged version of the equation shown above

$$B = \frac{\Phi}{A} = \frac{8.7 \times 10^{-6}}{32 \times 10^{-4}} = 2.7 \text{ mT}$$

quickfire

(39) The axis of a metal circular loop is at an angle of 27° to the B-field that passes through it and the area of the loop is $4.6 \times 10^{-2}\ m^2$. If the B-field is 0.034 T, calculate the magnetic flux of the loop.

Flux linkage

This is no more complicated than magnetic flux but refers to many loops rather than one loop.

If a coil has N loops and the magnetic flux through each loop is Φ then it should seem quite obvious that the total magnetic flux for all the loops is:

 total magnetic flux for the whole of the coil = **flux linkage** = $N\Phi$

The unit of flux linkage is also the weber (or even better the weber-turn) and most of the time you'll be able to write:

flux linkage $= N\Phi = BAN$

Because $\cos \theta = 1$ and the same flux passes through each of the N loops (or turns).

>> **Pointer**

Again, flux linkage by itself isn't much use but it's essential in applying Faraday's law.

Example

A solenoid (cylindrical coil of wire) has 3600 turns (or loops). A uniform magnetic flux density of 3.8 mT passes through the centre of the solenoid parallel to its axis. The solenoid has a circular cross-section of radius 5.3 cm. Calculate the flux linkage for the solenoid.

radius
5.3 cm

3.8 mT

Grade boost

Take the time to really make sure you understand and can explain electromagnetic induction. It often receives the lowest mark of all questions on the PH5 exam paper.

Answer

Once again, you have $\theta = 0$ and $\cos \theta = 1$ (the 3600 loops will be much flatter than the simplified diagram), so the flux for each turn is:

$$\Phi = AB = \pi r^2 B = \pi \times 0.053^2 \times 0.0038 = 3.35 \times 10^{-5} \text{ Wb}$$

Then you need to use the equation for the flux linkage:

$$\text{flux linkage} = N\Phi = 3600 \times 3.35 \times 10^{-5} = 0.12 \text{ Wb-turn}$$

Faraday's law

Key Term

Faraday's law = the induced EMF is equal to the rate of change of the magnetic flux linkage.

Only a short sentence (see Key term) but every single dynamo and transformer is based on this law.

Alternatively, you can state **Faraday's law** in mathematical form:

$$V = -\frac{\Delta(BAN)}{\Delta t} \qquad \text{or also acceptable} \qquad V = -\frac{(BAN)}{t}$$

where *BAN* is the flux linkage. As this is a law that you're often asked to quote, you will not find the equation on the WJEC data sheet.

You should realise that there are two ways of inducing an EMF from Faraday's law:

1 Varying the B-field.
2 Varying the area (through some sort of motion).

A transformer makes use of the first method:

A question that has been set in the past is the following:

'Explain, using Faraday's law, how an alternating current in the primary coil leads to an alternating induced EMF in the secondary.'

Answer

- The alternating current in the primary coil provides an alternating magnetic field inside it.
- The magnetic field lines follow the iron core to the secondary coil.
- The magnetic field inside the secondary coil is alternating because the current in the primary is alternating.
- An alternating EMF is induced in the secondary coil because of the changing flux linkage according to Faraday's law.

quickfire

(40) A solenoid has 830 turns and its radius is 0.125 m. The solenoid is in a uniform B-field of 2.5 mT making an angle of 26° with the axis of the solenoid. Calculate the flux linkage of the solenoid.

》 Pointer

Some students might prefer an alternative version of Faraday's law – *The induced EMF is equal to the rate of flux cutting.*

» Pointer

It's the flux inside the shaded area that's increasing for this set-up.

» Pointer

Alternatively, it's the flux lines inside the shaded area that have been cut.

▲ Grade boost

You can sometimes obtain many marks by remembering the equation $V = B\ell v$.

Example employing a changing area

This is a favourite set-up and actually comes from a 2008 paper. A thick conductor slides along the rail tracks at 34 m s^{-1} as shown. Calculate the EMF induced and the current flowing through the resistor.

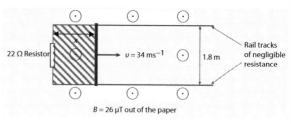

Answer

Start with Faraday's mathematical expression:

$$V = -\frac{\Delta(BAN)}{\Delta t} \quad \text{or} \quad -\frac{(BAN)}{t}$$

and you should note that N = 1 (there's definitely only 1 loop, shaded) and that the B-field is a constant. Hence,

$$V = -B\frac{\Delta A}{\Delta t} \quad \text{or} \quad -B\frac{A}{t}$$

but the area A is given by $A = l \times x$ where l is the length of the conducting bar (1.8 m)

$$V = -B\frac{\Delta(lx)}{\Delta t} = -Bl\frac{\Delta x}{\Delta t} \doteq -Blv \text{ ***} \quad \text{or} \quad -B\frac{lx}{t} \quad \text{etc.}$$

because $\frac{\Delta x}{\Delta t}\left(\text{or } \frac{x}{t}\right)$ is the speed v. Putting in the numbers gives an EMF of

$$V = Blv = 26 \times 10^{-6} \times 1.8 \times 34 = 1.59 \text{ mV}$$

Finally, to calculate the current

$$I = \frac{V}{R} = \frac{1.59 \times 10^{-3}}{22} = 72 \text{ μA}$$

There are some interesting things to point out here that should help your understanding of Faraday's law:

1. You don't have to use deltas (Δ) or any sort of calculus notation for the type of question that can be asked at A2 level.
2. If you prefer the flux cutting approach, you'll get exactly the same answer and exactly the same steps because the area ($l \times x$) is the area of the field lines that have been cut.

3. Notice the equation with a triple asterisk ($V = -Blv$). A very similar equation was given a triple asterisk in the Hall Effect also ($V = Bvd$ in 5.2 page 68). This is a useful result to remember if you get stuck in your derivations (for both the Hall probe and electromagnetic induction). Remember that l (or d) is the dimension that is perpendicular to both the velocity and the B-field.

An alternative approach to the last question might also help you understand Faraday's law. You can consider the moving conductor as a cell providing the EMF for the whole circuit. The free electrons within the conductor will experience a force of Bqv because they are moving within a magnetic field. If you apply FLHR to these electrons, they will move upward (note that all the other electrons and protons will experience a force too but they aren't free to move). The work done on an electron moving from the bottom of the conductor to the top is:

$$Bqv \times l$$

i.e. work = force × distance. But thinking of the moving conductor as a cell providing the (induced) EMF. The work done is also:

$$Vq$$

i.e. work done = pd × charge. Equating these gives exactly the same result:

$$Bqv \times l = Vq \qquad \rightarrow \qquad V = Blv$$

quickfire

41　The flux linkage in a solenoid changes from 7.3 Wb to 4.1 Wb and the EMF induced is 213 V. Calculate the time for the flux linkage to change.

Example using a changing B-field

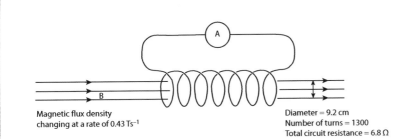

Magnetic flux density changing at a rate of 0.43 Ts⁻¹

Diameter = 9.2 cm
Number of turns = 1300
Total circuit resistance = 6.8 Ω

What is the reading on the ammeter?

Answer

Again, start with Faraday's mathematical expression:

$$V = -\frac{\Delta(BAN)}{\Delta t} \qquad \text{or} \qquad -\frac{BAN}{t}$$

and you should note that A and N are constants. Hence,

$$V = -AN\frac{\Delta B}{\Delta t} \qquad \text{or} \qquad -AN\frac{B}{t}$$

quickfire

42　The magnetic flux through a coil is 2.7 μWb and the coil is at right angles to a B-field of 5.1 mT. Calculate the area of the coil.

quickfire

43　A magnet is moved towards a solenoid and then away from it. A voltmeter connected across the solenoid reads positive then negative. Explain these observations using Faraday's law.

quickfire

(44) A uniform B-field along the axis of a solenoid changes from 0 T to 7.5 mT in 44 ms. The solenoid has 260 turns and a cross-sectional area of 25 cm². Calculate the induced EMF.

quickfire

(45) The B-field inside the last solenoid remains a constant 7.5 mT. Explain why the induced EMF is zero.

but the question states that the B-field is changing at a rate of 0.43 T s^{-1} i.e.

$$\frac{\Delta B}{\Delta t} = 0.43 \qquad \text{or} \qquad \frac{B}{t} = 0.43$$

Also, the area will be given by $\pi r^2 = \pi \dfrac{d^2}{4}$

$$V = -AN\frac{\Delta B}{\Delta t} = \pi\frac{d^2}{4}N\frac{\Delta B}{\Delta t} = \pi\frac{0.092^2}{4}\times 1300 \times 0.43 = 3.72 \text{ V}$$

Once again, you'll need $I = \dfrac{V}{R}$ to obtain the ammeter reading

$$I = \frac{V}{R} = \frac{3.72}{6.8} = 0.55 \text{ A}$$

Lenz's law

If an induced current flows due to a change in magnetic flux linkage (Faraday's law), then this current will oppose what's causing the current. If you like, it's the reason why there's a minus sign in the mathematical expression for Faraday's law:

& More blue mag. field than current! &

$$V = -\frac{\Delta(BAN)}{\Delta t}$$

What does Lenz's law mean in the previous examples?

In this set-up, Lenz's law means that the force on the moving conductor must be to the left (opposing the motion). You can check this using Fleming's right-hand rule (very similar to FLHR except you use your right hand). For the above set-up you'll need to point your right first finger towards your face (field) with your thumb pointing to the right (in the direction of motion). Your second finger should be pointing downward to indicate the direction of the current.

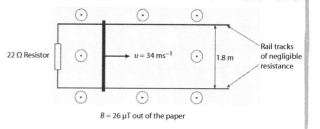

22 Ω Resistor $v = 34$ ms^{-1} 1.8 m   Rail tracks of negligible resistance

$B = 26$ μT out of the paper

Note that this direction of current is in exact agreement with using FLHR when you showed that the force on the free electrons was upward (and hence the current was downward, see page 81).

To get the direction of the force on the conductor you need to apply FLHR. You should find yourself pointing your left first finger towards your face (field) and your second finger pointing downward (current). Your thumb should be pointing to the left (indicating the direction of the force). This confirms that Lenz's law seems to be correct and that the magnetic force due to the induced EMF opposes the motion that's causing the induced current.

What does Lenz's law mean in this example?

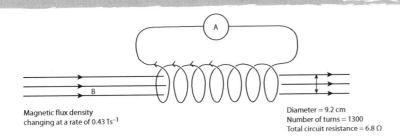

Magnetic flux density changing at a rate of 0.43 Ts⁻¹

Diameter = 9.2 cm
Number of turns = 1300
Total circuit resistance = 6.8 Ω

Now, the change in flux linkage is not caused by a motion but by an increasing B-field. Applying Lenz's law means that the B-field produced by the coil must oppose the increasing applied B-field, i.e. the B-field produced inside the solenoid must be to the left. You can use the right-hand grip rule to find the direction of the induced current and this direction is indicated by the arrows in the diagram.

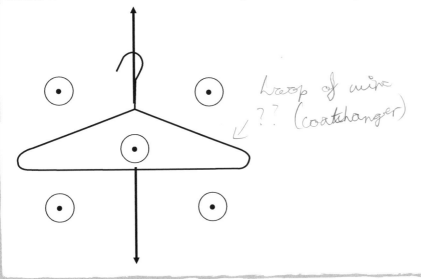

④⑥ A metal wire coat hanger is pulled apart perpendicular to a uniform magnetic field of 2.8 mT. The area inside the coat hanger is increased from 220 cm² to 560 cm² in a time of 0.050 s. The resistance of the coat hanger loop is 0.13 Ω. Calculate the current induced in the coat hanger.

④⑦ What does Lenz's law tell you about the magnetic force acting on the coat hanger in Quickfire 46?

④⑧ In which direction does the current flow in the coat hanger in Quickfire 46?

>> Pointer

There are three ways of obtaining the direction of the induced EMF/current when there's motion involved:

1. You can apply FLHR to the free electrons in the moving wire and note that the current will be in the opposite direction to the motion.
2. You can apply FRHR using your first finger for the field, second finger for the current and thumb for the motion.
3. You can use the right-hand screw rule to the loop so that the induced current provides a B-field opposing the change.

>> Pointer

Note that it's easier to use the 3rd method if there is no motion.

>> Pointer

The rotating coil in a magnetic field hasn't come up recently but it's only a matter of time . . .

quicнριre

⑭ Explain why the induced EMF is reversed in position D compared with position B.

Rotating coil in a magnetic field

Although you don't have to do calculations based on a rotating coil dynamo or generator, you do need to be able to explain the effect of the following on the induced EMF:

1 Coil position

2 Flux density

3 Coil area

4 Angular velocity.

All four effects can be explained with reference to the diagram and Faraday's law.

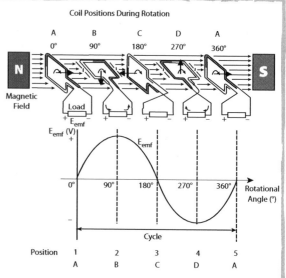

1 Coil position

This is far easier to explain in terms of flux cutting but the alternative explanation in terms of changing flux is also given.

In position A, the induced EMF is zero because the coil is not cutting lines of magnetic flux (the long sides of the coil are moving parallel with the field lines and so are doing no cutting). Alternatively, you can state that the flux linkage of the coil is at its maximum (because $\cos \theta = 1$). If the flux linkage is a maximum then the rate of change of flux linkage is zero.

In position B, the induced EMF is a maximum because the coil is cutting lines of magnetic flux at right angles (i.e., cutting field lines at the greatest rate). Alternatively, you can state that the flux linkage of the coil is changing at its greatest rate (this is true even though the flux linkage of the coil is zero since $\cos \theta = 0$).

2 Flux density

The induced EMF is proportional to the strength of the B-field. This is easily explained because a stronger B-field results in more lines of magnetic flux being cut. Alternatively, a stronger B-field results in a larger magnetic flux linkage for the coil.

3 Coil area

The induced EMF is proportional to the coil area. This is because a larger area results in a larger magnetic flux linkage for the coil. Alternatively, the larger the area of the coil the more lines of magnetic flux will be cut.

4 Angular velocity

The induced EMF is proportional to the angular velocity. Again, both flux cutting and change in flux linkage approaches are valid. As the angular velocity increases, it's obvious that the rate of change of flux linkage increases, it's also obvious that the rate of cutting of flux increases.

» Pointer

Suppose you plot a graph of some variable against time. When the variable reaches its maximum or minimum value, the line plotted must be horizontal (otherwise it couldn't be a maximum or minimum because it would still be increasing or decreasing). If the line is horizontal the gradient is zero and hence the rate of change of the variable is zero.

Alternating current and the root mean square (rms)

All circuit analysis so far has been based on dc circuits but it's also important to have some idea of the very basics of ac circuits.

All alternating pd's will be sinusoidal in this section. Here's a graph of what the sinusoidally varying pd entering your home from the national grid looks like:

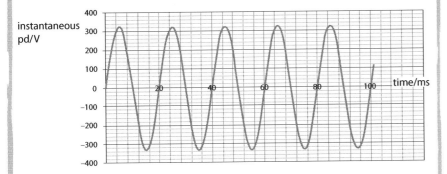

You should see that the period of the voltage is 20 ms and that this corresponds to a frequency of 50 Hz $\left(\text{remember } f = \dfrac{1}{T} \right)$. However, one unfamiliar thing that you should notice is that the peak pd is around 325 V and that this is different from the standard 230 V that you associate with the electricity supply of your house. The reason why 230 V is associated with the above graph is not at all obvious at first but it's related to the power dissipation.

» Pointer

The mean value of a sinusoidally varying pd or current is zero (see the graph of pd against time). However, if a sinusoidally varying pd is applied to a resistor, the resistor can still get hot even though the mean current and pd is zero.

Grade boost

If you understand Faraday's law well, there's nothing to memorise for the rotating coil – it's all explainable using Faraday's law.

» Pointer

At this point in the syllabus there aren't many types of question the examiner can ask you about rms pd and current – it'll probably be one of these two equations:

$$I = I_0 \big/ \sqrt{2} \text{ or}$$

$$V = V_0 \big/ \sqrt{2}$$

followed by some power calculation.

Consider the following simple circuit

The instantaneous power dissipated in the resistor will be given by:

$$P = \frac{V^2}{R}$$

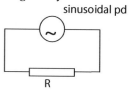

sinusoidal pd

where V is the instantaneous pd. Because the pd is varying quickly we're not concerned with instantaneous power but rather with the mean power. That means you have to obtain the mean value of $\frac{V^2}{R}$ which means obtaining the mean value of V^2. Very similar to the concept of the root mean square velocity in PH4 (page 28), we use a root mean square pd value which is written as V_{rms}. The mean power dissipated in the resistor is given by:

$$P = \frac{V_{rms}^2}{R}$$

Due to the sinusoidal variation of the pd, the rms pd (V_{rms}) is given by:

$$V_{rms} = \frac{V_0}{\sqrt{2}}$$

If you calculate $\frac{1}{\sqrt{2}}$ you'll obtain 0.707 which means that the rms pd (V_{rms}) is always 70.7% of the peak pd (V_0).

Example

The rms pd supplied to a house is 230 V. Calculate the peak pd (V_0).

Answer

$$V_{rms} = \frac{V_0}{\sqrt{2}} \quad \rightarrow \quad V_0 = \sqrt{2}V_{rms} = 1.4142 \times 230 = 325\,V$$

which explains the unfamiliar peak pd of 325 V shown in the earlier graph. The relationship is also true for the root mean square current I_{rms}

$$I_{rms} = \frac{I_0}{\sqrt{2}}$$

and all the expressions for electrical power are true when the rms values are used:

$$P = I_{rms}V_{rms} = \frac{V_{rms}^2}{R} = I_{rms}^2 R$$

Example

Hair straighteners are rated 26 W and operate from a peak pd of 340 V. Calculate:

(i) the rms pd
(ii) the rms current
(iii) the peak current
(iv) the resistance of the straighteners.

Answers

(i) $V_{rms} = \frac{V_0}{\sqrt{2}} = \frac{340}{1.4142} = 240\text{ V}$

(ii) using $P = I_{rms}V_{rms} \rightarrow I_{rms} = \frac{P}{V_{rms}} = \frac{26}{240} = 0.11\text{ A}$

(iii) $I_{rms} = \frac{I_0}{\sqrt{2}} \rightarrow I_0 = \sqrt{2}I_{rms} = 1.4142 \times 0.11 = 0.15\text{ A}$

(iv) using $R = \frac{V}{I}$ you can use either the peak values or the rms values of the pd and current:

$$R = \frac{V}{I} = \frac{240}{0.11} = 2200\ \Omega$$

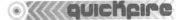

quickfire

(52) A kettle element has a resistance of 19.6 Ω and the peak current supplied to it is 16.1 A. Calculate:

(i) The mean power supplied to the kettle.
(ii) The rms pd supplied to the kettle.

quickfire

(53) An electric heater has a rms current of 8.3 A and a peak pd across it of 340 V. Calculate its mean output power.

The oscilloscope

Gone are the days when A-level students needed to know how an oscilloscope worked and this makes sense now that freeware software can turn your PC and soundcard into an oscilloscope for free. However, the syllabus does state clearly that you should know how to use an oscilloscope.

Take a look at the oscilloscope trace showing a sinusoidally varying pd. You should be able to tell that the 'amplitude' of the trace is about 1.4 squares (vertically) and that the 'wavelength' of the trace is about 9.4 squares (horizontally). Now to understand the full significance of the trace you need to use the volts/div and seconds/div settings.

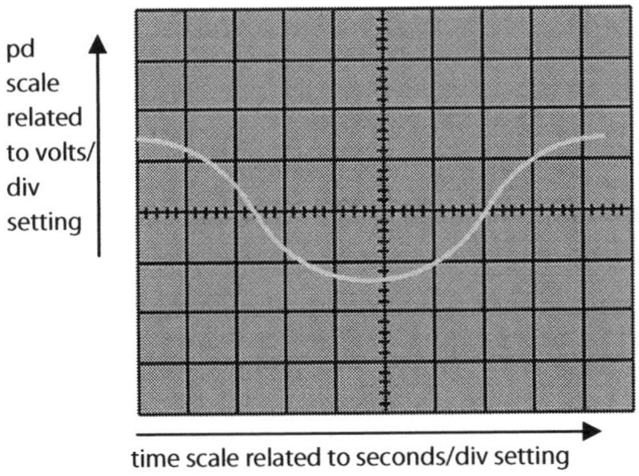
pd scale related to volts/div setting
time scale related to seconds/div setting

Pointer

The oscilloscope effectively gives you a graph of pd against time.

Looking at the VOLTS/DIV setting below you should note that the setting is 50 mV per division. This means that the height of each square on the oscilloscope represents 50 mV. Hence, the peak pd of the trace on the screen is

$$1.4 \times 50 = 70 \text{ mV}$$

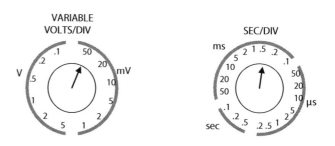

>> **Pointer**

The oscilloscope screen is just a pd against time graph. The volts per division (volts/div) effectively tells you what numbers to put on the vertical axis.

Looking at the SEC/DIV setting, the knob is set to .5 ms. This means that the width of each square on the oscilloscope represents 0.5 ms. Hence, the period of the waveform shown on the oscilloscope is:

$$9.4 \times 0.5 = 4.7 \text{ ms}$$

You can convert this period to frequency using the relationship from PH2

$$f = \frac{1}{T} = \frac{1}{0.0047} = 210 \text{ Hz}$$

>> **Pointer**

Note that the small divisions of the squares on the oscilloscope screen are 0.2 squares.

At this stage, a particularly nasty question that an examiner could ask is: 'Draw the trace on the oscilloscope screen for the same input waveform when the VOLTS/DIV is adjusted to 20 mV and the SEC/DIV is adjusted to 1 ms.'

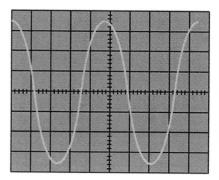

>> **Pointer**

Again, the oscilloscope screen is just a pd against time graph. The seconds per division (sec/div) effectively tells you what numbers to put on the horizontal axis.

Answer

To find the height of the trace, peak pd = 70 mV, hence

$$\text{max height} = \frac{70 \text{ mV}}{20 \text{ mV}} = 3.5 \text{ squares}$$

Also, period = 4.7 ms, hence:

$$\text{'wave width'} = \frac{4.7 \text{ ms}}{1 \text{ ms}} = 4.7 \text{ squares}$$

Grade boost

Oscilloscope questions don't rear their heads too often but when they do they're tricky. Not many students understand the concepts of volts per division or seconds per division.

Using an oscilloscope

This is easier than you might think. Once you've input your pd into the oscilloscope, you simply twiddle the VOLTS/DIV until your signal is the maximum height that fits on the screen. Then you twiddle the SEC/DIV until you have a few complete waveforms on the screen.

Measuring dc voltage

Again, this is easier than you might think. A constant pd just gives a horizontal line on the oscilloscope screen. In the following example, the oscilloscope has been adjusted so that the zero volt level is not in the centre of the oscilloscope screen.

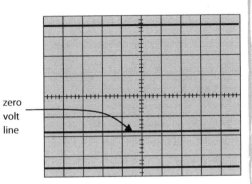

zero volt line

Example

Calculate the two dc voltages represented by the top and bottom lines on the oscilloscope screen. The VOLT/DIV setting of the oscilloscope is 5 mV.

Answer

The top line is 5.3 squares above the zero volt line, hence

$$pd = 5.3 \times 5 = 26.5 \text{ mV}$$

The bottom line is 1.8 squares below the zero volt line, hence

$$pd = -1.8 \times 5 = -9.0 \text{ mV}$$

Measuring currents using an oscilloscope

This is not directly possible because an oscilloscope measures pd. However, the current can be calculated if you know the device for which you're measuring the pd. For example, in the last dc voltage example the pd's were measured across a 680 Ω resistor. Calculate the current in the resistor corresponding to the pd's shown.

Answers

$$I = \frac{V}{R} = \frac{0.0265}{680} = 39 \text{ μA}$$

and

$$I = \frac{V}{R} = \frac{0.009}{680} = 13 \text{ μA}$$

quickfire

54
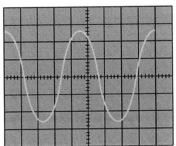

The oscilloscope is set to 0.1 s/div and 0.2 V/div. Calculate:

  (i) the peak pd

  (ii) the rms pd

  (iii) the period

  (iv) the frequency.

quickfire

55 Draw a diagram of the trace you would see on an oscilloscope when the input pd is the mains pd (i.e. 230 V rms and 50 Hz). The oscilloscope is set to 100 V/div and 5 ms/div.

quickfire

56 Calculate the constant pds represented by the top and bottom lines on the oscilloscope traces. The oscilloscope is set to 50 μV/div.

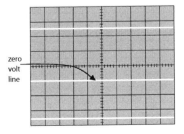

zero volt line

Radioactivity and radioisotopes

Properties of α, β and γ radiation

>> **Pointer**

You need to learn the penetration of the three types of radiation.

>> **Pointer**

You also need to know the ionising powers of the three types of radiation but this is just the reverse order of the penetration, i.e. α – highest ionising, β – intermediate ionising and γ – low ionising.

>> **Pointer**

Once you know the penetration and ionising properties, you can explain the relative dangers of the radiation, i.e. α – most dangerous but only if inside the body (it can't penetrate skin), β – intermediate danger, γ – lowest danger but most difficult to shield against.

These are the three types of nuclear radiation and are all types of ionising radiation. They are ionising because they knock out electrons from atoms or molecules. The ionised particles that are produced will be highly reactive and will react with other molecules nearby. In living tissue this can lead to all sorts of damage at the cellular level including damage to DNA, possibly leading to cancer. However, our bodies are subject to attacks from background radiation every minute of the day and life expectancy, remarkably, is no shorter in places with very high background radiation. On the other hand, an absorbed radiation dosage of only 8 J per kilogram is lethal to all humans.

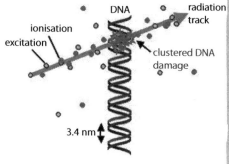

An alpha (α) particle is a fast moving helium nucleus (i.e. $^4_2\text{He}^{2+}$ or $^4_2\alpha$ but the 2+ is usually dropped). It is more highly ionising than both β and γ radiation. In contrast, the fact that α radiation is so ionising means that it loses its energy very quickly and has low penetration. In fact, the range of α particles is only a few cm in air and it's absorbed by a sheet of paper. Example of α decay:

$$^{238}_{92}\text{U} \rightarrow \,^{234}_{90}\text{Th} + \,^4_2\text{He}$$

A beta (β) particle is a fast-moving electron and is usually written as $^0_{-1}e$ or $^0_{-1}\beta$. It is more highly ionising than γ radiation but less so than α radiation. Likewise, β has an intermediate penetrating power – it's usually stopped by a few mm of aluminium or a few metres of air. Example of β decay:

$$^{14}_{6}\text{C} \rightarrow \,^{14}_{7}\text{N} + \,^0_{-1}\beta$$

γ radiation is a high energy, low wavelength electromagnetic wave or photon that originates from an excited nucleus. It is less ionising than both α and β particles but is consequently more penetrating. γ radiation is stopped by around 15 cm of lead (Pb) or around a metre of concrete. Example of γ decay:

$$^{60}_{28}\text{Ni}^* \rightarrow \,^{60}_{28}\text{Ni} + \,^0_0\gamma$$

The asterisk denotes that the original Ni (nickel) nucleus is in an excited state.

The relative absorption of the three nuclear radiation types is represented in the following diagram.

This leads nicely to a simple experiment to investigate which type(s) of radiation are present in a radioactive source.

Consider the following set-up.

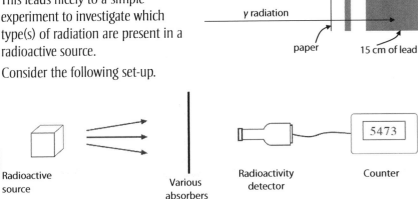

By placing various absorbers between the source and detector you can work out which radiation is emitted by the source. Here are the relevant steps:

Place a sheet of paper between the source and detector. If there's a significant drop in count rate (say from 5473 down to 4000), there must be α radiation present. Then place a piece of aluminium a couple of mm thick between the source and detector. If there's a further significant drop (say down to 2000), there must be β radiation present also. Whatever signal that's left (above background radiation of ~0.5 counts s^{-1}) must be due to γ radiation. Note that you don't need a γ absorber to do this experiment because anything significant that's left over after the β absorber must be due to γ radiation. With the above quoted results you would conclude that the count rate due to α radiation is around 1500 Bq, that due to β radiation is around 2000 Bq and that due to γ radiation is around 2000 Bq.

Example (taken from 2008)

The following results were obtained using a similar set-up of radioactive source, absorber, detector. Explain which types of radiation are present in the radioactive source.

Absorber	Count rate/s^{-1}
None	8894
3 sheets of paper	5473
None	8921
0.5 mm of Aluminum foil	5455
None	8860
10 cm of Lead	56
None	8888

Answer

The count rate drops by about 3500 s^{-1} when 3 sheets of paper are used as an absorber. This is a sure sign that α radiation is present.

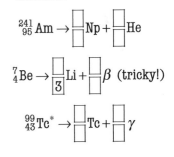

> ### ≫ Pointer
> In these nuclear reaction equations remember that the A number and Z number are conserved, i.e. the individual totals of the A and Z numbers on the right-hand side (RHS) is equal to the total on the LHS.

quickfire

(57) Balance the equations by putting in the missing numbers:

$$^{241}_{95}\text{Am} \rightarrow \square_{\square}\text{Np} + \square_{\square}\text{He}$$

$$^{7}_{4}\text{Be} \rightarrow \square_{3}\text{Li} + \square_{\square}\beta \text{ (tricky!)}$$

$$^{99}_{43}\text{Tc}^* \rightarrow \square_{\square}\text{Tc} + \square_{\square}\gamma$$

⏶ Grade boost
The syllabus states that you should be able to describe ways of differentiating between the three types of radiation. You should be able to describe the experiment using a source, different absorbers and a counter.

quickfire

⑤⑧ Explain which radiation is present in a radioactive source considering the following data collected using the relevant absorber between source and detector:

Absorber	Count rate/s^{-1}
None	9562
Paper	9482
None	9715
2 mm Al	6723
None	9642
15 cm Pb	11
None	9613

quickfire

⑤⑨ If you swallowed the source in Quickfire 58, explain why you would be at greatest risk from β radiation.

quickfire

⑥⓪ The source that was swallowed in Quickfire 59 passes through your body in 24 hours. The rate of absorption of β particles absorbed by your body for that time was 89 000 s^{-1}. The energy of the β particles is 1.7 MeV. Calculate the total energy of the absorbed β particles in J.

quickfire

⑥① Does a significant amount of radiation pass through the 15 cm of lead in Quickfire 58 or is this attributable to background radiation?

There is a very similar drop when 0.5 mm of aluminium is used, which suggests that there is no β radiation (i.e. the aluminium doesn't absorb any more than the paper). However, there must be γ radiation present because there's a large count rate after using 0.5 mm of aluminium. Confirmation of the presence of γ radiation is given when the count rate is significant after using 10 cm of lead (it's still detecting 56 s^{-1} which is considerably greater than background radiation).

Some things to beware in this type of data:

1. Paper will absorb some of the β radiation.
2. Aluminium will absorb some of the γ radiation.
3. There is a substantial random error in all radioactive count readings (see the variation in count rate with no absorber).
4. Normally, you'll have to take account of the background radiation (it's around 0.5 counts s^{-1} but that's insignificant in the above results).

When you take all these things into account, you need to be looking for *significant* drops in count rates and not drops of a few percent as different absorbers are put in place.

Other methods of distinguishing between α, β and γ radiation

You've already covered the effect of a magnetic field on charged particles and if your teacher has a cloud chamber you might well have seen a demonstration of this effect (if not there are plenty of good videos of working cloud chambers on YouTube). Here's a picture of what you might see if you had $^{226}_{88}$Ra as the radioactive source and a cloud chamber in a magnetic field ($^{226}_{88}$Ra emits all three types of nuclear radiation and a cloud chamber is a clever device that gives a vapour trail where ionising radiation has been).

For practice, you should use FLHR to check that the directions of the curvature of the α and β tracks are correct. Also, note that γ radiation doesn't curve because it isn't charged.

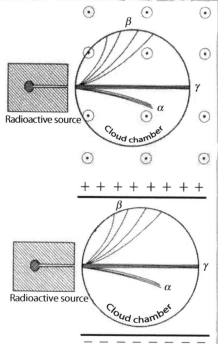

Very similar results can be obtained if you use an electric field instead of a magnetic field. The shapes of the paths will be slightly different – the magnetic field will give arcs of circles whereas the electric field will give parabolas.

Background radiation

Here's a typical pie chart to explain where we get most of our dosage of ionising radiation.

Three of the five sources are essentially the same because they come from naturally occurring elements on the Earth. Radon gas that we breathe, food and drink and buildings and the ground are all natural sources coming originally from radioactive

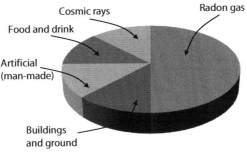

elements such as potassium-40, carbon-14, uranium and thorium. Cosmic rays are completely different and mainly arise from high-energy particles arriving at the Earth's atmosphere. The vast majority of our man-made radiation dosage is a direct result of having an X-ray image taken but a tiny percentage is a result of nuclear power or nuclear weapon testing. Although the sources of nuclear radiation are everywhere and seemingly vast, in nearly all the world a radiation detector will sit quietly clicking randomly at an average rate of half a count every second – telling us that there's nothing to fear.

Theory of radioactivity

All the mathematical theory that follows is based on one simple principle – that radioactivity is an entirely random process and depends purely on the number of radioactive nuclei present. Therefore, for a radioactive sample, the number of nuclei disintegrating per second is proportional to the number of nuclei present, i.e.:

disintegration per second $\propto N$ (the number of nuclei)

We now define a **decay constant** λ (see Key term) as the constant of proportionality and λ will depend on the nucleus that's decaying. We also define the **activity** A as the number of disintegrations per second (see Key term).

disintegration per second $= A = \lambda N$

but every time a nucleus disintegrates, the number of nuclei decreases, so the number of disintegrations per second $= -\dfrac{\Delta N}{\Delta t}$. The minus sign is there because

Key Terms

Becquerel = one disintegration per second (it's the unit of activity).

Activity = the rate of decay (number of disintegrations per second) of a sample of radioactive nuclei $\left(A = -\dfrac{\Delta N}{\Delta t} = \lambda N\right)$.

Decay constant = the constant in the exponential decay law $\left(\dfrac{\Delta N}{\Delta t} = -\lambda N\right)$ and it determines the rate of decay of a particular nucleus (the greater λ, the more rapid the rate of decay – it's the probability per second of a particular nucleus decaying).

Half-life = the time taken for the number of radioactive nuclei N (or the activity A) to reduce to one half of the initial value. Unit: s but often given as year.

» Pointer

You can also derive $\lambda = \dfrac{\ln 2}{T_{\frac{1}{2}}}$ from the equation $N = N_0 e^{-\lambda t}$. You'll need to put in the time $t = T_{\frac{1}{2}}$ for the number of nuclei to drop from N_0 to $\frac{1}{2} N_0$.

the number N is decreasing and $\dfrac{\Delta N}{\Delta t}$ must be negative. Hence, the equation that is the foundation of all nuclear decay theory is:

$$\frac{\Delta N}{\Delta t} = -\lambda N$$

As discussed in PH5.1, this leads to an exponential decay in N. If you compare the above equation with $\dfrac{\Delta Q}{\Delta t} = -\dfrac{Q}{CR}$ you'll see that our final result is:

$$N = N_0 e^{-\lambda t}$$

which tells you that the number of radioactive nuclei, N, decreases exponentially from an initial number N_0 of nuclei. Now, let's multiply the equation $N = N_0 e^{-\lambda t}$ by the decay constant λ, i.e.

$$\lambda N = \lambda N_0 e^{-\lambda t}$$

but the activity $A = \lambda N$ and the initial activity $A_0 = \lambda N_0$, hence:

$$A = A_0 e^{-\lambda t}$$

Therefore the activity, A, also decreases exponentially from an initial value of A_0. These three equations ($N = N_0 e^{-\lambda t}$, $A = \lambda N$ and $A = A_0 e^{-\lambda t}$) appear on the WJEC data sheet and you don't need to remember them. However, the syllabus states that you should be able to derive the equation involving the **half-life** (see Key term).

Let's use the definition of the half-life and the equation $A = A_0 e^{-\lambda t}$ to derive an expression for the half-life ($T_{\frac{1}{2}}$). When the time reaches $t = T_{\frac{1}{2}}$ the activity drops from A_0 to $\frac{1}{2} A_0$ (this is the definition of $T_{\frac{1}{2}}$). Putting these values into the equation you get:

$$\frac{1}{2} A_0 = A_0 e^{-\lambda T_{\frac{1}{2}}} \quad \rightarrow \quad \frac{1}{2} = e^{-\lambda T_{\frac{1}{2}}} \quad \rightarrow \quad 2 = e^{\lambda T_{\frac{1}{2}}}$$

and, taking logs:

$$\ln 2 = \lambda T_{\frac{1}{2}} \text{ or } \lambda = \frac{\ln 2}{T_{\frac{1}{2}}} \text{ as the equation appears on the data sheet.}$$

Examples

A sample of carbon-14 has a mass of 150 g. Calculate:

(i) The number of nuclei present (the mass of a carbon-14 atom is 14.00 u).

(ii) Its decay constant (the half-life of carbon-14 is 5730 years).

(iii) The initial activity of the 150 g sample of carbon-14.

(iv) The activity after 2500 years.

(v) The mass of carbon-14 after 11 460 years.

(vi) The time for the activity of carbon-14 to decrease to 10% of its initial value.

Answers

(i) mass of atom $= 14.00 \times 1.66 \times 10^{-27} = 2.324 \times 10^{-26}$ kg

number of atoms (and nuclei) $= 0.150 \div 2.324 \times 10^{-26} = 6.45 \times 10^{24}$

or number of moles $= 150 \div 14 = 10.71$
number of nuclei $= 10.71 \times 6.02 \times 10^{23} = 6.45 \times 10^{24}$

(ii) $\lambda = \dfrac{\ln 2}{T_{\frac{1}{2}}} = \dfrac{\ln 2}{5730 \times 365 \times 24 \times 60 \times 60} = 3.84 \times 10^{-12}\,\text{s}^{-1}$

(iii) $A = \lambda N = 3.84 \times 10^{-12} \times 6.45 \times 10^{24} = 2.48 \times 10^{13}$ Bq

(iv) $A = A_0 e^{-\lambda t} = 2.48 \times 10^{13}\, e^{-3.84 \times 10^{-12} \times 2500 \times 365 \times 24 \times 60 \times 60}$

$= 1.83 \times 10^{13}$ Bq

(v) This is easier than it looks but you have to be numerate and notice that 11 460 year is two half-lives. Therefore, the mass will quarter, i.e. mass $= 37.5$ g

(vi) This is trickier and requires taking logs

$$A = A_0 e^{-\lambda t} \quad \rightarrow \quad \frac{A}{A_0} = e^{-\lambda t}$$

taking logs and remembering that $\dfrac{A}{A_0} = 10\% = 0.1$

$$\ln\left(\frac{A}{A_0}\right) = -\lambda t \quad \rightarrow \quad t = -\frac{1}{\lambda}\ln\left(\frac{A}{A_0}\right) = -\frac{1}{3.84 \times 10^{-12}}\ln(0.1)$$

giving a final answer of $t = 6.00 \times 10^{11}$ s   or   19 000 years

Uses of radioisotopes

A radioisotope is simply an isotope that's radioactive (see Key term). You should be able to describe briefly two applications of their use. For example:

1 You can use a gamma emitter (e.g. cobalt-60) to sterilise medical equipment or food. Although gamma has the lowest ionising capabilities of the three types of radiation, it can penetrate many centimetres of metal and in large enough doses will kill all germs, bacteria and viruses. Hence, the tomatoes inside a tin of tomatoes can be sterilised after the tin has been sealed ensuring long life and bacteria-free tomatoes. Alternatively, you can sterilise surgical instruments as shown (the surgical instruments are in the crates).

Key Term

Radioisotope = an isotope that is radioactive (remember that isotopes have the same atomic number Z but different mass number A).

≫ Pointer

Calculating the number of nuclei is often the least well-done of all these parts.

≫ Pointer

Although part (vi) looks difficult, you should be familiar with this type of calculation from capacitors (PH5.1) and the practical test in PH6.

quickfire

(63) Uranium-238 has a half-life of 4.47×10^9 years. An initial sample of uranium-238 has a mass of 25.2 kg. Calculate:

(i) The decay constant in s^{-1}.

(ii) The number of nuclei of uranium-238 in the initial sample (the mass of a uranium atom is 238 u).

(iii) The initial activity of the sample.

(iv) The activity of the sample after 3 half-lives.

(v) The activity of the sample after 5 billion years (5.00×10^9 years).

(vi) The time (in years) for the activity of the sample to decrease to 30% of its initial value.

64 Explain how an alpha emitter might be used in a smoke detector.

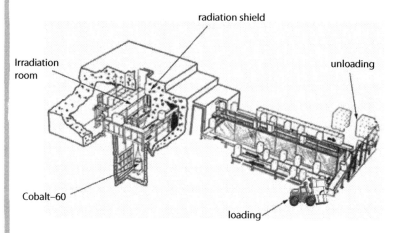

radiation shield

Irradiation room

unloading

Cobalt–60

loading

2 You can use a beta emitter (e.g. strontium-90) to check the thickness of paper as it rolls off a paper mill. All you need is a source and detector with paper in between, the count rate will tell you the thickness of the paper.

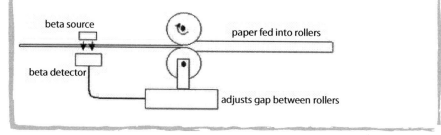

beta source

paper fed into rollers

beta detector

adjusts gap between rollers

Nuclear energy

Mass–energy equivalence $E = mc^2$

Perhaps the most famous of all physics equations is: $E = mc^2$, which actually gives a relationship between mass and energy – two seemingly completely different concepts. Nuclear energy is based on this equation and benefits greatly from c^2 being a large number (9×10^{16}). This means that the energy produced when 1 kg of matter is 'lost' is:

$$E = mc^2 = 1 \times (3 \times 10^8)^2 = 9 \times 10^{16} \text{ J (or 90 000 000 000 000 000 J)}$$

One way of 'losing' 1 kg of mass is to annihilate 0.5 kg of antimatter with 0.5 kg of matter. Unfortunately (or possibly fortunately), 0.5 kg of isolated antimatter does not exist on Earth and hence, more subtle methods of using nuclear energy must be employed.

The first confirmation of the equation $E = mc^2$ came from Cockcroft and Walton's experiment that also 'split the atom' for the first time in 1932 (they received a Nobel Prize in 1951). This is the reaction they used and these are the results that they obtained:

$$^7_3\text{Li} + ^1_1\text{H} \rightarrow ^4_2\text{He} + ^4_2\text{He} + 17.1 \text{ MeV of energy}$$

They bombarded ^7_3Li nuclei with hydrogen nuclei (protons) and obtained two helium nuclei (α-particles) along with a considerable sum of extra energy. This extra energy must come from 'lost' mass according to Einstein's equation but did the numbers tie in?

Here are the masses of the nuclei involved presented in a new unit – the unified atomic mass unit (1 u = 1.66×10^{-27} kg).

mass of ^7_3Li = 7.0144 u   mass of ^1_1H = 1.0073 u   mass of ^4_2He = 4.0015 u

Total mass of LHS = 7.0144 + 1.0072   = 8.0216 u
Total mass of RHS = 4.0015 + 4.0015   = 8.0030 u
i.e. the mass lost   = 0.0186 u
to use $E = mc^2$ you need 1 u = 1.66×10^{-27} kg from the data sheet.
$E = 0.0186 \times 1.66 \times 10^{-27} \times (3 \times 10^8)^2 = 2.779 \times 10^{-12}$ J
To convert from J to eV, you need to divide by e (1.6×10^{-19} C)
$E = 2.78 \times 10^{-12} \div 1.6 \times 10^{-19} = 1.737 \times 10^7 = 17.37$ MeV
which is very close to Cockcroft and Walton's result of 17.1 MeV.

⑥⑤ The mass loss in a nuclear reaction is 0.542 u. How much MeV is released in the reaction? (1 u ≡ 931 MeV)

⑥⑥ Convert the following:
(i) 12.0 u into kg.
(ii) 401 × 10⁻²⁷ kg into u.

» Pointer
When calculating nuclear energies of reactions always do:
(LHS mass – RHS mass) × 931 and you have your answer in MeV. Note, for reactions that don't release energy, the answer will be zero or negative.

⑥⑦ How much energy is released in a nuclear reaction when:
(i) 0.666 × 10⁻⁹ kg of mass is 'lost'?
(ii) 0.007892 u of mass is 'lost'?

Key Term

Unified atomic mass unit u = one twelfth of the mass of an atom of carbon 12 ($1u = 1.6605 \times 10^{-27}$ kg and 1u mass loss gives 931 MeV of energy).

quickfire

(68) Calculate the energy released in the nuclear reaction:

$$^6_3Li + ^2_1H \rightarrow ^4_2He + ^4_2He$$

The masses of the nuclei involved are:

mass of ^6_3Li = 6.014 u

mass of ^2_1H = 2.013 u

mass of ^4_2He = 4.002 u

>> *Pointer*

Nuclear reactions and stability are quite similar to chemical reactions and stability of atoms and molecules.

>> *Pointer*

Nuclear reactions involve forces within the nuclei and the larger forces lead to larger energies.

>> *Pointer*

In chemical reactions everything is to do with rearrangement of electrons but nuclear reactions involve rearrangement of nucleons within the nuclei.

There is, in fact, an easier way of obtaining the correct answer because you will always be given the information 1 u ≡ 931 MeV. This means that a mass of 1 u is equivalent to 931 MeV of energy. So, all you have to do is multiply your mass loss in u by 931 and you get your final answer in MeV i.e. $0.0186 \times 931 = 17.32$ MeV (the slight discrepancy is because all the constants are only given to 3 s.f.).

The **unified mass unit** is a particularly useful unit of mass at the atomic or nuclear scale and you will see a lot of it in this section. You will also be converting regularly from u to MeV using the information 1 u ≡ 931 MeV.

What makes some nuclei stable and others unstable?

A complete answer to this question is impossible but at A-level you need to be able to explain in terms of binding energy.

First, let's consider the stability of electrons in orbits. There's an attractive force between the nucleus and the electron (+ve and –ve) which holds the electrons in place. The same is true of nucleons in the nucleus. There's an attractive force (strong nuclear force) to hold the nucleons together in the nucleus (it's about 100 times greater than the +ve/+ve repulsion of protons).

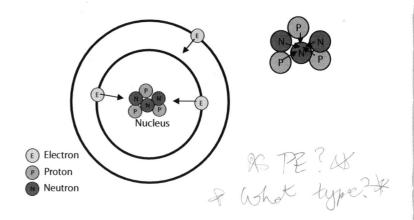

E Electron
P Proton
N Neutron

Whenever an attractive force exists, as the particles come closer they lose potential energy and this is the energy that can be given out. In a chemical reaction, the electrons are more stable in the final products so they've lost potential energy and energy has been given out. It's very similar in nuclear reactions, when the nuclei become more stable they lose PE and give out energy but about a million times more than is given out in chemical reactions.

What happens is that as the particles come closer together the total mass decreases – the potential energy was just a greater mass before the particles were brought together. This is true even in chemical reactions – the mass of the system will decrease after an exothermic reaction but this change in mass is difficult to detect. In a nuclear reaction, the change in mass is a million times greater and is easily measured with a mass spectrometer (even in 1932 this was measured quite accurately).

The name given to this change in PE as nucleons are brought together to form a nucleus is **binding energy** (BE) and it's defined formally in the Key term. It's a useful concept and when you divide the binding energy by the number of nucleons it's an excellent measure of the stability of an individual nucleus.

Key Term
Binding energy = the energy that has to be supplied in order to separate a nucleus into its constituent nucleons. Alternatively, it's the energy given out (or the decrease in PE) when the constituent nucleons form the nucleus. **Unit: J** or **MeV**

Example

Calculate the nuclear binding energy and binding energy per nucleon of $^4_2$He. (mass of $^4_2$He nucleus = 4.001506 u, mass of proton (m_p) = 1.007276 u, mass of neutron (m_n) = 1.008665 and 1 u $\equiv$ 931 MeV)

Answer

First, you know that you have 2 protons (from the atomic number) and that you have 2 neutrons (mass number – atomic number).

Next, add up the individual masses of the particles:

$$2 \times m_p + 2 \times m_n = 2 \times 1.007276 + 2 \times 1.008665 = 4.031882 \text{ u}$$

This is the mass of the nucleons before they were brought together and the mass after they were brought together is 4.001506 (i.e. the mass of $^4_2$He). The difference is: 4.031882 – 4.001506 = 0.030376 u, which is the decrease in mass

Finally for the first answer:

$$\text{Binding energy} = 0.030376 \times 931 = 28.28 \text{ MeV}$$

All you have to do for the second answer is divide by the number of nucleons (i.e., divide by 4, because of the 2 neutrons and 2 protons)

$$\text{BE/nucleon} = 28.28/4 = 7.07 \text{ MeV/nucleon}$$

Tricky synoptic example

A spring is extended 8.2 cm using a force of 360 N. Calculate the increase in mass of the spring.

Answer

This question may seem like science fiction nonsense but it's actually quite easy and real.

$$PE = \frac{1}{2}Fx = \frac{1}{2} \times 360 \times 8.2 \times 10^{-2} = 14.8 \text{ J (from PH1 last year)}$$

$$E = 14.8 = mc^2 \quad \rightarrow \quad m = \frac{14.8}{c^2} = 1.6 \times 10^{-16} \text{ kg}$$

The increase in mass is because the atoms are being pulled farther apart as the spring is being extended and the PE is increasing.

» Pointer
Remember that binding energy is an energy given out that's associated with lost mass – it's not an energy that a nucleus possesses (alternatively it's an energy you have to provide in order to increase mass when the nucleons are pulled apart).

⑥⑨ Calculate the binding energy per nucleon of $^{56}_{26}$Fe. (nuclear mass of $^{56}_{26}$Fe = 55.9207 u, m_p = 1.0073 u, m_n = 1.0087 u)

⑦⑩ A mass of 250 kg is lifted 2.14 m. Calculate the increase in GPE and the increase in the mass of the Earth-mass system (it's easier than you think just use $E = mc^2$).

The binding energy per nucleon vs. nucleon number graph

This is the graph that shows the stability of nuclei. It also tells you if nuclei are likely to perform fusion or fission reactions.

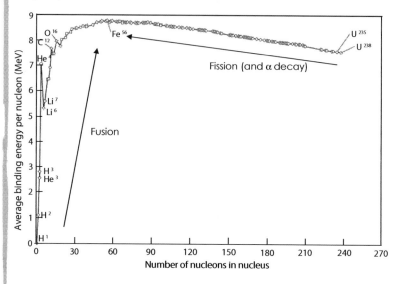

You should notice that $^4_2$He and $^{56}_{26}$Fe are plotted correctly (if you got the correct answer to Quickfire 69). You should also notice that $^1_1$H has 0 binding energy per nucleon – that's quite obvious after you've thought about it. $^1_1$H nucleus is just a proton which cannot have any binding energy because there's nothing else in the nucleus with it. Furthermore, $^{56}_{26}$Fe is close to the maximum of the curve and is one of the most stable of all nuclei.

All this means that smaller nuclei can undergo fusion to increase their nucleon number and move towards the stable part of the graph (see the fusion arrow on the graph). Heavy nuclei will undergo fission (or α decay) to decrease their nucleon number and move towards stability.

Trickier example

One of the fission reactions of $^{235}_{92}$U (uranium-235) is the following:

$$^{235}_{92}U + {}^1_0n \rightarrow {}^{95}_{37}Rb + {}^{137}_{55}Cs + 4{}^1_0n$$

i.e. $^{235}_{92}$U is hit by a neutron and breaks up into $^{95}_{37}$Rb, $^{137}_{55}$Cs and 4 neutrons.

mass of $^{235}_{92}$U = 235.0439 u,   mass of $^{95}_{37}$Rb = 94.9293 u,

mass of $^{137}_{55}$Cs = 136.9071 u,   mass of neutron = 1.0073 u

Calculate the energy released in the reaction and explain your answer in terms of binding energy and stability.

Answer

Total mass of LHS $= 235.0439 + 1.0073 \qquad = 236.0512$ u

Total mass of RHS $= 94.9293 + 136.9071 + 4 \times 1.0073 \qquad = 235.8656$ u

mass lost $\qquad$ *How do* $= 0.1856$ u

Finally, energy released $= 0.1856 \times 931 = 173$ MeV $\qquad$ *we know ??*

In terms of binding energy, the products $^{137}_{55}$Cs and $^{95}_{37}$Rb have fewer nucleons than $^{235}_{92}$U and their binding energy per nucleon is greater than $^{235}_{92}$U (i.e. followed the fission arrow on the graph). The products therefore are more stable and an extra 173 MeV of energy is released.

If you really wanted to give a complete answer, you could also state that the binding energy of the free neutrons is zero and that they decay into a proton, electron and anti-neutrino with a half-life of 10–15 minutes (this would not be expected though).

quickfire

(73) Another possible fission reaction involving uranium-235 is shown. Calculate the energy released from the data provided:

$$^{235}_{92}\text{U} + ^{1}_{0}\text{n} \rightarrow ^{89}_{36}\text{Kr} + ^{144}_{56}\text{Ba} + 3^{1}_{0}\text{n}$$

mass of $^{235}_{92}$U $= 235.0439$ u,

mass of $^{144}_{56}$Ba $= 143.9230$ u,

mass of $^{89}_{36}$Kr $= 88.9176$ u,

mass of neutron $= 1.0073$ u

Fission reactors

The last example of a fission reaction of uranium leads you nicely to the next topic in nuclear energy – the chain reaction. In the reaction, three extra neutrons are produced. What was not mentioned earlier is the fact that $^{235}_{92}$U does not split up by itself, it needs to capture a neutron to produce $^{236}_{92}$U and it's $^{236}_{92}$U that's unstable and spontaneously undergoes fission. The full reaction is:

$$^{235}_{92}\text{U} + ^{1}_{0}\text{n} \rightarrow ^{236}_{92}\text{U} \rightarrow ^{95}_{37}\text{Rb} + ^{137}_{55}\text{Cs} + 4^{1}_{0}\text{n}$$

The reason why this reaction can lead to a chain reaction is that one neutron, after fission, can produce 4 neutrons. These other 4 neutrons can produce 4 fission reactions and 16 neutrons which can produce 16 fission reactions and 64 neutrons, etc. This type of reaction can soon get out of control and end up as a bomb. In a nuclear reactor producing electricity, you ensure a controlled reaction where, on average, exactly one of the product neutrons causes another neutron reaction and you have equilibrium.

≫ Pointer

Learn the basic details of the fission reactor and the chain reaction – if it comes up there'll be a reward of around 7 marks.

>> *Pointer*

Chain reaction – more neutrons out than in and possible exponential increase (bomb) or equilibrium (controlled reaction).

>> *Pointer*

Control rods – absorb neutrons and control reaction.

>> *Pointer*

Moderator – slows neutrons down to increase probability of reaction.

>> *Pointer*

Coolant – takes away thermal energy and can also be moderator e.g. water.

>> *Pointer*

Waste – problems because highly radioactive for long time.

How does a nuclear reactor work?

You can see a simplified diagram of a nuclear reactor to the right. You don't need to know the diagram but you do need to know the roles of the moderator, control rods and coolant.

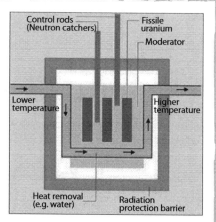

Control rods

These absorb neutrons to decrease the total number of neutrons available for fission. The control rods start off lowered and are raised until a sustainable chain reaction is achieved. The material of the control rod must be a neutron absorber but it also needs a high melting point and other mechanical properties, e.g. high boron steel.

Moderator

The neutrons produced during fission are travelling too fast; the moderator slows them down so that the probability of fission is increased. The moderator material needs to be a poor absorber (you need to slow the neutrons down not take them out). Also, the moderator must be a material with a light nucleus – the neutrons slow down through transferring KE in collisions with the moderator nucleus. In a collision with a heavy nucleus, practically no KE is transferred – the neutron just bounces off at the same speed. Examples of moderators include water and graphite.

Coolant

This controls the temperature of the reactor and also takes away the thermal energy to the steam turbine and generator. The coolant ideally is a gas or liquid with high heat capacity that doesn't absorb neutrons or become radioactive. Water or super-heated steam is often used as a coolant, too.

There are many more interesting things that could be mentioned about a fission nuclear reactor but the information herein should be sufficient to obtain full marks on any question the examiner might ask.

Finally, you need the common sense to answer questions about the disposal of waste products of nuclear reactors. All you need to do is make sensible comments about radioactive waste that is radioactive for thousands of years needing a stable, safe place to store it. You might even go further and give details regarding security of the storage or geological stability of the area or problems in transporting the radioactive waste.

Summary: PH5 Magnetism, Nuclei and Options

Capacitance

- Capacitance defined $\left(C = \dfrac{Q}{V} \right)$ and the parallel plate capacitor
- Factors affecting capacitance, $C = \dfrac{\varepsilon_0 A}{d}$ and dielectric
- Electric field, $E = \dfrac{V}{d}$
- Energy stored in a capacitor, $U = \dfrac{1}{2}QV = \dfrac{1}{2}CV^2 = \dfrac{Q^2}{2C}$
- Capacitors in parallel and series $\left(C = C_1 + C_2 + C_3 \right.$ and $\left. \dfrac{1}{C} = \dfrac{1}{C_1} + \dfrac{1}{C_2} + \dfrac{1}{C_3} \right)$
- Discharging a capacitor $Q = Q_0 e^{\frac{-t}{RC}}$ and RC = time constant

B-fields

- Force on a wire in a B-field $F = BI\ell \sin\theta$ and Fleming's LHR
- Force on a charge in a B-field $F = Bqv \sin\theta$ leading to circular motion
- The Hall Effect, $Bev = Ee$ with $I = nAve$, etc.
- Fields due to long wire and solenoid – shapes and use of equations $B = \dfrac{\mu_0 I}{2\pi a}$, $B = \mu_0 n I$ and the right-hand grip rule
- Force between two current carrying wires and the ampere
- Magnetic and electric field theory applied to particle accelerators

Electromagnetic induction

- Magnetic flux ($\Phi = AB \cos\theta$) and flux linkage $N\Phi$
- Faraday's law $V = -\dfrac{\Delta(BAN)}{\Delta t}$ and Lenz's law
- Rotating coil in a B-field – explanations
- Peak and rms values of I and V and $P = I_{rms}V_{rms}$ etc.
- Using an oscilloscope

Radioactivity and radioisotopes

- Properties of α, β and γ radiation
- Distinguishing between α, β and γ with absorbers, E and B-fields
- Radioactive decay theory $N = N_0 e^{-\lambda t}$, $A = \lambda N$, $A = A_0 e^{-\lambda t}$ and $\lambda = \dfrac{\ln 2}{T_{\frac{1}{2}}}$
- Uses of radioisotopes

Nuclear energy

- Mass–energy equivalence $E = mc^2$ and $1u \equiv 931$ MeV
- Calculating energy released in nuclear reactions from masses
- Binding energy graph, stability and calculating binding energy per nucleon
- Nuclear fission – chain reaction, moderator, control rods, coolant and waste

Knowledge and Understanding

PH5 Option A: Further Electromagnetism and Alternating Currents

This option continues from Faraday's law of electromagnetic induction and starts by applying Faraday's law to a transformer. Aspects of the design and theory of a transformer are then introduced in some detail. Faraday's law also leads to the concept and theory of self-induction which, in turn, leads to inductors in ac circuits. The main part of the ac theory is based on series LCR circuits and resonance by employing phasor diagrams. The Q-factor of a LCR circuit is defined and this leads to the sharpness of the resonance curve and frequency tuning using a variable capacitor. Option A finishes with the theory of CR circuits as high- and low-pass filters.

Revision checklist

Tick column 1 when you have completed brief revision notes.

Tick column 2 when you think you have a good grasp of the topic.

Tick column 3 during final revision when you feel you have mastered the topic.

		1	2	3	Notes
p104	**Option A - Further EM & AC**				
p105	Transformers and Faraday's law				
p105	Pd, current and power of a transformer				
p106	Design of a transformer				
p107	Self-inductance				
p108	Phasor diagrams and ac circuits				
p111	Resonance in an LCR circuit				
p113	Q-factor and tuning				
p116	CR circuits as low- and high-pass filters				

Unit PH5 Option A – Further Electromagnetism and Alternating Currents

Induction, transformers and self-induction

Key Terms

Flux leakage = not all the magnetic flux produced by the primary of a transformer is linked with the secondary (and vice versa).

Eddy current = charge flowing in closed loops in a conducting material (rather than being constrained to flow along wires).

These first topics follow on from electromagnetic induction (PH5.3). You already know that a changing current in one coil can induce an EMF in another coil from the explanation of how a transformer works (see page 79). This is true for any two coils brought into proximity:

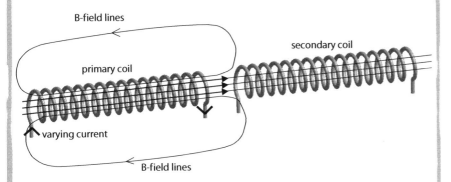

Some (but not all) of the B-field lines of the primary coil will provide a changing flux for the secondary coil. This leads to an EMF in the secondary coil according to Faraday's law. There are two important differences between the two coils shown above and a transformer:

1. The core of a transformer increases the strength of the B-field by a factor of thousands.
2. The closed core of a transformer ensures that there is almost no **flux leakage**, i.e. all the field lines from the primary coil go through the secondary coil.

Ideal transformer equations

If a transformer has no flux leakage and heat losses in the wires of the coil then the following equations are valid:

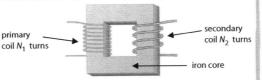

power in primary coil = power in secondary coil

$$I_1 V_1 = I_2 V_2$$

and

$$\frac{V_1}{V_2} = \frac{N_1}{N_2}$$

≫ Pointer
Although these equations apply to ideal transformers, you won't come across anything other than an ideal transformer for your calculations. In any case, modern transformers are highly efficient and these equations are excellent approximations.

Grade boost

Remember, the pd's in the primary and secondary coils are in the same ratio as the number of turns. If there are 20 times more turns, there'll be a 20 times bigger pd.

Grade boost

The currents are in the inverse ratio of the numbers of turns. If there are 15 times fewer turns then there'll be 15 times greater current.

$$\frac{V_1}{V_2} = \frac{N_1}{N_2} = \frac{I_2}{I_1}$$

quickfire

(A1)

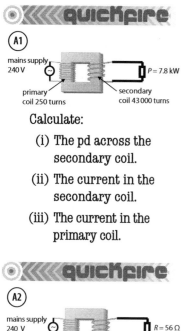

mains supply 240 V
primary coil 250 turns
secondary coil 43 000 turns
$P = 7.8\ kW$

Calculate:

(i) The pd across the secondary coil.

(ii) The current in the secondary coil.

(iii) The current in the primary coil.

quickfire

(A2)

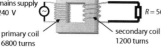

mains supply 240 V
primary coil 6800 turns
secondary coil 1200 turns
$R = 56\ \Omega$

Calculate:

(i) The power supplied to the 56 Ω resistor.

(ii) The current supplied to the primary coil.

Example

Calculate:

(i) The number of turns in the secondary coil.

(ii) The current in the lamp.

(iii) The current in the primary coil.

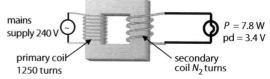

mains supply 240 V
primary coil 1250 turns
secondary coil N_2 turns
$P = 7.8\ W$
pd = 3.4 V

Answers

(i) Using $\dfrac{V_1}{V_2} = \dfrac{N_1}{N_2}$ → $N_2 = \dfrac{V_2}{V_1} \times N_1 = \dfrac{3.4}{240} \times 1250 = 18$ turns

(ii) $P = IV$ → $I = \dfrac{P}{V} = \dfrac{7.8}{3.4} = 2.3$ A

(iii) for the primary $P = IV = 7.8$ W (same power)

Hence, $I = \dfrac{P}{V} = \dfrac{7.8}{240} = 33$ mA

In addition to avoiding flux leakage, you need to know about three ways in which transformers can dissipate energy and how to reduce these losses.

1. Resistance of the wires in the primary and secondary coils. The power dissipated by the wires is given by $I^2 R$ so you need to ensure that the wires have as low a resistance as possible. In practice, this is accomplished by using the thickest appropriate copper wires. However, high temperature superconductor transformers have been used successfully since 1997 in the power supply network of Geneva, Switzerland.

2. **Eddy currents** in the iron core (see Key term). These are unwanted currents in the core itself that increase the internal (thermal) energy of the core. The eddy currents flow in a plane perpendicular to the B-field and can be eliminated by laminating the core (the individual laminations are insulated electrically).

3. Magnetising and demagnetising energy losses. The magnetisation of the core is changed continuously (due to the input alternating current) and this itself leads to power losses. You need to choose a suitable alloy that has very low magnetising and demagnetising losses (sometimes called hysteresis losses). The most commonly used alloy is iron with 3% silicon known as electrical steel (or silicon steel).

Self-induction

A coil that has a changing current in it also has a changing magnetic field inside it. This changing magnetic field provides the coil with a changing magnetic flux and flux linkage. According to Faraday's law an EMF is induced inside the coil. This is what is meant by self-induction – a changing current in a coil means that an EMF is induced in the coil itself. In fact, the induced EMF is proportional to the rate of change of current and this is the basis of the definition of **self-inductance** (see Key term).

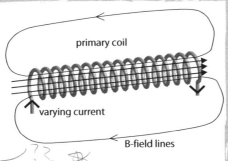

primary coil

varying current

B-field lines

Example

Use Faraday's law to show that the self-inductance of a long solenoid is given by:

$$\mu_0 \frac{N^2}{\ell} A.$$

B-field

Answer

You should recall from PH5.2 that the B-field inside a long solenoid is on the data sheet and is given by:

$$B = \mu_0 n I$$

Also (from PH5.3), the induced EMF is given by Faraday's law:

$$V = -\frac{\Delta(BAN)}{\Delta t}$$

All you have to do is substitute the expression for the B-field:

$$V = -\frac{\Delta(BAN)}{\Delta t} = -\frac{\Delta(\mu_0 n I A N)}{\Delta t} = -\mu_0 n A N \frac{\Delta I}{\Delta t}$$

compare this with the definition of self-inductance (see Key term)

$$\text{Induced EMF} = -L\frac{\Delta I}{\Delta t}$$

Hence, the self-inductance of a long solenoid is $L = \mu_0 n A N$. This expression can be modified slightly if you remember that n is the number of turns per unit length i.e. $n = \frac{N}{\ell}$. Hence,

$$L = \mu_0 n A N = \mu_0 \frac{N}{\ell} A N = \mu_0 \frac{N^2}{\ell} A \quad \text{QED}$$

Key Term

Self-inductance = L in the equation:

Induced EMF $= -L\dfrac{\Delta I}{\Delta t}$

$\dfrac{\Delta I}{\Delta t}$ is the rate of change of current and L is usually referred to as the self-inductance of a coil or an inductor. Unit: henry (H) = V s A^{-1}.

» Pointer

The self-induced EMF is often called the back EMF. As you would expect from Lenz's law, it opposes the change that's causing it.

Grade boost

Learn the three methods of power losses in a transformer and how to avoid them; it's come up regularly so far.

quickfire

(A3) The magnetic field inside a flat coil of N turns is given by $B = \dfrac{\mu_0 N I}{2r}$.

B-field

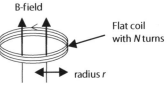

Flat coil with N turns

radius r

Use Faraday's law to show that the self-inductance of the flat coil is $\frac{1}{2}\mu_0 \pi r N^2$.

Currents

& Phase differences!?

Example

A long solenoid of length 0.75 m has 4600 turns per metre. It is cylindrical in shape and the radius of its circular cross-section is 5.5 cm. Calculate the self-inductance of the solenoid.

Answer

Here, the examiner's been deliberately awkward and has provided you with n rather than N – you need to use $N = n\ell$. He's given you the radius rather than the area so you'll also need $A = \pi r^2$.

$$L = \mu_0 \frac{N^2}{\ell} A = \mu_0 \frac{n^2\ell^2}{\ell} A = \mu_0 n^2 \ell A$$

$$L = \mu_0 n^2 \ell A = \mu_0 n^2 \ell \pi r^2$$

$$= 4\pi \times 10^{-7} \times 4600^2 \times 0.75 \times \pi \times 0.055^2 = 0.19 \text{ H}$$

Empire

...self-
...a long
solenoid with a total of 9800 turns and of length 1.20 m. The diameter of the cross-section of the solenoid is 6.2 cm.

≫ Pointer

A useful mnemonic: CIVIL - in a capacitor the current leads the voltage; the voltage leads the current in an inductor.

≫ Pointer

The current in a LCR circuit is $I = I_0 \sin \omega t$ but the pd **applied** to an inductor is $V_L = +L\frac{\Delta I}{\Delta t}$, hence,

$$V_L = L\frac{\Delta (I_0 \sin \omega t)}{\Delta t}$$

$$= \omega L I_0 \cos \omega t$$

$$= \omega L \times I_0 \sin\left(\omega t + \frac{\pi}{2}\right)$$

≫ Pointer

For a capacitor in an LCR circuit, $I = \frac{\Delta Q}{\Delta t} = I_0 \sin \omega t$. You can integrate this expression

$$\int \Delta Q = \int I_0 \sin \omega t \Delta t$$

$$Q = -\frac{1}{\omega} I_0 \cos \omega t$$

but $Q = CV_C$

$$CV_C = -\frac{1}{\omega} I_0 \cos \omega t$$

$$V_C = -\frac{1}{\omega} I_0 \cos \omega t$$

$$V_C = \frac{1}{\omega C} \times I_0 \sin\left(\omega t - \frac{\pi}{2}\right)$$

Phasor diagrams and ac circuits

You need to know how to apply ac circuit analysis to series circuits involving capacitors, inductors and resistors. This is done using vector or **phasor** (see Key term) diagrams. The reason why these vector diagrams work won't be discussed here – only how to apply the analysis.

Consider the following LCR circuit – it's called an LCR circuit because it has an inductor (*L*), capacitor (*C*) and resistor (*R*).

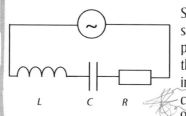

Similar to a dc circuit, the current is the same through all three components but the pd's are different. Added to this, however, is the complexity of phase differences. For an inductor, the pd across it is 90° in front of the current (see Pointer). For a capacitor, the pd is 90° behind the current (see Pointer). However, a resistor is simpler, the current and pd are always in phase for a resistor. The phasor or vector diagram is drawn as follows:

First draw the resistor pd as a horizontal vector, you don't need to draw the current vector but it's been added for completeness. Then draw V_L as going vertically upward. This signifies that V_L is 90° ahead of V_R (increasing phase goes anticlockwise). Draw V_C going vertically downwards, signifying that V_C is 90° behind V_R. You obtain the resultant in the same way as normal vectors – first

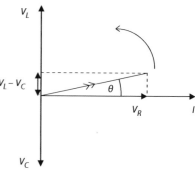

obtain $V_L - V_C$ then obtain the resultant of $V_L - V_C$ and V_R. Hence, the resultant is the vector (or phasor) shown in the diagram with the double arrow. The size (magnitude) of the resultant is V_S and the phase angle θ can be obtained from

$$V_S = \sqrt{(V_L - V_C)^2 + V_R^2} \quad \text{and} \quad \tan\theta = \frac{V_L - V_C}{V_R}$$

The resultant (V_S) shown in the phasor diagram is actually the supply pd. In general there's a phase difference between the applied pd and the current, it's represented by θ in the above diagram and can be calculated from $\tan\theta = \dfrac{V_L - V_C}{V_R}$.

In order to calculate the individual pd's, you need to know the 'effective resistance' of the inductor and capacitor. This 'effective resistance' of the inductor is called the **reactance** (see Key term) of the inductor and is given the symbol X_L. Likewise, the capacitor also has a reactance that's given the symbol X_C. Unlike resistance, these reactances are frequency dependent and are given by the following formulae that appear on the WJEC data sheet (also see Pointers):

$$X_L = \omega L \quad \text{and} \quad X_C = \frac{1}{\omega C} \quad \text{Why??} \quad \text{Nature?}$$

By definition (see Key terms), the pd's across the inductor and capacitor can be written:

$$V_L = IX_L = I\omega L \quad \text{and} \quad V_C = IX_C = \frac{1}{\omega C}$$

When combined with $V_R = IR$, you can obtain an expression for the 'effective resistance' of the LCR combination.

From earlier:

$$V_S = \sqrt{(V_L - V_C)^2 + V_R^2} = \sqrt{\left(I\omega L - \frac{I}{\omega C}\right)^2 + (IR)^2} = I\sqrt{\left(\omega L - \frac{1}{\omega C}\right)^2 + R^2}$$

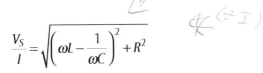

leading to:

$$\frac{V_S}{I} = \sqrt{\left(\omega L - \frac{1}{\omega C}\right)^2 + R^2} \qquad (= I)$$

This is where yet another new term is introduced. The name given to the 'effective resistance' of the LCR combination is the **impedance** (see Key term). By definition, $\dfrac{V_S}{I}$ is the impedance of the LCR combination (V_S and I both represent rms values). R_{eff}
Hence the impedance of an LCR circuit is:

$$Z = \sqrt{\left(\omega L - \frac{1}{\omega C}\right)^2 + R^2}$$

» Pointer

Remember the relationship between ω and f i.e.

$$\omega = 2\pi f \quad \text{and} \quad f = \frac{\omega}{2\pi}$$

 **quickfire**

(A5) Draw a phasor diagram for an LR circuit (it's the phasor diagram for an LCR circuit but without the capacitor phasor).

 **quickfire**

(A6) Draw a phasor diagram for a CR circuit.

Key Term

Impedance $= Z = \dfrac{V_{rms}}{I_{rms}}$, for some combination of resistor, inductor and capacitor. V_{rms} and I_{rms} are the rms values of the pd across and the current in the combination. It is equal to $Z = \sqrt{\left(\omega L - \dfrac{1}{\omega C}\right)^2 + R^2}$

or $Z = \sqrt{(\omega L)^2 + R^2}$ if there is no capacitor or

$Z = \sqrt{\left(\dfrac{1}{\omega C}\right)^2 + R^2}$ if there is no inductor. **UNIT:** Ω

≫ Pointer

It's actually easier to derive $Z = \sqrt{\left(\omega L - \dfrac{1}{\omega C}\right)^2 + R^2}$ from the phasor diagram of resistance and reactance:

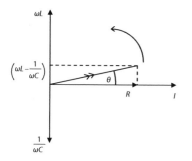

Example

Calculate:

(i) The reactance of the inductor.

(ii) The reactance of the capacitor.

(iii) The impedance of the circuit.

(iv) The rms current.

(v) The phase difference between the supplied pd and the current.

(vi) The frequency when the reactances of the inductor and capacitor are equal.

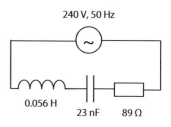

240 V, 50 Hz

0.056 H   23 nF   89 Ω

Answers

(i) $X_L = \omega L = 2\pi f L = 2\pi \times 50 \times 0.056 = 17.6\ \Omega$

(ii) $X_C = \dfrac{1}{\omega C} = \dfrac{1}{2\pi f C} = \dfrac{1}{2\pi \times 50 \times 23 \times 10^{-9}} = 138\ \text{k}\Omega$

(iii) $Z = \sqrt{\left(\omega L - \dfrac{1}{\omega C}\right)^2 + R^2} = \sqrt{(17.6 - 138 \times 10^3)^2 + 89^2} = 138\ \text{k}\Omega$

(iv) $I = \dfrac{V_{rms}}{Z} = \dfrac{240}{138 \times 10^3} = 1.7\ \text{mA}$

(v) This is tricky but the answer is very close to $-90°$ $\left(\text{or } -\dfrac{\pi}{2}\right)$ because the circuit is, more or less, behaving like a capacitor (see above figures where the capacitor reactance is dominant i.e. $Z \approx X_C$). Mathematically you can do:

$$\tan\theta = \frac{V_L - V_C}{V_R} = \frac{IX_L - IX_C}{IR} = \frac{0.0017 \times 17.6 - 0.0017 \times 13800}{0.0017 \times 89} = -1550$$

$$\theta = \tan^{-1}(-1550) = -89.96°$$

(vi) $\omega L = \dfrac{1}{\omega C} \rightarrow \omega^2 = \dfrac{1}{LC} \rightarrow \omega = \sqrt{\dfrac{1}{LC}} = \dfrac{1}{\sqrt{LC}}$

$\rightarrow f = \dfrac{1}{2\pi\sqrt{LC}} = \dfrac{1}{2\pi\sqrt{0.056 \times 23 \times 10^{-9}}} = 4.4\ \text{kHz}$

Again, notice in the last example that the reactance of the capacitor (138 kΩ) is far greater than the reactance of the inductor (17.6 Ω) at 50 Hz and also far greater than the resistance 89 Ω. This meant that the final impedance was almost exactly the reactance of the capacitor. However, at a higher frequency of 4.4 kHz the reactances of the capacitor and inductor were equal. This is because the reactance of the capacitor $\left(\dfrac{1}{\omega C}\right)$ decreases with frequency whereas the reactance of the inductor (ωL) increases with frequency.

You can actually draw a graph of the reactances, impedance and resistance of the circuit against frequency.

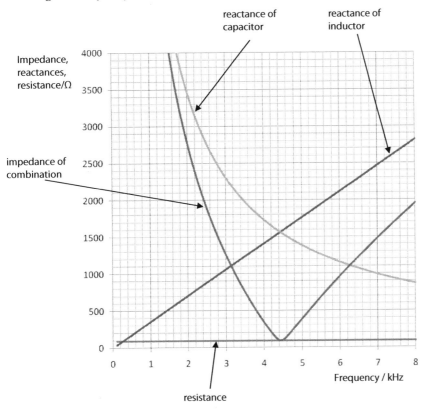

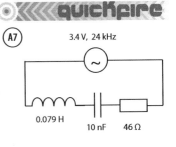

quicKfire

(A7) 3.4 V, 24 kHz

0.079 H   10 nF   46 Ω

Calculate:

(i) The reactance of the inductor.

(ii) The reactance of the capacitor.

(iii) The impedance of the circuit.

(iv) The rms current.

(v) The phase difference between the supplied pd and the current.

(vi) The frequency when the reactances of the inductor and capacitor are equal.

If you notice how the impedance of the circuit becomes a minimum at 4.4 kHz, it brings you nicely to the next topic – resonance.

Resonance in an LCR circuit

Looking carefully at the previous graph there are three crucial things to notice and remember:

1. The impedance is a minimum at resonance (4.4 kHz for the given circuit).
2. When the impedance is a minimum, the lines for the reactances of the capacitor and the inductor cross i.e. the reactances are equal.
3. The minimum value of the impedance is the resistance.

So, for resonance, the important condition is that the reactances of the inductor and capacitor are equal:

$$X_L = X_C \text{ or } \omega L = \frac{1}{\omega C}$$

but this is also reasonably obvious from the equation for the impedance:

$$Z = \sqrt{\left(\omega L - \frac{1}{\omega C}\right)^2 + R^2}$$

Grade boost

Know your resonance LCR circuit, it comes up very regularly.

Grade boost

The three essential points of resonance are important. Understand them and you'll do well. Resonance – minimum impedance, $X_L = X_C$ and $Z = R$.

quickfire

(A8) The following circuit is at resonance.

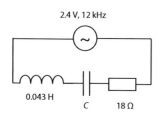

2.4 V, 12 kHz

0.043 H
C
18 Ω

Calculate:

(i) The current.

(ii) The capacitance of the capacitor.

(iii) The pd across the capacitor and inductor.

(iv) The phase difference between the applied pd and the current.

quickfire

(A9) The frequency of the supply is changed in Quickfire 8, first to 6 kHz and then to 24 kHz. Calculate the current at both these new frequencies and explain briefly why they are equal.

You want the impedance to be as small as possible in order to obtain a large current. Because the resistance R is a constant, the only way to achieve this minimum impedance is to have the two terms in the brackets cancel each other out. This gives:

$$Z = \sqrt{\left(\omega L - \frac{1}{\omega C}\right)^2 + R^2} = \sqrt{(0)^2 + R^2} = \sqrt{R^2} = R$$

and this explains why the minimum impedance in the graph is actually the resistance of the resistor R. The expression for the resonance frequency has already been derived in the last example of an LCR circuit but here it is again to make sure you learn it:

$$\omega L = \frac{1}{\omega C} \quad \rightarrow \quad \omega^2 = \frac{1}{LC} \quad \rightarrow \quad \omega = \sqrt{\frac{1}{LC}} = \frac{1}{\sqrt{LC}}$$

$$\rightarrow \quad f = \frac{1}{2\pi\sqrt{LC}} \quad \text{since} \quad f = \frac{\omega}{2\pi}$$

Example

The following circuit is at resonance. Calculate:

(i) The current.

(ii) The inductance of the inductor.

(iii) The pd across the capacitor and inductor.

(iv) The phase difference between the applied pd and the current.

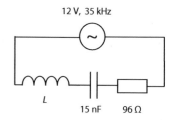

12 V, 35 kHz

L
15 nF   96 Ω

Answers

(i) Because the circuit is at resonance the reactances of the inductor and capacitor cancel and $Z = R$. Hence:

$$I = \frac{V}{Z} = \frac{V}{R} = \frac{12}{96} = 0.125 \text{ A}$$

(ii) This is trickier and you need to use the resonance condition:

$$\omega L = \frac{1}{\omega C} \quad \rightarrow \quad \omega^2 = \frac{1}{LC} \quad \rightarrow \quad L = \frac{1}{\omega^2 C}$$

$$\rightarrow \quad L = \frac{1}{(2\pi f)^2 C} = \frac{1}{(2\pi \times 35000)^2 \times 15 \times 10^{-9}} = 1.38 \text{ mH}$$

(iii) $V_L = IX_L = I\omega L = I \times 2\pi f L$

$$= 0.125 \times 2\pi \times 35\,000 \times 0.00138 = 38 \text{ V}$$

you don't need to calculate the pd across the capacitor because it must be equal to 38 V but here it is just as a check:

$$V_C = IX_C = \frac{1}{\omega C} = \frac{1}{2\pi f C}$$

$$= \frac{0.125}{2\pi \times 35000 \times 15 \times 10^{-9}} = 38 \text{ V}$$

Key Term

Quality (Q) factor of an LCR circuit $= \dfrac{\omega_0 L}{R} = \dfrac{1}{\omega_0 CR}$ (at resonance). It's a measure of the sharpness of the resonance curve – the larger the Q factor the sharper the resonance curve.

(iv) The resultant phasor at resonance is the resistance. This means that the current and applied pd are in phase and the phase angle is zero.

A very surprising result in that last example is that the pd across the inductor and capacitor is 38 V, which is larger than the applied pd of 12 V. Although this is surprising, you must remember that the phase difference between the pd across the inductor and the pd across the capacitor is 180° – they are in anti-phase. When the pd across the inductor is positive, the pd across the capacitor is equal but negative, leaving the whole of the applied pd across the resistor.

The quality (Q) factor of a resonance circuit

The **quality (Q) factor of a LCR circuit** is related to the sharpness of the resonance curve. A high Q factor gives a sharp resonance curve, while a low Q factor gives a broad resonance curve (see the diagram below with $Q = 8$, $Q = 2$ and $Q = 0.5$).

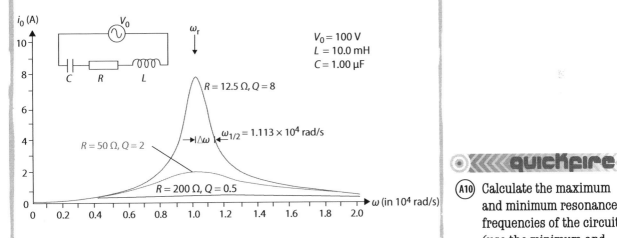

The **main** component in determining the Q factor of the circuit is the resistance of the circuit because it is the resistance that dissipates energy away from the circuit. This is similar to pushing a swing back and forth – if there's a lot of friction taking energy away from the swing it's difficult to achieve a high amplitude and 'sharp' resonance. The easiest way to define the Q factor is as follows:

$$Q = \frac{\text{rms pd across inductor at resonance}}{\text{rms pd across resistor at resonance}}$$

quickfire

(A10) Calculate the maximum and minimum resonance frequencies of the circuit (use the minimum and maximum values of the variable capacitor).

quickfire

(A11) For the circuit in Quickfire 10, calculate the maximum and minimum Q factors.

quickfire

(A12) Write down the maximum and minimum resonance frequencies of the circuit.

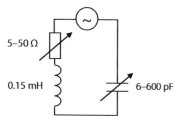

5–50 Ω

0.15 mH   6–600 pF

(A13) For the circuit in Quickfire 12, calculate the maximum and minimum Q factors.

>> **Pointer**

Notice how you can change the resonance frequency of an LCR circuit with a variable capacitor – this is how radios tune to different frequencies.

As the capacitor and inductor have equal reactance at resonance, the Q factor can also be written:

$$Q = \frac{\text{rms pd across capacitor at resonance}}{\text{rms pd across resistor at resonance}}$$

These definitions lead to the equations:

$$Q = \frac{I\omega_0 L}{IR} = \frac{\omega_0 L}{R} \text{ and also } Q = \frac{I/\omega_0 C}{IR} = \frac{1}{\omega_0 CR}$$

If you incorporate the expression for the resonance frequency, $\omega_0 = \dfrac{1}{\sqrt{LC}}$, then:

$$Q = \frac{\omega_0 L}{R} = \frac{\frac{1}{\sqrt{LC}}L}{R} = \frac{1}{R}\sqrt{\frac{L}{C}}$$

So you have three expressions for the Q factor (only the first appears on the data sheet):

$$Q = \frac{\omega_0 L}{R} = \frac{1}{\omega_0 CR} = \frac{1}{R}\sqrt{\frac{L}{C}}$$

Note that, in the expressions for the Q factor, you can eliminate L, C and ω_0 but you cannot eliminate R – it is in all three expressions. Note also that the Q factor is a ratio and it has no unit.

Now consider this circuit:

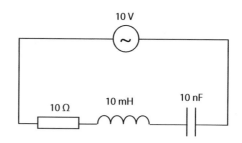

10 V

10 Ω   10 mH   10 nF

These values for R, C, L make your arithmetic extremely easy and give you a quick exercise in dealing with powers of 10. You should obtain the following figures:

$$\omega_0 = \frac{1}{\sqrt{LC}} = \frac{1}{\sqrt{10^{-2} \times 10^{-8}}} = \frac{1}{\sqrt{10^{-10}}} = 10^5 \ s^{-1}$$

and

$$Q = \frac{\omega_0 L}{R} = \frac{10^5 \times 10^{-2}}{10} = 100$$

You can also calculate the current flowing at resonance because the whole of the supply pd is across the resistor at resonance (pd's across the inductor and capacitance are equal and opposite, so cancel).

$$I = \frac{V}{R} = \frac{10}{10} = 1 \text{ A}$$

All seems nice and straight forward until you look at the pd across the capacitor or inductor:

$$V_L = I\omega_0 L = 1 \times 10^5 \times 10^{-2} = 1000 \text{ V}$$

How can you have 1000 V across the inductor (and capacitor) when the supply voltage is only 10 V? There's no simple answer to this question but a better understanding can be drawn from considering another type of resonance. Again, consider a swing with very little friction. You only need to provide a small push regularly in order to obtain a large amplitude – you might only be pushing the swing for a distance of 30 cm each swing but the amplitude of oscillation could easily be 2 m.

Grade boost

Don't drop silly marks for not converting the kΩ and the nF.

Grade boost

(if you have an EXP button on your calculator)
When putting 10^{-9} in your calculator you cannot type 10 exp –9 because this is the same as 10×10^{-9}. You must type (and this might seem strange until you think about it carefully) 1 exp –9 because this is 1×10^{-9}.

Example

For the circuit shown:

(i) Calculate the resonance frequency.

(ii) Calculate the Q factor.

(iii) State what happens to the resonance curve if the resistance doubles.

(iv) State what happens to the resonance curve when the inductance is doubled.

(v) State what happens to the resonance curve when the capacitance is doubled.

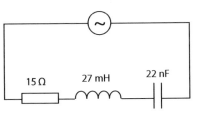

15 Ω   27 mH   22 nF

Answers

(i) From the equation derived earlier:

$$f = \frac{1}{2\pi\sqrt{LC}} = \frac{1}{2\pi\sqrt{0.027 \times 22 \times 10^9}} = 6530 \text{ Hz}$$

(ii) $Q = \dfrac{\omega_0 L}{R} = \dfrac{2\pi \times 6530 \times 0.027}{15} = 74$

(iii) The Q factor $\left(\dfrac{\omega_0 L}{R}\right)$ halves and the resonance curve becomes flatter.

(iv) The Q factor $\left(\dfrac{\omega_0 L}{R}\right)$ doubles and the resonance curve becomes sharper.

(v) The Q factor $\left(\dfrac{1}{\omega_0 CR}\right)$ halves and the resonance curve becomes flatter.

Using CR circuits as low-pass and high-pass filters

Low-pass filter

Compare with

The easiest way to explain how the above circuit behaves as a low-pass filter is to compare it with a voltage divider.

In the circuit on the right, the supply voltage is shared between the two resistors. In the low-pass filter, on the left, the voltage is divided between the capacitor and the resistor.

Remember that the reactance of the capacitor is given by: $X_C = \dfrac{1}{\omega C}$

From the above equation, at low frequencies X_C will be very large. So at low frequencies you have a voltage divider with a very large 'resistance' in the R_2 position. This means that nearly all the supply voltage will be across the capacitor at low frequencies.

At high frequencies X_C will be very small. So at high frequencies you have a voltage divider with a very low 'resistance' in the R_2 position. This means that nearly all the supply voltage will be across the resistor at high frequencies, i.e. there will be a very low pd across the capacitor.

If you were to draw a graph of V_{out}/V_{in} against frequency you would get:

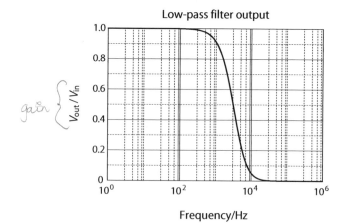

Low-pass filter output

Note that V_{out}/V_{in} is usually called the gain and that it starts at 1 and drops to zero (this is because $V_{out} = V_{in}$ at very low frequencies and $V_{out} = 0$ at very high frequencies).

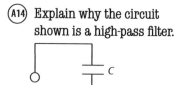

Example

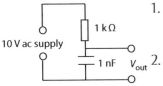

10 V ac supply
1 kΩ
1 nF V_{out}

1. Calculate the frequency when the rms pd across the resistor is equal to the rms pd across the capacitor.
2. Calculate the rms pd across both the resistor and the capacitor at the frequency of Q1.

→ Question ①
not Q-factor ! ✗

Answers

1. Equating the pd's across the capacitor and resistor you get:

   $IX_C = IR$. Cancelling I gives you: $X_C = R$

   But $X_C = \dfrac{1}{\omega C}$, hence $\dfrac{1}{\omega C} = R$ and rearranging you get $\omega = \dfrac{1}{CR}$.

   Using $\omega = 2\pi f$, you get: $f = \dfrac{\omega}{2\pi} = \dfrac{1}{2\pi CR} = \dfrac{1}{2\pi \times 10^{-9} \times 1000} = 159$ kHz.

2. There are many ways of obtaining the correct answer,

   e.g. using $Z = \sqrt{X_C^2 + R^2}$ and $I = \dfrac{V}{Z}$ etc.,

   but it's probably more direct and simple to do as follows:

   Remember that $V_S^2 = V_C^2 + V_R^2$ and that $V_C = V_R$ from question 1.

   So $V_S^2 = 2V_C^2$, ∴ $V_C^2 = \dfrac{V_S^2}{2}$ and hence $V_C = \dfrac{V_S}{\sqrt{2}} = \dfrac{10}{\sqrt{2}} = 7.07$ V

So the correct answer is that the pd across both the capacitor and the resistor is 7.07 V.

Beware: Don't fall into the trap of saying that both rms pd's must be 5 V so that they add up to 10 V. Although this sort of argument applies to **instantaneous** pd's it is completely wrong for obtaining **rms** pd's because the pd across the capacitor is out of phase with the pd across the resistor.

High-pass filter

(Resistor)
"High output pd at high frequencies! ✗"

In the low-pass filter of the previous section you noted that when the pd was low across the capacitor, the pd was high across the resistor. If you now swap the capacitor and resistor, the output pd will be the pd across the resistor instead of the capacitor (see diagram on page 118). In this circuit you will have a high output where you previously had a low output, and a low output where you previously had a high output, i.e. a high output at large frequencies and a low output at low frequencies. See the graph below and compare it with the previous low-pass filter graph. The graph below is characteristic of a high-pass filter.

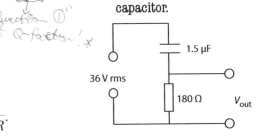

QUICKFIRE

(A15) Calculate the frequency when the rms pd across the resistor is equal to the rms pd across the capacitor.

36 V rms
1.5 µF
180 Ω
V_{out}

QUICKFIRE

(A16) Calculate the output pd in the circuit of Quickfire 15 when the frequency of the supply is 1.2 kHz.

Grade boost

The explanation for the high-pass filter hasn't been given in full. Make sure you can change the explanation for the low-pass filter correctly for a high-pass filter.

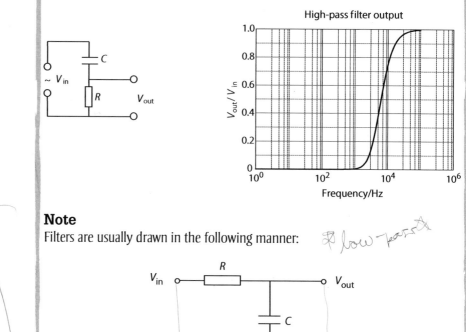

High-pass filter output

Note

Filters are usually drawn in the following manner: *low pass*

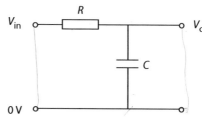

This makes it easier to draw higher order filters (i.e., one filter feeding into another to provide more filtering, see below). This notation has not been used here so that you can compare the circuit more easily with a potential divider. However, the above notation may well be used in an examination.

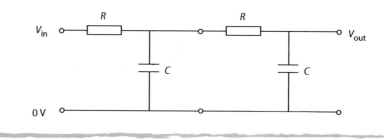

Knowledge and Understanding

PH5 Option C: Materials

This option picks up where PH1 left off in terms of forces, energy and materials. As the title suggests, the emphasis is on the mechanical properties of materials (e.g. steel) rather than objects (e.g. springs), though there is some crossover. This unit is particularly useful if you are interested in mechanical engineering or materials science.

Option C is tested as a single 20-mark question in section C of the PH5 exam.

Revision checklist

Tick column 1 when you have completed brief revision notes.

Tick column 2 when you think you have a good grasp of the topic.

Tick column 3 during final revision when you feel you have mastered the topic.

		1	2	3	Notes
p120	**Hooke's law**				
p120	Basic definitions and experiment				
p121	**Young modulus**				
p121	Stress, strain and Young modulus				
p121	Units and magnitudes				
p122	Experiment				
p123	Strain energy				
p125	Stress–strain graphs				
p126	**Material structure**				
p126	Molecular structure – edge dislocations				
p127	Properties of ductile materials				
p127	Superalloys				
p128	Brittle facture and crack propagation				
p129	**Polymers and their mechanical properties**				
p129	Rubber				
p130	Polythene				

Hooke's law

>> *Pointer*

Learn a description of the spring experiment.

>> *Pointer*

Learn Hooke's law.

(c1) A spring extends by 10.0 cm when a mass of 200 g is suspended from it. Calculate the spring constant, k. [Hint: $F = mg$ and $F = k\Delta x$]

(c2) The spring constant, k, for a spring is 25.3 N m^{-1}. The largest mass it can support without permanent extension is 0.65 kg. What is the extension at the elastic limit?

If a **load** is hung from a spiral spring, it extends, i.e. it gets longer. The increase in length is called the **extension**.

Extension Δx = length – original length.

A simple arrangement to investigate the relationship between the extension and the load is shown. The apparatus is set up with just the hanger; the reading on the rule indicated by the pointer is taken. Additional masses are added and the position readings taken.

The values of Δx are calculated as above and the load, F, is calculated using $F = mg$.

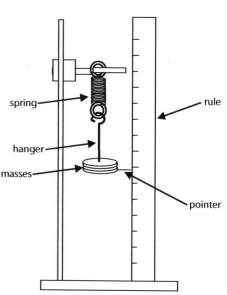

The load extension graph is typically as shown.

In the initial, straight-line region, the spring is *elastic*, i.e. it returns to its original length when the load is removed. Beyond the elastic limit (see graph) the spring is permanently stretched.

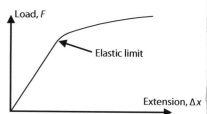

Hooke's law summarises this:

'Provided the elastic limit is not exceeded, the extension of a spring is [directly] proportional to the load.'

The relationship, $F = k\Delta x$ relates to this elastic region. The constant k is called the **spring constant**: it is the force per unit extension of the spring and gives an indication of the stiffness of the spring – the stiffer the spring, the larger k is. Its unit is N m^{-1}.

Young modulus

Stress, strain and Young modulus

F ← [diagram of cylinder] → F

Cross-sectional area, A

Length, l

If a force, F, called the *tension*, is applied to each end of a specimen of a solid material, the extension Δx is proportional to the original length. So, when comparing materials, it makes sense to use the **strain**, ε which is defined by:

$$\varepsilon = \frac{\Delta l}{l_0}, \text{ where } l_0 \text{ is the original length.}$$

The effect of the tension depends upon the cross-sectional area (csa) A of the specimen, so engineers work with the *stress, σ*, defined by:

$$\sigma = \frac{F}{A}$$

The **Young modulus**, E, of a material is defined by: $E = \dfrac{\sigma}{\varepsilon}$. The value of E relates to the stiffness of a material – not the stiffness of a particular specimen.

Units and magnitudes of ε, σ and E

From its definition, ε has no unit – it is one length divided by another. In most engineering situations, the values of ε are very small, e.g. the girder of a bridge may be about 5 m long when unloaded and extend by 0.5 mm when under tension.

In this example $\varepsilon = \dfrac{5 \times 10^{-4}\,\text{m}}{5\,\text{m}} = 1 \times 10^{-4}$. The figure tells us that the girder has extended by 1×10^{-4} m for every metre of its length, or 1×10^{-4} mm for every mm of its length.

Looking at the definition of **stress**:

Unit of stress $= \dfrac{\text{unit of force}}{\text{unit of area}} = \dfrac{\text{N}}{\text{m}^2} = \text{N m}^{-2} = \text{Pa (pascal)}$. This is the same as the unit of pressure.

quickfire

(C4) A load of 5 kN is applied to a steel rope of csa 2 cm². Calculate the stress in (a) N cm⁻², (b) Pa, (c) MPa.

The values of σ in Pa tend to be large, e.g. the girder in the above example might have a load of 2×10^5 N [~20 tonnes] and a csa of 10^{-2} m²:

So $\sigma = \dfrac{2 \times 10^5 \text{ N}}{1 \times 10^{-2} \text{ m}^2} = 2 \times 10^7 = 2 \times 10^7$ Pa or 20 MPa. 10s or even 100s of MPa are typical in engineering situations.

Unit of the Young modulus $= \dfrac{\text{unit of stress}}{\text{unit of strain}} = \dfrac{\text{Pa}}{\text{no unit}} = $ Pa. Because stress is typically in the 10s of MPa and strain is typically less than 10^{-3}, the value of the Young modulus is typically in the GPa range.

In this example: $E = \dfrac{\sigma}{\varepsilon} = \dfrac{2 \times 10^7 \text{ Pa}}{1 \times 10^{-4}} = 2 \times 10^{11}$ Pa $= 200$ GPa, which is a typical value for steel.

》Pointer

With hard engineering materials (steel, concrete, glass) the value for the Young modulus will be typically 10–200 × GPa. If your answer is a lot smaller, you've probably not converted your units, e.g. cm² to m².

》Pointer

The Young modulus of natural materials, e.g. tendons or rubber, is of the order of MPa rather than GPa.

》Pointer

Learn the Young modulus experiment.

Sample calculation

A 5.00 m long wire, of diameter 0.315 mm, is made of steel with a Young modulus of 200 GPa. Calculate its extension when a load of 10 N is applied to it.

$$\sigma = \frac{F}{A} \text{ and } A = \pi r^2. \text{ So } \sigma = \frac{10 \text{ N}}{\pi \times \left(\dfrac{0.315 \times 10^{-3} \text{ m}}{2} \right)^2} = 1.28 \times 10^8 \text{ Pa}$$

$$E = \frac{\sigma}{\varepsilon}, \text{ so } \varepsilon = \frac{\sigma}{E} = \frac{1.28 \times 10^8 \text{ Pa}}{200 \times 10^9 \text{ Pa}} = 6.4 \times 10^{-4}.$$

$$\varepsilon = \frac{\Delta l}{l_0}, \text{ so } \Delta l = \varepsilon l_0 = 6.4 \times 10^{-4} \times 5.00 \text{ m} = 3.2 \times 10^{-3} \text{ m} = 3.2 \text{ mm}.$$

Care with units

Remember 1 cm² $= 10^{-4}$ m², so 1 N cm⁻² $= 1 \times 10^4$ Pa [i.e. 1×10^4 N m⁻²]. In the sample calculation above, notice how the diameter of the wire was converted to m straightaway.

Experiment to determine the Young modulus

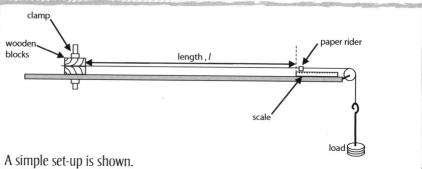

A simple set-up is shown.

A long piece of wire is used, with *l* typically about 2 m. The blocks are to prevent damage to the wire.

The original length *l* is measured using a metre rule (giving an uncertainty of ~ 0.1 %). The extension is measured using the paper rider (or a paint blob) and the mm scale – this is the least precise part of the experiment. For accurate work a travelling microscope can be used. The tension is determined from the mass of the load – typically increased in 0.1 kg steps – and use of $W = mg$. After the maximum load is reached, the load is decreased and the mean of the Δl values for each value of the load is calculated.

The diameter of the wire is determined using a micrometer/digital calliper (giving an uncertainty of 0.01 mm, i.e 3% for a 0.3 mm diameter wire).

A graph is plotted of *F* against Δl. From the definition of *E*, σ and ε we have $E = \dfrac{Fl_0}{A\Delta l}$.

So $F = \dfrac{EA}{l_0}\Delta l$, giving a gradient of $\dfrac{EA}{l_0}$. *A* is calculated using $A = \pi\dfrac{d^2}{4}$ allowing *E* to be calculated from the gradient.

Sample data: Copper wire; $l_0 = 2.105 \pm 0.001$ m; $d = 0.38 \pm 0.01$ mm; gradient $= 6200 \pm 300$ N m^{-1}.

Calculation: Gradient $= \dfrac{EA}{l_0}$, so $E = \dfrac{l_0 \times \text{gradient}}{A} =$

$$\frac{2.105 \text{ m} \times 6200 \text{ N m}^{-1}}{\pi\left(\dfrac{0.38\times10^{-3}}{2}\right)^2 \text{m}^2} = 115 \text{ GPa}$$

Uncertainty: % uncertainties: d – 2.6%; gradient – 4.8%; l_0 – 0.05% [ignore].

So total uncertainty $= 2.6\% + 4.8\% = 7.4\%$. 7.4% of 115 $= 8.5$

So $E = 115 \pm 9$ GPa

Key Term

Strain energy = the energy stored in a specimen when it is deformed elastically.

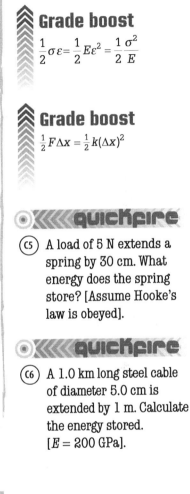

Grade boost

$$\frac{1}{2}\sigma\varepsilon = \frac{1}{2}E\varepsilon^2 = \frac{1}{2}\frac{\sigma^2}{E}$$

Grade boost

$$\tfrac{1}{2}F\Delta x = \tfrac{1}{2}k(\Delta x)^2$$

quickfire

(C5) A load of 5 N extends a spring by 30 cm. What energy does the spring store? [Assume Hooke's law is obeyed].

quickfire

(C6) A 1.0 km long steel cable of diameter 5.0 cm is extended by 1 m. Calculate the energy stored. [$E = 200$ GPa].

Strain energy

If an object is stretched, the tension does work on the object, i.e. it transfers energy to the internal energy of the object. If the object is elastic, this process is reversible – in relaxing, the elastic object can transfer energy back, so this stored energy is the elastic potential energy.

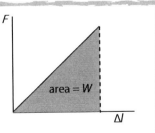

How much energy is transferred?

Work = force × distance moved in the direction of the force.

But the force is not constant, so how do we calculate the work done? As in so many other examples, it is the area under the graph – in this case the *F*, Δl graph.

Key Term

Strain energy per unit volume = the strain energy divided by the (original) volume of the specimen.

For an object which obeys Hooke's law, the area is triangular, so:

$$W = \tfrac{1}{2}F\Delta l.$$

Hence the elastic potential energy $E_P = \tfrac{1}{2}F\Delta l.$

Grade boost

Look out for the use of SI multipliers in the information provided for calculations, e.g. stress = 25 MPa = 25×10^6 Pa
Young modulus = 200 GPa = 200×10^9 Pa
Length = 2.5 km = 2.5×10^3 m

Grade boost

Convert quantities to basic SI units before doing any calculations, e.g. a cylinder of diameter 5.0 mm has a csa of $\pi \times \left(\dfrac{5.0 \times 10^{-3}\ \text{m}}{2}\right)^2 =$
2.0×10^{-6} m^2

Grade boost

Remember 1 cm^2 = 1×10^{-4} m^2.

Strain energy per unit volume

Consider an object with csa A and length l. The volume $V = Al$.

Using $E_P = \tfrac{1}{2}F\Delta l$, we can divide by Al to find the strain energy per unit volume (aka strain energy density):

$$\text{Strain energy per unit volume} = \frac{1}{2}\frac{F\Delta l}{Al} = \frac{1}{2}\frac{F}{A} \times \frac{\Delta l}{l} = \frac{1}{2}\sigma\,\varepsilon.$$

Note that csa and length of a specimen are not constant but the variation in A and l is generally so small that the unstretched values can be used. Rubber, which does have large extensions, also has a virtually constant volume when stretched. It gets noticeably thinner and the product length × csa is almost constant.

Example

The band of a catapult consists of two 10-cm length pieces rubber of 4 mm × 4 mm cross-section. A 25 g stone inserted, the band drawn back a distance of 10 cm and released. The Young modulus of the rubber is 20 MPa. Calculate the speed that the stone will leave the catapult.

Answer

csa of each piece of rubber = $(4 \times 10^{-3}\ \text{m})^2 = 1.6 \times 10^{-5}$ m^2.
So Total csa = 3.2×10^{-5} m^2.
Volume of rubber = $0.1\ \text{m} \times 3.2 \times 10^{-5}\ \text{m} = 3.2 \times 10^{-6}$ m^3
$$\Delta l = 10\ \text{cm}; l_0 = 10\ \text{cm so } \varepsilon = 1.$$

Energy stored per unit volume = $\tfrac{1}{2}\sigma\varepsilon = \tfrac{1}{2}E\varepsilon^2 = \tfrac{1}{2} \times 20 \times 10^6$ Pa $\times 1$
$$= 1 \times 10^7\ \text{J m}^{-3}$$

So Total energy stored = 1×10^7 J m$^{-3} \times 3.2 \times 10^{-6}$ m^3 = 32 J.

If all this energy is transferred to the stone, $E_k = \tfrac{1}{2} \times 0.025\ v^2 = 32$ J
So $v^2 = 2560$ m^2 s^{-2}
So $v = 51$ m s^{-1} (2 s.f.)

Stress–strain graphs

Some engineering materials (e.g. copper and steel) are classed as *ductile*, which means that they can be drawn out into a wire. Others (e.g. glass) cannot – they just snap – and are classed as *brittle*. Their stress–strain graphs are clearly different as shown.

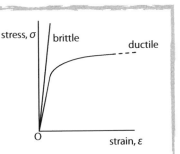

The following diagrams compare the $\sigma - \varepsilon$ graphs for copper and steel:

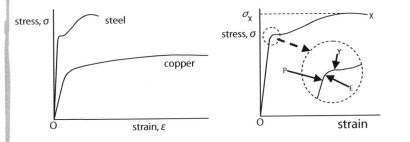

The materials both have an initial linear region – the elastic region. The Young modulus is a constant here and the following equation is valid:

$$\text{Elastic potential energy stored per unit volume} = \tfrac{1}{2}\,\sigma\varepsilon.$$

At higher values of strain, the graph curves to the right and the material becomes *plastic*, i.e. it becomes permanently stretched. Significant features shown on the second graph are:

P – the limit of proportionality;

E – **the elastic limit**;

Y – **the yield point**, at which the material shows a large increase in strain for little or no increase in stress;

σ_X – the breaking stress, aka ultimate tensile strength (UTS)

X – the breaking point.

Why do the graphs turn down at the end? At very large strains, the specimen under test starts to form a 'neck'. In this region the true stress is higher because  the csa is lower: engineers usually measure the apparent stress which is the load divided by the original csa.

Key Terms

Elastic limit = the point at which deformation ceases to be elastic. For a specimen it is usually measured by the maximum force, and for a material, by the maximum stress, before the strain ceases to be elastic.

Yield point = the point at which a large increase in strain occurs for little or no increase in the stress.

≫ Pointer

The $\sigma - \varepsilon$ graph for steel is easier to label than that for copper.

⟫ *Pointer*

An edge dislocation does not move back when the tension is removed. The movement of dislocations therefore produces plastic deformation.

⟫ *Pointer*

Dislocations cannot migrate across grain boundaries, so these act to stiffen the material in polycrystalline materials.

Material structure

The molecular structure of materials – edge dislocations

Metals are **polycrystalline**. This means that they are composed of large numbers of interlocking *crystals* – in which the metal ions are arranged in a regular repeating pattern. A typical **crystalline** structure is shown to the right. Some materials, e.g. diamond, are single crystals but a large metal sample has many of these crystals arranged in all possible orientations.

 The diagram to the left shows an approximately 100 μm square surface of a piece of metal. The individual crystals, or *grains*, are clearly seen. The diagram to the right is a model showing arrangements of particles  [ions]. The number of ions in an individual grain is much more than shown [~100 000 planes of ions per grain]. Some materials are **amorphous**, meaning that there is no regular arrangement of ions. See the discussion of the properties of glass.

Because the crystals grow randomly, they are not perfect and very often an **edge dislocation** is produced [millions per crystal]. This is an extra $\frac{1}{2}$ plane of ions. In the diagram to the right, the dislocation is at X. If forces are applied as shown, the dislocation will move 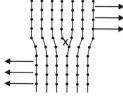 irreversibly to the right, i.e. the crystal will suffer permanent deformation. There are many animations of this – type edge dislocation into a search engine.

The movement of edge dislocations can cause large deformations in the following way: large stresses can cause a crystal plane to snap producing two edge dislocations, which migrate in opposite directions. This makes the crystals elongate in the direction of the stress. Foreign (impurity) atoms, grain boundaries and other dislocations impede the movement of edge dislocations and act against this tendency.

The properties of ductile metals

Property	Relation to dislocations
plastic deformation	caused by the movement of edge dislocations
yield	the stress is great enough to cause edge dislocations to move and to create new edge dislocations
necking and **ductile** fracture	the movement of edge dislocations causes the metal to flow away from a point of higher stress, leading to even higher stress and failure
creep	slow increase in length caused by the movement of dislocations at lower stress if maintained over a long period of time – increased at higher temperature
work hardening	deforming, e.g. by hammering, causes dislocation entanglement, and accumulation at grain boundaries impeding subsequent movement
annealing	(in copper) heating to a high temperature to cause recrystallisation followed by quenching – to restore ductility to a work hardened material
quench hardening (of steel)	heating to a high temperature ($\sim$ 900°C) produces a fine grain structure which obstructs the movement of dislocations
fatigue	see brittle facture

Key Terms

Ductile = a material which can be drawn out into a wire. This implies that plastic strain occurs under enough stress.

Creep = an increase of strain with time, which may sometimes occur even if the stress is kept constant.

Work hardening = the process of causing inelastic strain in a metal, through at least one application of stress. It raises the elastic limit, but reduces the extent of the ductile region between elastic limit and fracture.

Superalloys

Metallic mixtures of different elements are called alloys. Everyday examples are *mild steel*, an alloy of iron and 0.3% carbon, and *brass*, an alloy of copper and zinc. Superalloys have been developed to withstand extreme conditions, e.g. those encountered in gas turbine blades. Such a turbine blade needs to be: low density; corrosion resistant; strong; stiff [i.e. have a high Young modulus]; creep resistant; stable over a long period of time.

This revision guide is too short to do justice to this topic. You are advised to read the WJEC publication '*Superalloy Notes*' which you can find on the website www.wjec.co.uk. One major technique used in the development of these alloys is the inclusion of selected impurities, e.g. hard precipitates, which hinder dislocation movement, and therefore plastic deformation. Another is the development of turbine blades, which are single crystals, thus avoiding the weakness associated with grain boundaries.

≫ Pointer

Read the WJEC superalloy notes and be familiar with two examples of their uses.

(c7) A glass fibre of diameter 0.12 mm just breaks when a mass of 650 g is hung from it. Its Young modulus is 100 GPa.

(a) Calculate the UTS.

(b) Calculate the strain at fracture.

(c) Sketch the stress-strain graph.

Brittle fracture = sudden failure of a specimen with no plastic deformation. This occurs in, e.g., concrete, glass, cast iron.

Stress lines = lines that indicate how the tension is transmitted through the specimen; strain occurs along these lines and fracture is approximately at right angles to them.

Crack propagation = increase in length of a crack, usually when the specimen is under tension. This can be very rapid and leads to failure (i.e. breaking).

Metal fatigue = when a ductile metal is subject to many cycles of loading and unloading, microscopic cracks are produced.

Prestressed = manufactured so that the surface is under compression.

≫ Pointer

In prestressed glass, the surface is under compression and the centre under tension. Any cracks on the surface do not propagate until the specimen is under a tension big enough to overcome the initial compression.

≫ Pointer

Old churches were built with towers at the corners of the walls. The weight of these helps keep the walls in compression.

Brittle fracture

Many **brittle** materials, e.g. glass, ceramics, are *amorphous*, i.e. their molecules show no long-range regularity. The stress–strain graph is a straight line up to fracture, with no plastic deformation. The material fractures because of the existence of microscopic cracks in the surface.

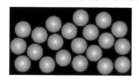

The diagram shows a highly exaggerated crack. The dotted lines are so-called **stress lines**, which indicate how the tension is transmitted through the specimen. The stress lines are concentrated around the tip of the crack, magnifying the stress and causing the crack to extend, which produces an even higher stress at the new tip: the result is that the **crack propagates** rapidly through the material.

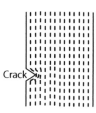

This mechanism is responsible for failure due to **metal fatigue**. If a ductile metal is subject to many cycles of loading and unloading, microscopic cracks are produced which eventually will propagate as above. Manufactured objects with small, especially irregular, holes are especially susceptible [enter *metal fatigue* into a search engine and ignore references to a video game!].

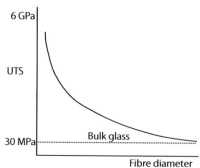

The theoretical UTS of glass is ~ 6 GPa. Bulk glass has a UTS of ~ 30 MPa. However, experiments on thin glass fibres have shown that, if care is taken not to damage the surface, the UTS of a freshly drawn glass fibre increases with decreasing diameter. The thinner the glass fibre, the smaller the thermal stresses when it cools, so the problem with surface cracks is less. Very thin (~ 1 μm) glass fibres have strengths approaching the theoretical value.

Stopping cracks propagating

Brittle materials can be used in engineering if the propagation of cracks can be avoided. This is done in the following ways:

1. With concrete and brick structures – design the structure so that the brittle material is always *under compression*. In this way the cracks do not open up.
2. With glass – use **prestressed** *glass*, manufactured so that the surface is under compression. This is done by a rapid cooling of the surface. A tension can be applied without the crack-bearing surface being put under tension. Search on *prestressed glass* and *prestressed concrete*.
3. Use *composite* materials, e.g. fibre glass, reinforced concrete. A crack propagating through the material is stopped when it hits a new component of the composite.

Polymers and their mechanical properties

Key Terms

Thermoplastic = see main text.

Thermoset = see main text.

Elastic hysteresis = when a material such as rubber is put under stress and the stress is then relaxed, the stress–strain graphs for increasing and decreasing stress do not coincide, but form a loop.

Polymers consist of molecules with long chains of repeated units, e.g. polythene has chains produced from ethene molecules [C_2H_4]. Two types of polymer are:

- **Thermoplastics** – or thermosoftening plastics – which soften with increasing temperature, e.g. polythene, natural rubber. The long chains are tangled but are not bound together.
- **Thermosets** – or thermosetting polymers – which cannot be liquefied once they have cured, e.g. melamine. The chains have cross links – chemical bonds, which prevent re-melting. They are generally hard, brittle and have a high decomposition temperature. Melamine is used in worktop surfaces.

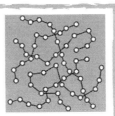

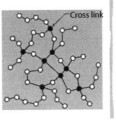
Cross link

Rubber

The stress–strain and load-extension graphs have the following features:

- Non-linear: steep → less steep → very steep.
- Large strains: up to ~5 depending on the type of rubber.
- The stress needed to stretch is low.
- Loading and unloading curves different: called **elastic hysteresis**.

Because the area under a load-extension curve is the work done, the work done *by* the rubber band in contracting is less than the work done *on* the rubber band in stretching.

The area between the curves represents the energy dissipated in moving once around the hysteresis loop. It manifests itself as random vibrational energy of the rubber molecules.

Why does rubber behave like this?

1. The C–C bonds in the long chains can rotate;
2. Successive C–C bonds are at an angle [actually 110°] to each other.

A rubber molecule in the unstressed state is naturally tangled up: it is very unlikely to form in a linear state [see diagram – remember it's 3D]. Applying a

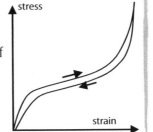

Grade boost

Facts about rubber:
- Poly-isoprene. The isoprene molecule is ~1 nm long.
- ~ 10^5 isoprene units per molecule.
- Size of molecules ~500 nm, so a lot of room for stretching out!
- Natural rubber is very soft but can be stiffened by introducing cross-links.

≫ *Pointer*

Rubber has a roughly constant volume when being stretched [see page 124] because bonds are not stretched, just realigned. This is also the reason why the force needed is much lower than other engineering materials.

small longitudinal force rotates the bonds and straightens out the molecules: no bonds are stretched; large extensions are produced. When the force is relaxed, the natural vibration of the molecules tangles up the long chains again. Because of the work done, the molecules end up vibrating more, i.e. energy is dissipated.

The energy losses in hysteresis can be *useful*, e.g. in shock absorbers. It can be a *nuisance*, e.g. the rolling resistance in car tyres. It can be reduced by introducing cross-linkages in the process of *vulcanisation*.

Grade boost

Polythene is an example of a thermoplastic.

Polythene

The polythene molecules are partly folded into crystals called *lamellae* and partly tangled in an amorphous phase. The strands of the lamellae are held together by van der Waals forces. At low loads the lamellae are stretched (like a concertina) – OA on the graph. In AB a neck forms in the polythene as the strands in the amorphous phase start to align. In BC the strands of the lamellae progressively unfold. Eventually the load increases – after C – as the stronger covalent bonds take the strain. From A onwards the deformation is a plastic.

This behaviour is familiar to all who have put too many potatoes in a plastic shopping bag!

Grade boost

The initial extension (OA on the graph) of polythene is elastic.

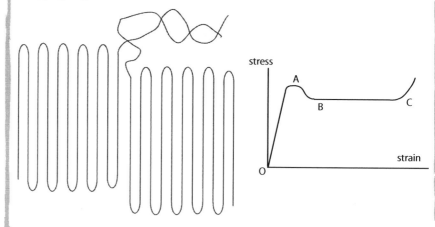

Knowledge and Understanding

PH5 Option D: Medical Measurement and Medical Imaging

The emphasis in this option is in the use of physics to obtain information about the body in a medical context. The assessment of biological knowledge is restricted to basic properties of the heart as a pump. The option covers X-rays, ultrasound, MRI and the use of radioisotopes in imaging.

Option D is tested as a single 20-mark question in section C of the PH5 exam.

Revision checklist

Tick column 1 when you have completed brief revision notes.

Tick column 2 when you think you have a good grasp of the topic.

Tick column 3 during final revision when you feel you have mastered the topic.

		1	2	3	Notes
p132	**X-rays**				
p132	Production				
p133	Attenuation				
p133	**Ultrasound**				
p133	Production				
p134	Reflection				
p135	Doppler probe				
p135	**Magnetic resonance imaging (MRI)**				
p135	Basic physics				
p136	Comparison with X-rays and ultrasound				
p137	**Electrocardiograms (ECG)**				
p137	Structure and function of the heart				
p138	**Nuclear radiation in medicine**				
p138	The effects of radiation				
p139	Radionuclides in medicine				

X-rays

In PH2 you learnt that **X-rays** are high-energy, ionising electromagnetic radiation. Their penetration depends on the concentration of electrons, so high density materials such as heavy metals can block X-rays, but low density materials such as flesh are relatively transparent to them. Because they are ionising, they are also mutagenic, i.e. can damage biological molecules, including DNA.

The production of X-rays

This is a schematic diagram of an X-ray tube:

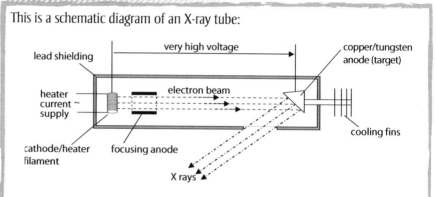

Grade boost

The optimum photon energy for radiography is ~ 30 keV, achieved with a tube voltage of 50–100 keV.

» Pointer

λ_{min} can be calculated from
$$\frac{hc}{\lambda_{min}} = eV$$

The heated cathode emits electrons by thermal emission; they are accelerated and focused by the focusing anode and then accelerated by an EHT voltage and hit a tungsten anode, where they are absorbed. The rapid deceleration of the electrons produces a continuous spectrum, the details of which depend upon the voltage.

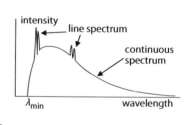

Some electrons knock out inner electrons from the target atoms; electrons from higher energy levels drop into the empty energy levels, producing a line spectrum that is characteristic of the element.

Controlling the X-ray beam and images:

- Intensity – the higher the heater current, the hotter the cathode, so the more electrons are given off per second and the more X-ray photons are produced.

- Photon energy – the higher the accelerating voltage, the more energetic the electrons and the smaller the cut-off wavelength λ_{min}. The maximum photon energy $= eV$.

- The image sharpness – placing a directional grid on the exit window increases sharpness (but cuts down the beam intensity).

- Contrast – selecting the accelerating voltage to produce a suitable range of wavelengths which are absorbed differently by the different materials, e.g. the softer the X-rays (lower energy) the better they will be absorbed by low density materials. Contrast agents, highly absorbent materials, can be used to increase the contrast in soft tissue, e.g. barium sulfate for alimentary canal imaging, or an iodine-based solution to make the coronary blood vessels show up.

- 3D images – computerised axial tomography (CT) scans use rotating beams which move along the body to produce images from all directions, from which 3D images can be constructed. Although useful, this technique is restricted to urgent cases because the X-ray dose received is high.

X-ray attenuation

When X-rays pass through a material, the intensity, I, of the beam falls with distance, x, according to the equation $I = I_0 e^{-\mu x}$, where μ is a constant that is characteristic of the material, called the attenuation (or absorption) coefficient.

Example: The attenuation coefficient of a material for an X-ray beam is 0.30 m^{-1}. What fraction of the incident photons remain after 5 m?

Answer: $I = I_0 e^{-0.3 \times 5} = I_0 e^{-1.5} = 0.22 I_0$. So the fraction remaining $= 0.22$, ie. 22%.

The value of μ depends on the wavelength of the X-rays as well as the material. Because of this, different X-ray wavelengths are chosen for imaging different structures.

Ultrasound

The production of ultrasound

This is produced using a piezoelectric crystal. This deforms in response to an electric field. Electrodes apply a high frequency alternating pd to the crystal, which vibrates at the same frequency and generates the sound wave. The process also works in reverse: the crystal produces an alternating pd in response to an incident sound wave – thus the transmitter is also a detector. This is a typical ultrasound probe:

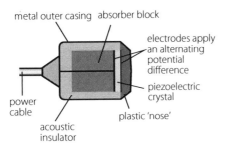

metal outer casing absorber block
electrodes apply an alternating potential difference
piezoelectric crystal
plastic 'nose'
power cable
acoustic insulator

quickfire

(D3) The wavelength of the Kβ line in the X-ray spectrum of copper is 0.14 nm. What is the minimum tube voltage needed to produce this line?

quickfire

(D4) Show that the unit of the attenuation coefficient is m^{-1}.

quickfire

(D5) Calculate the distance for X-rays to halve their intensity if $\mu = 10$ cm^{-1}.

(Hint: keep the unit as cm^{-1})

>> **Pointer**

The fraction of sound reflected at a boundary does not depend on the direction of the sound.

>> **Pointer**

The fractional change in frequency $\dfrac{\Delta f}{f} = -2\dfrac{v}{c}$

Grade boost

Show that the unit of Z is kg m^{-2} s^{-1}.

The absorber soaks up the sound waves which would be sent to the left (in the diagram). These would be subsequently reflected and interfere with the reflected signals from the body. A pulse of high frequency (MHz) alternating pd is applied to the crystal; a pulse of sound waves is produced and travels to the right into the body; reflections are received (see below); the crystal converts these into electrical pulses which are sent back along the power cable and analysed. This is repeated many times per second.

Types of scan	Description	Example
A-scan	1-dimensional: return pulses detected on CRO; time delay used for determining distances or existence of structures	A tumour would alter the time for a reflected pulse from a known structure
B-scan	2-dimensional: an array of detectors or a single moving transmitter/detector used; return pulses displayed on screen; images of structures seen	Foetal/prenatal scans

The reflection of ultrasound

Ultrasound is reflected whenever it crosses a boundary between two media. The property of the materials which determines the fraction reflected is the **acoustic impedance**, Z, of each of the media. This is defined by:

$$Z = c\rho,$$

where c is the speed of sound (in the medium) and ρ = the density of the medium.

$$Z_{air} \sim 400 \text{ kg m}^{-2}\text{ s}^{-1} \text{ and } Z_{skin} \sim 2 \times 10^6 \text{ kg m}^{-2}\text{ s}^{-1}.$$

The fraction, R, of the ultrasound energy reflected is given by:

$$R = \frac{(Z_2 - Z_1)^2}{(Z_2 + Z_1)^2}.$$

If you need it in the examination you will be given this equation in the question paper. Using the above values of Z for air and skin, you should be able to show that R between air and skin is almost 100%, i.e. hardly any ultrasound (<0.1%) would penetrate into the body from air, and hardly any sound from within the body would emerge back into the air. There would always be a thin layer of air between the ultrasound probe and dry skin, so a **coupling medium**, a gel, is applied to the skin and the probe placed in contact with the gel. The gel has a value of Z which is almost the same as skin so hardly any ultrasound is reflected at the gel-skin boundary – it all gets across in both directions. Another result of this impedance mismatch between tissues and air is that ultrasound cannot be used to probe the lungs.

Doppler probe $\frac{\Delta f}{f}$

This is an alternative way of using ultrasound to study the flow of blood. The technique is based on the same physics as the detection of extra-solar planets by looking at the star's spectrum.

Consider an ultrasound wave of wavelength λ, hitting an erythrocyte (a red blood cell) moving with velocity v.

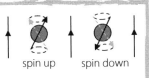

From PH4, the wavelength of the of the sound wave which the red blood cell 'sees' is shifted by $\Delta\lambda$, given by the equation:

$$\frac{\Delta\lambda}{\lambda} = \frac{v}{c},$$

The red blood cell reflected the wave back along its original direction to the detector. Because the erythrocyte is moving away from the detector, the wave is Doppler shifted for a second time by the same amount. So the received wave has a value of $\Delta\lambda$ given by:

$$\frac{\Delta\lambda}{\lambda} = 2\frac{v}{c}$$

Measurement of the fractional change on wavelength (or frequency) reveals the speed of the blood flow. The strength of the reflected pulse reveals the volume of blood, so the two together can be used to estimate the flow rate.

The Doppler shift of microwaves reflected from a moving car is used in speed traps by police. It works on the same principle.

Magnetic resonance imaging (MRI)

Basic physics

Hydrogen nuclei, i.e. protons, spin. If they are in a magnetic field, these spins can be aligned as in the diagram. They can either be aligned 'spin-up' or 'spin-down' (the diagonal arrows show the spin axis). The spin down direction has a higher energy than the spin up (the difference is small).

spin up   spin down

In both cases the spin direction **precesses**, i.e. it rotates around the magnetic field direction, rather like a child's top. The frequency of this precession depends on the strength of the magnetic field and is called the Larmor frequency. If radio waves at this frequency hit the nuclei, they will absorb the energy (it is a resonance effect) and most nuclei will be in the higher energy state. If the radio waves are turned off, the nuclei will flip back, giving out radio waves – the

Key Term

Precession = see main text.

quickfire

(D6) Calculate the acoustic impedance of skin.

Data:
density = 1075 kg m^{-3};
speed of sound = 1600 m s^{-1}

quickfire

(D7) What fraction of sound is reflected at a boundary between fresh and sea water?

$Z_{fresh} = 1.43 \times 10^6$ kg m^{-2} s^{-1}; $Z_{sea} = 1.45 \times 10^6$ kg m^{-2} s^{-1}.

quickfire

(D8) A police speed-trap radar, operating on 12.3 GHz, is Doppler shifted by 1.23 kHz by a moving car. Is the driver breaking the 30 mph (13 ms^{-1}) speed limit?

Key Term

Relaxation time = see main text.

>> *Pointer*

λ for the waves needed for imaging must be less in the tissue than the size of the structure to be imaged.

Grade boost

Learn the comparisons between X-rays, ultrasound and MRI for medical examinations.

detection of these waves reveals the location of the nuclei. The time taken for them to flip back – the **relaxation time** – depends upon the details of the surroundings of the hydrogen atoms, i.e it will be different for different tissues.

All tissues contain water and therefore hydrogen nuclei in different concentrations, and this difference can be used to build up a detailed image of the body tissues. It works very well for soft tissues but is less good for bones, for which X-rays are superior.

As far as is known, MRI is an entirely safe procedure. Its use is restricted because of its claustrophobic nature and the expense.

Comparison of X-rays, ultrasound and MRI

This table is taken from the medical imaging notes on the WJEC website:

Technique	Advantages	Disadvantages
X-rays	X-rays are absorbed by bone and so produce good shadow images. Unlike ultrasound they can produce images of, e.g. cancer on the lungs.	High radiation dose [see page 138] for the patient. People working with X-rays need to take care to limit their annual dosage.
Ultrasound	No known side effects. Good quality images of soft tissue. Moving images can be obtained. Machines are relatively cheap and portable.	Doesn't penetrate bone and so cannot study the brain. Cannot pass through air and so cannot study the lungs. Low resolution.
MRI	No known side effects. High quality images of soft tissue. Image can be made for any part/orientation of the body.	Images of hard tissue such as bone are poor. Uncomfortable for the patient, causes claustrophobia. Very expensive.

Electrocardiograms (ECG)

The functioning of the heart

The blood flows around the body in a double circulatory system. The sequence is:

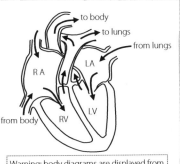

1. Blood low in oxygen (*deoxygenated*) enters the top right-hand chamber, RA (**right atrium**), of the heart.

2. The right atrium pushes the blood past a non-return value into the bottom right-hand chamber, RV (**right ventricle**), which pumps it (via the *pulmonary artery*) to the lungs, where it picks up oxygen.

> Warning: body diagrams are displayed from the front so left and right are inverted!

3. The oxygen-rich (*oxygenated*) blood returns to the top left-hand chamber, LA (*left atrium*).

4. The left atrium pushes the blood past a non-return valve into the bottom left hand chamber, LV (*left ventricle*), which pumps it around the body where it gives up its oxygen to the tissues before returning to the heart.

The heart is a set of muscles which comprise four pumps in one that operate together. The muscles contract to force the blood from one chamber of the heart to another or to the body. They are triggered to contract by a signal from the **sinoatrial node** which is located at the top-right of the heart (see arrow on the diagram) and is controlled by the central-nervous and hormonal systems. The nervous impulses associated with the

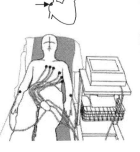

heartbeat can be detected outside the body to produce an **electrocardiogram** (ECG – not to be confused with an EEG, which is a brain scan!). A conducting gel is applied to the shaved skin and 12 electrodes placed into position – most over the heart but some on the ends of the arms and legs. The pd between the various electrodes is monitored and displayed on a voltage–time chart. Because the voltages detected are so low, they need to be amplified first.

A typical chart for a healthy heart looks like this – note the typical values of the **surface potential** and time. For a pulse rate of 75 per minute, this shape would be repeated every 0.8 s (800 ms).

The labelled features are:

P   – the **contraction** of the atria
       (atria = *plural of atrium*)

QRS – the contraction of the ventricles

T   – the relaxation of the ventricles

Key Terms

ECG = see main text.

Atrium/atria = see main text.

Ventricle = see main text.

Sinoatrial node = see main text.

Surface potential = voltage measured on the skin due to nerve signal within the body.

Contraction = shortening of muscles in response to nerve stimulus.

Grade boost

A typical surface potential is 1 mV.

Grade boost

The duration of a heart beat is less than 1 s.

Pointer

A conducting gel is used in ECG because dry skin has a large contact resistance.

Key Terms

Activity = see main text.

Absorbed dose = the radiation energy (for α, β, or γ radiation, or for X-rays) absorbed per kilogram of tissue.

Dose equivalent = $Q \times$ *absorbed dose*, in which Q is a factor (with no units) which depends on the type of radiation, and takes account of the degree of biological effect of the radiation.

Quality factor = see main text.

≫ Pointer

An exam question will always give the value of Q.

Grade boost

Read up on some of the health effects of radiation.

Nuclear radiation in medicine

The effects of radiation

Alpha, beta and gamma radiation (as well as uv and X-rays) are ionising. When nuclear radiation passes through a biological molecule it interacts with the electrons, knocking them out of the molecule and therefore modifying it. DNA molecules can suffer mutations, which the body usually repairs, but sometimes repairs incorrectly, leading to genetic change. Many genetic changes are negligible but a change which affects the cell's control mechanisms can lead to uncontrolled cell division, i.e. is carcinogenic (causes cancer). This sort of damage can be caused by long-term exposure to low levels of radiation.

Cells which are dividing are more susceptible to radiation damage. Examples are cells of the hair follicles and *epithelial* cells, such as the lining of the alimentary canal and the lungs – these cells suffer constant damage and need to be replaced continuously in life. Again, low radiation doses can usually be accommodated by these tissues but a large dose over a short time produces such damage to the biological molecules that the cells are killed off – for example, patients undergoing radiation therapy often lose their hair.

Measuring radiation

There are several different ways of measuring radiation and each has its own unit (or units!) and it is easy to get them confused.

The quantity which expresses how much nuclear radiation a radioactive source is emitting is the **activity** of the source. This is expressed in *becquerel* (Bq), which is equivalent to the number of decays per second.

Health workers are concerned with how much radiation is absorbed by the body. This will depend upon many factors including the distance of the source, the penetrating power of the radiation and its activity. The unit of **absorbed dose** is the *gray* (Gy) which is the energy absorbed per kg of body tissue, i.e. $1 \text{ Gy} \equiv 1 \text{ J kg}^{-1}$.

The absorbed dose doesn't tell the whole story as far as the effects of the radiation are concerned. Alpha particles are much more heavily ionising than β or γ, which is why their range is so low. Medical physicists express this in terms of the **dose equivalent**, for which the unit is the *sievert* (Sv). This relates to the absorbed dose as follows:

Dose equivalent (Sv) = quality factor (Q) × absorbed dose (Gy).

The **quality factor** is usually given as 20 for α radiation and 1 for β and γ, but it also depends upon the energy of the particles. The dose equivalent is the absorbed dose of gamma rays which will have the same biological effect.

Example 1

Calculate the power radiated by a 2.0 GBq source of 1 MeV beta particles.

Solution

Power radiated $= $ particles per second $\times$ energy per particle

$= 2.0 \times 10^9 \text{ s}^{-1} \times 1 \text{ MeV}$

$= 2.0 \times 10^9 \text{ s}^{-1} \times 1.6 \times 10^{-13} \text{ J}$

$= 0.32 \text{ mW}$

Example 2

A beam of β particles of intensity 2 nW cm^{-2} is directed onto a 10 cm^2 area of skin for a period of 10 minutes. The density of the tissue $= 1200$ kg m^{-3}. If the β particles are absorbed within 1 cm depth, calculate:

(a) the absorbed dose,

(b) the dose equivalent.

Solution

(a) Power delivered $= 2 \text{ nW cm}^{-2} \times 10 \text{ cm}^2$

$= 20 \text{ nW}$

Energy delivered $= 20 \text{ nW} \times 600 \text{ s}$

$= 1.2 \text{ µJ}$

Mass of tissue $=$ volume $\times$ density

$= 1.0 \times 10^{-5} \text{ m}^3 \times 1200 \text{ kg m}^{-3}$

$= 1.2 \times 10^{-2} \text{ kg}$

Absorbed dose $= \dfrac{1.2 \times 10^{-6} \text{ J}}{1.2 \times 10^{-2} \text{ kg}} = 100 \text{ µGy}$

(b) Q $= 1$, so Effective absorbed dose $= 1 \times 100 = 100$ µSv.

Key Terms

Radioactive tracers = chemical compounds with an atom replaced by a radioactive isotope – used to track the uptake of the compound by the body.

Tracer = see main text.

Electron capture = see main text.

quickfire

(D9) What is the unit of Q?

quickfire

(D10) Protons are sometimes used in radiotherapy. Between what values would you expect Q to lie?

Radionuclides in medicine

Radioactive tracers are used to investigate the function of particular organs. A good example is the thyroid gland, which concentrates the element iodine. Iodine has the stable isotope I-127 and a whole range of radioisotopes. The decay of I-123 results in the emission of γ rays, which can be detected outside the body. It has a half-life of 13.3 hours, which is ideal for tracer use as this is long enough for production and administration but short enough so that the body is rid of it in a few days.

I-123 decays by **electron capture** to an excited state of tellurium-123, Te-123*, which immediately decays by γ-emission:

$$^{123}_{53}\text{I} + {}^{0}_{-1}\text{e} \rightarrow {}^{123}_{52}\text{Te}^* \rightarrow {}^{123}_{52}\text{Te} + \gamma$$

Grade boost

Do a search on electron capture and positive beta decay.

≫ Pointer

Medical tracers must have a short half-life, be biologically safe and have safe decay products.

The iodine is injected in the form of NaI (sodium iodide), which is biologically safe. Tellurium is mildly toxic but safe in the quantities involved. The emitted γ rays are monitored to investigate the thyroid function.

Note: This mode of decay occurs in proton-rich nuclei. The electrons in the innermost orbital [called the 1s orbital] spend some of their time actually within the nucleus. An electron combines with a proton in the nucleus to produce a neutron (and an electron neutrino)

$$_{-1}^{0}e + _{1}^{1}p \rightarrow _{0}^{1}n + _{0}^{0}\nu_e$$

Because neutrons are more massive than protons, this interaction only happens if there is a lower energy level available for the newly created neutron to occupy. The nucleus is formed in an excited state – this is what the Te* indicates – and then the neutron drops down to a lower energy level, emitting the balance of the energy as a photon (γ).

Another isotope of iodine, I-131, is used in *radioisotope therapy* in treating some thyroid cancers. Again it is useful because it is absorbed by the thyroid. I-131 decays by β⁻ decay to an excited state of xenon-131, which rapidly decays by γ-emission:

$$_{53}^{131}I \rightarrow _{54}^{131}Xe^* + _{-1}^{0}\beta \text{ followed by: } _{54}^{131}Xe^* \rightarrow _{54}^{131}Xe + \gamma$$

The β particles damage the surrounding tissues, including the cancerous tissue. The γ is also useful because it is detected outside the body and can be used to monitor the effectiveness of the iodine uptake. Because of its β emission, I-131 is rarely used directly as a **tracer**.

Gamma camera

The origin of gamma rays, e.g. from I-123 or I-131, can be difficult to pinpoint as they cannot be focused onto a film using lenses. A gamma camera allows the origin of γ rays to be determined and imaged. The camera consists of:

- A **collimator**, which is a piece of lead with narrow parallel channels – the lead absorbs all γ rays apart from those which travel along the channels.
- A **scintillation crystal** – this emits a flash of light when it absorbs a γ photon.
- **Photomultipliers** – electronic devices in contact with the scintillation crystal which amplify the light and turn it into an electrical signal.
- Scintillation counter – which registers the arrival of the photons.
- Output display which builds up the image.

A schematic diagram:

The collimator absorbs about 99% of the incident γ photons – hence a strong γ-source and a long exposure time (during which the patient must be immobile) are both needed. This limits the use to urgent cases.

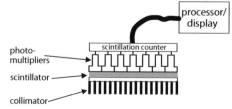

Positron emission tomography (PET) scanning

This technique makes use of the fact that some radionuclides decay by β^+ (i.e. **positron**) emission. A useful example is fluorine-18. The decay is:

$$^{18}_{9}\text{F} \rightarrow {}^{18}_{8}\text{O} + {}^{0}_{1}e^+$$

The positron slows down to a very low speed by collision and eventually undergoes mutual **annihilation** with an electron, resulting in the emission of 2 γ photons. Because momentum has to be conserved, the two photons must have equal and opposite momenta, i.e. they have the same wavelength and travel in opposite directions. This interaction is:

$$^{0}_{1}e^+ + {}^{0}_{-1}e^- \rightarrow \gamma + \gamma$$

The energy of each of these photons is 0.511 MeV (= the mass-energy of an electron).

The patient lies inside a PET scanner, a suitable tracer having been administered by injection, inhalation or ingestion. The γ scanner is lined with γ detectors which register coincidental and opposite events, i.e. they look for γ photons which are detected at the same time and on opposite sides of the patient.

The detectors are set to register when two γ-capture events on opposite sides of the patient are registered within a few nanoseconds. This is very unlikely to occur by chance. Because the positron moves typically less than 1 mm before annihilation, the site of its emission can be quite accurately pinpointed.

Over time the analysis of these can reveal a 3D image of the source.

One of the most common uses of this is in the search for *metastases*, or secondary cancers. The tracer is fluorodeoxyglucose (FDG) in which the fluorine is F-18. This is absorbed by rapidly dividing cells, including cancers, more than normal tissue, so a PET scan will reveal the metastases by looking for 'hot spots' in the γ emission. The half-life of F-18 is only 110 minutes; nevertheless, this is long enough to allow F-18 labelled FDG to be prepared and used in PET scanning.

F-18 is made on site in the medical facility using high-speed protons, produced in a particle accelerator, to bombard water that is enriched with the O-18 isotope. The reaction is:

$$^{18}_{8}\text{O} + {}^{1}_{1}\text{p} \rightarrow {}^{1}_{0}\text{n} + {}^{18}_{9}\text{F}$$

The oversight of the routine production of F-18 is one of the jobs of a medical physicist.

Information box

Rubidium-82 generators contain strontium-82 which decays by electron capture to Rb-82, which decays by positron emission.

quickfire

(D11) Find the momentum of a 0.511 MeV photon.

quickfire

(D12) Use the Information Box to write down the nuclear equations associated with Rb-82.

You may need to use a periodic table!

Knowledge and Understanding

PH6 Experimental Physics

PH6 builds on the practical skills which were assessed in PH3. Once again, the recall of learned physics theory is not tested. You will need to develop your ability to produce straight-line graphs for more difficult functions, such as log and exponential functions. In addition to plotting 'best-fit' lines, where appropriate, you should use error bars and go on to draw the steepest and least steep graphs consistent with the data. These extreme graphs will be used to determine values for the uncertainty in the gradient and intercept.

In PH6, you will be expected to plan an investigation.

This unit is internally assessed. It consists of two components:

- An experimental task, which is a practical exam lasting $1\frac{1}{4}$ hours – you will be expected to plan and carry out an investigation.
- A data analysis task, which is a written exam lasting $\frac{3}{4}$ hour – you will be given experimental data to analyse.

Your teacher will mark both these tasks.

Revision checklist

Tick column 1 when you have completed brief revision notes.

Tick column 2 when you think you have a good grasp of the topic.

Tick column 3 during final revision when you feel you have mastered the topic.

		1	2	3	Notes
p143	**6.1 Uncertainties**				
p143	Recap from PH3				
p144	**6.2 Graphs**				
p144	Linearising equations				
p145	Analysing data using log plots				
p145	Power law relationships				
p146	Exponential relationships				
p147	Use of error bars in PH6				
p151	**6.3 Planning investigations**				
p151	Information sheets				

Uncertainties

Recap from PH3

You should make sure that you are familiar with all the techniques which are examined in PH3. These are detailed in *WJEC AS Physics: Study and Revision Guide* by the same author team as this book, and also published by Illuminate Publishing.

The following sections of the AS guide are unchanged at A2:

- Making measurements
- Displaying data.

The following sections from PH3 are developed further for PH6:

- Graphs
- Relationships between variables
- Uncertainties
- Planning investigations.

Uncertainties in quantities

In PH3, you are assessed on your ability to estimate uncertainties in measured quantities and also in quantities which are derived by multiplying, dividing or raising measured quantities to powers. This is all required for PH6. In addition you may be asked to estimate the uncertainties in quantities which are added or subtracted.

If two or more quantities are added or subtracted, the *absolute* uncertainties are added.

Example
A rectangle has length 10.5 ± 0.2 cm and width 5.6 ± 0.1 cm. What is its perimeter?

Answer
Perimeter $= 10.5 \pm 0.2 + 5.6 \pm 0.1 + 10.5 \pm 0.2 + 5.6 \pm 0.1$ cm $= 32.2 \pm 0.6$ cm

The principle that we generally express an uncertainty (or percentage uncertainty) to 1 s.f. is still applied.

① What volume of water is formed from the addition of 30.8 ± 0.4 cm^3 and 5.2 ± 0.1 cm^3 of water from different measuring cylinders?

② A coil of wire is wound tightly on a cylinder. The wire forms a single layer of 40 turns and the coils are touching. The diameter of the cylinder is measured as 2.54 ± 0.02 cm and the outside diameter of the coils is 2.68 ± 0.02 cm. What length of wire is in the coil?

>> *Pointer*

Remember when plotting graphs:
- linear (uniform) scales
- points occupy >50% of the space
- label axes and include units.

Grade boost

When plotting graphs, it is sometimes sensible to turn the graph grid on its side to make better use of the space.

>> *Pointer*

The equation of a straight line is written
$y = mx + c$,
where x and y are the variables, m is the gradient and c is the intercept on the y-axis.

Graphs

In PH3 you are assessed on your ability to choose scales, draw appropriate axes, plot points, draw best-fit lines, take readings from graphs and use them to interpret relationships. These skills are also required in PH6. In addition, you will need to do the following:

- Analyse data using log plots.
- Display data using error bars.

Note that you will not be expected to do both at the same time.

Linearising equations

For PH3, you were assessed on your ability to plot data from variables with a non-linear relationship, in a way which would give a straight-line graph, e.g. for the kinematic equation for constant acceleration,

$$v^2 = u^2 + 2ax,$$

a graph of v^2 against x is a straight line of gradient $2a$ and an intercept of u^2 on the v^2 axis. You will be assessed on this on PH6, too.

In the data analysis part of PH6, you may be given more complicated relationships to linearise.

③ For the compound pendulum:

(a) What is the gradient of the graph?

(b) What is the intercept on the yT^2 axis?

(c) Suggest a unit for k.

Example

A length of wood, e.g. a metre rule, pivoted as shown, will oscillate. This is referred to as a *compound pendulum*. The period of the pendulum is given by:

$$\frac{T}{2\pi} = \sqrt{\frac{k^2 + y^2}{gy}},$$ where k is a constant.

What plot will give a straight-line graph?

Squaring: $\dfrac{T^2}{4\pi} = \dfrac{k^2 + y^2}{gy}$

Re-arranging: $yT^2 = \dfrac{4\pi k^2}{g} + \dfrac{4\pi}{g} y^2$

So a graph of yT^2 against y^2 should be a straight line.

(See Quickfire 3 and also the Practice questions section.)

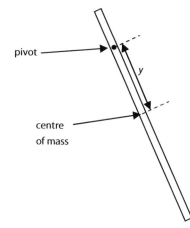

pivot

y

centre of mass

Analysing data using log plots

There are two kinds of logarithms (logs for short) in common use. These are $\log_{10}$ ('logs to the base 10') and ln ('natural logarithms' or 'logs to the base e'). The most useful ones in PH6 are natural logarithms. In PH6 you do not need the $\log_{10}$ function.

We write a log function as follows: ln 2, ln A (where A is a variable). What do these mean?

If $x = \ln 2$, this means that $e^x = 2$. In other words $e^{\ln x} = x$ – this is the definition of the ln function.

Important note

ln ab means $\ln(ab)$; in other words it is the logarithm of ab. If you want to multiply ln a by b, we write it $b \ln a$. Sometimes it is worth using brackets to avoid confusion, e.g. $\ln (3.5 \times 10^{-16})$. If we wrote ln 3.5×10^{-16} it might be confused as $10^{-16} \ln 3.5$.

Calculator practice

To find the ln of a number, use the ln button on the calculator. This is similar to using the sin, cos or tan functions. On some calculators, you will need to put in the number first and then press ln. On modern calculators you usually press ln first and then the number.

Check these answers (to 3 s.f.): ln 2 = 0.693 ; ln 1000 = 6.91; 4 ln 2 = 2.77

If ln $x = 2.5$, what is x?

Answer: Use the e^x button. Check that ln $x = 2.5 \rightarrow x = 1.22$ (3 s.f.)

The following properties of the log function are important:

$$\ln ab = \ln a + \ln b \qquad (1)$$
$$\ln x^n = n \ln x \qquad (2)$$
$$\ln e^x = x \qquad (3)$$

The ln function is important for the following two sorts of relationships.

Power law relationships

Relationships of the form $y = Ax^n$, where A and n are constants.

First find the logarithm of each side of the equation:

$$\ln y = \ln Ax^n$$

Using property (1) we can write:

$$\ln y = \ln A + \ln x^n$$

④ (a) What is ln 3.6?

(b) What is $\ln (2 \times 10^6)$?

(c) What is 5 ln 8?

(d) What is $e^{2.5}$?

(e) Without using a calculator, what is ln 12.2?

⑤ For a filament lamp, the current varies with voltage according to the relationship $I = kV^n$.

(a) What graph is suitable for testing this relationship?

(b) How could you use the graph to determine k and n?

(c) Draw a sketch-graph to illustrate this.

⑥ The activity A of a radioactive source varies with time according to $A = A_0e^{-\lambda t}$, where λ is the decay constant.

To determine λ, what graph should be plotted and how will λ be found?

⑦ The activity A of a radioactive source varies according to $A = A_0 2^{-n}$, where n is the number of half-lives and A_0 is the initial activity. What is the gradient of a graph of $\ln A$ against n?

⑧ The luminosity L of stars of mass $M > M_\odot$, where $M_\odot$ is the mass of the sun, is known to be given approximately by:

$$\frac{L}{L_\odot} = 1.5\left(\frac{M}{M_\odot}\right)^{3.5}. \text{ How}$$

could this relationship be verified?

⑨ A graph of $\ln y$ against $\ln x$ has gradient 2 and an intercept of 2.5 on the $\ln y$ axis. What is the relationship between y and x?

Using property (2) we can further write the relationship

$$\ln y = \ln A + n \ln x$$

(For convenience!)
Comparing with the straight-line equation:

So a graph of $\ln y$ against $\ln x$ is a straight line with gradient n and an intercept of $\ln A$ on the $\ln y$ axis. This sort of plot is referred to as a 'log-log plot'.

$\ln y = n \ln x + \ln A$

$y = m x + c$

Caution: A log-log plot is useful when the value of n is to be found. If n is known and the value of A is to be found, it is better to avoid a log-log plot: a plot of y against x^n has a gradient A – gradients usually have a lower uncertainty than intercepts.

Exponential relationships

Relationships of the form $y = Ak^x$, where A and k are constants.
First find the logarithm of each side of the equation:

$$\ln y = \ln (Ae^{kx})$$

Using property (1) we can write:

$$\ln y = \ln A + \ln e^{kx}$$

or

$$\ln y = \ln e^{kx} + \ln A \qquad \text{for convenience!}$$

Using property 3, this becomes:

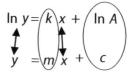

$\ln y = k x + \ln A$

Comparing with the straight-line equation:

$y = m x + c$

So, a graph of $\ln y$ against x is a straight line with gradient k and intercept $\ln A$. This sort of plot is referred to as a 'semi-log plot'.

Use of error bars in PH6

Note that you will not be expected to use error bars if you are undertaking log-log or semi-log plots.

Uncertainty in only one variable

Consider the following experimental point: (2.50 s, 35 ± 2 m s^{-1}). The data tell us that, at a time of 2.50 s, the speed is between 33 and 37 m s^{-1}. This is plotted as on the grid: This shape is referred to as an *error bar*. The cross-bars at the ends have no function apart from showing the error bar clearly.

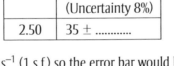

Some additional points:

(i) Sometimes, the examiner gives the *percentage* uncertainty rather than the absolute uncertainty – see the table opposite:

Time/s	Speed/m s^{-1} (Uncertainty 8%)
2.50	$35 \pm$ ....

You need to work out the absolute uncertainty: in this case 8% of 35 = 3 m s^{-1} (1 s.f.) so the error bar would be from 32 to 38 m s^{-1}.

(ii) Sometimes the examiner will give data which needs to be manipulated, e.g. finding a square, a square root or reciprocal.

x/m (Uncertainty 5%)	$\left(\dfrac{1}{x\text{/m}}\right)^2$
0.250	.... $\pm$ ....

In this case $\left(\dfrac{1}{0.250}\right)^2 = 16.0$ with an uncertainty of 10%, i.e. 16 ± 2 m^{-2} or 16.0 ± 1.6 m^{-2}.

Sometimes the data may be more complicated, e.g. the plot of yT^2 against y^2 for the compound pendulum. In this case the rules for combining the uncertainties from PH3 hold.

Note

Sometimes the *x*-variable will have the uncertainty, in which case the error bar will be horizontal.

> **Pointer**
> You should remember the following properties of uncertainties from PH3:
> - $p(xy) = p(x) + p(y)$
> - $p(x^n) = n.p(x)$
> - $p\left(\dfrac{x}{y}\right) = p(x) + p(y).$

(10) If $y = 0.50 \pm 0.01$ m and $T = 1.88 \pm 0.05$ s, between which values will the error bar for of yT^2 be?

Grade boost

Before drawing the error bar(s), plot the point using one of the following:

⊙

×

+

This will help to ensure that the error bars are correctly positioned.

Grade boost

Take care with the scales when drawing in the error bars, especially when the horizontal and vertical scales are different.

⑪ A graph of v^2 against x from the relationship $v^2 = u^2 + 2ax$ has a gradient of 3.20 ± 0.10 and an intercept of 6.25 ± 0.15. The units m and s are used.

Give the values and uncertainties of u and a.

Uncertainty in both variables

Often there is a significant uncertainty in both variables, e.g. (2.0 ± 0.2 s, 86 ± 3 cm). In this case two error bars are plotted at right angles as shown.

As an *alternative*, some people like to plot a rectangle, or 'error box'. This is perfectly acceptable; indeed it can be very useful when drawing best-fit lines.

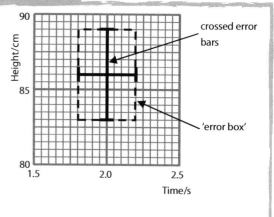

Drawing graphs using error bars

Once you have plotted the error bars, rather than being asked to draw a best-fit line, you are told to draw the steepest and least-steep lines consistent with the data. Once you have done this you will be expected to find the gradient (with its uncertainty) and the intercept (with its uncertainty).

To see how this is done, it is best to use an example. Note: In this example and the subsequent diagrams, the error bars are all shown on the **y**-variable, i.e. the error bars are all vertical. Exactly the same principles hold for horizontal error bars.

The following graph relates to the equation: $x = ut + \frac{1}{2}at^2$

If we divide by t we get $\frac{x}{t} = u + \frac{1}{2}at$, so a plot of $\frac{x}{t}$ against t should be a straight line. Its gradient is $\frac{1}{2}a$ and the intercept on the vertical axis is u.

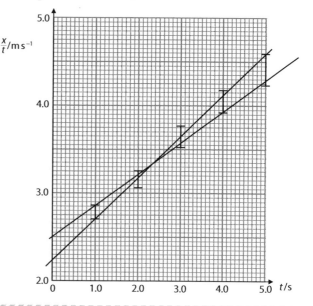

The sequence is:

1. Work out the scales, draw and label the axes as in PH3.
2. Plot the points with error bars.
3. Draw the *steepest possible* straight line passing through the error bars (Note: **Not** the straight line through the tops of the error bars!)
4. Draw the least steep line through the error bars (**Not** the straight line through the bottoms of the error bars!)

The aims are to *verify the relationship* and to *determine u and a*.

It is possible to draw a straight line through the error bars, so the data are consistent with a linear relationship between $\frac{x}{t}$ and t.

Is the relationship verified? Most scientists would say that it is not possible to show that a law or a relationship is true – but we can attempt to falsify it. In this case, we can say that the results are consistent with the suggested relationship because it is possible to draw a straight line passing through all the error bars.

Determining u and a: assuming the relationship, we note that the steepest line passes through (0.00, 2.23) and (5.00, 4.59) and the least steep line passes through (0.00, 2.50) and (5.00, 4.28). Using these points and the rules we learnt in unit PH3, the maximum and minimum gradient values are:

$$m_{max} = \frac{4.59 - 2.23}{5.00} = 0.472 \text{ m s}^{-2} \quad \text{and} \quad m_{min} = \frac{4.28 - 2.50}{5.00} = 0.350 \text{ m s}^{-2}$$

So
$$m = \frac{0.472 + 0.350}{2} \pm \frac{0.472 - 0.350}{2} \text{ m s}^{-2} = 0.41 \pm 0.06 \text{ m s}^{-2}$$

And the intercept
$$c = \frac{2.50 + 2.23}{2} \pm \frac{2.50 - 2.23}{2} \text{ m s}^{-1} = 2.37 \pm 0.14 \text{ m s}^{-1}$$

Now, u = the intercept. So $u = 2.37 \pm 0.14 \text{ m s}^{-1}$ **or** $2.4 \pm 0.1 \text{ m s}^{-1}$

And $a = 2 \times$ gradient $= 0.82 \pm 0.12 \text{ m s}^{-2}$ or $0.8 \pm 0.1 \text{ m s}^{-2}$.

Grade boost

When finding the gradient of the steepest and least steep lines:

1. Use points on the line that are as far apart as possible.
2. Indicate clearly which points you are using, e.g. By drawing a gradient triangle or labelling them on the graph.
3. Make sure you read the scales correctly when reading the horizontal and vertical separation of the points.

Pointer

If the intercept on the y-axis is off the scale at the bottom or top of the grid, don't panic! You can calculate the intercept using your value of the gradient and any two (x, y) values from the line, using the equation $y = mx + c$.

Example

If a line has gradient 3.0 and passes through the point (50, 80), putting these values into $y = mx + c$, gives $80 = 3.0 \times 50 + c$, which leads to $c = -70$.

Three common mistakes with lines

1. Forcing the lines through the origin – (0,0)

   Candidates often do this when they expect the graph to pass through (0,0). The correct method is either to ignore zero when drawing the steepest and least-steep lines or to treat it as having error bars itself.

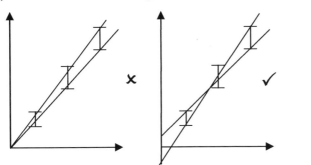

> **Pointer**

Sometimes sneaky examiners might produce data which have a straight-line portion and a curved portion or two straight line portions. They will usually tell you to expect this:

e.g., how would you draw in the lines with these error bars?

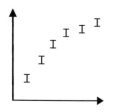

With these error bars, we would say that the data are consistent with a proportional relationship – it is possible to draw a straight line through the origin and all the error bars.

2. Taking the lines through the cross-bars.

   Remember that these cross-bars have no status – they just clarify the ends of the error bar.

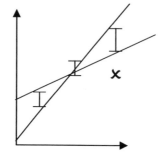 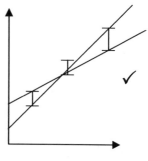

NB – steepest and least-steep lines can go down as well as up.

3. Drawing 'tram lines'.

   This is just wrong – don't do it!

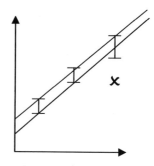

With error-bars in two directions

These are treated just the same as those in one direction. You just need to remember that the 'true' position of the point could be anywhere in the rectangle defined by the error bars, i.e. the shaded part of the diagram to the right. This is why some people use the 'error box' method of drawing the error bars – the error box is the same as the shaded area. The lower diagram shows an example of a graph with x and y error bars.

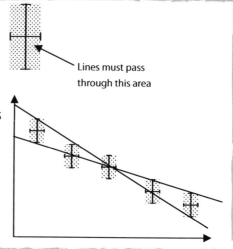

Lines must pass through this area

Planning investigations

This is tested in the Experimental Task part of PH6. In this paper you are presented with a problem to investigate and given a selection of apparatus. You will be told that the variables are expected to be related by a given equation. The first part of the task is to devise the experiment.

The first thing to do is to establish in your own mind what you are going to do. Do this by setting up the apparatus and possibly making some preliminary/trial observations and measurements. Then communicate the following to the examiner:

1. The experimental setup, i.e. a diagram of the arrangement of the apparatus.

2. The variables involved: the independent variable (the variable you plan to set to a series of values); the dependent variable (the variable whose value you will determine for each value of the independent variable); any control variables (variables whose values will remain the same, allowing the investigation to be valid).

3. A description of the procedure including how you will vary the value of the independent variable, the instruments used for taking all measurements with their resolution.

4. The range and number of the independent variable to be used and values of control variables, justified by reference to trial readings, if any. You can always change these if necessary whilst doing the experiment. Normally you would expect to take readings at least five values of the independent variable, with as wide a range as conveniently possible.

5. How you will handle the data, e.g. taking logs, plotting a graph of .... against ...., and how you will use the results to form conclusions.

Information sheets

The Experimental Task will have two (or possibly three) offers of Information Sheets. They come with a mark penalty – usually 2. There is always one sheet to go with the experimental plan and usually another with the graph. You should think carefully about whether to ask for these. They are intended to help you out of situations in which you do not know what to do.

What will these sheets tell you? They will identify the variables to investigate, with some details of a suggested procedure. They will also tell you how to manipulate the suggested relationship to obtain a linear graph.

If you have understood the advice in this chapter, you should not need to take the sheets. If you cannot make progress, on the other hand, you should ask for the sheet. Your teacher may also notice that you need help and offer you the sheet.

Grade boost

For an analogue instrument, the resolution can be taken to be the scale increment. On a digital instrument it is the smallest change in reading which is registered.

Pointer

When planning the investigation it is best to set up the apparatus first so that you can get a feel for how it works.

Grade boost

Sometimes the range of the independent variable to use will be obvious. In others it may not be. So, before you finish your plan, take some trial readings. This will let you make a sensible decision on ranges to use. It also lets you see if the apparatus is working properly.

Pointer

If you don't think the apparatus is in order, put up your hand and tell your supervisor, who will be able to check it [that's what he/she is there for!].

Practice questions

Definition-type questions

Note: the section numbers below agree with the specification and not necessarily the sections of this book.

1. A body undergoes *simple harmonic motion* with a *period* 2.5 ms and *amplitude* 16 cm. Say what is meant by each of the phrases in *italics*.
   [Vibrations – PH4.1]

2. A body undergoes simple harmonic motion described by the equation:

$$x = A\sin\frac{2\pi}{T}t$$

   Where x is the displacement, $A = 10$ cm, $T = 0.5$ s and t is the time.
   Sketch a graph of x against t between 0 and 2 seconds.
   [Vibrations – PH4.1]

3. A system may undergo *free oscillations* or *forced oscillations*. Explain the difference between these two types of oscillation.
   [Vibrations – PH4.1]

4. In an experiment to investigate resonance, a lightly damped oscillatory system of natural frequency f_0, is subject to a periodic driving force of constant amplitude and variable frequency f. The graph shows the variation of the amplitude, A, with f.

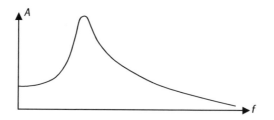

   (a) Label the graph with features of interest.
   (b) Add a second curve to show the expected behaviour with heavier but less than critical damping.
   [Vibrations – PH4.1]

5. State the principle of conservation of momentum.
   [Momentum concepts – PH4.2]

6. Explain what is meant by the Avogadro constant, N_A.
   [Thermal Physics – PH4.3]

7. The first law of thermodynamics deals with energy transfers between a system and its surroundings. It may be written:

$$\Delta U = Q - W$$

Explain what is meant by each of the three terms in the equation.

[Thermal Physics – PH4.3]

8. The *specific heat capacity* of water is approximately 4200 J kg^{-1} K^{-1}.

Define the term specific heat capacity and explain the above statement.

[Thermal Physics – PH4.3]

9. State Kepler's 3rd law of planetary motion and show how it can be derived for the case of circular orbits from Newton's law of gravitation.

[Orbits – PH4.5]

10. The diagram shows magnetic field lines linking a circuit at right angles.

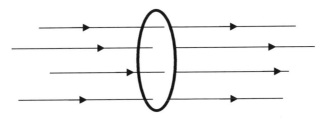

Use the diagram to define the magnetic flux linking the circuit, defining any symbols you use.

[Induction – PH5.3]

11. The following equation relates to the decay of radioactive materials:

$$A = \lambda N$$

Define the symbols used in the equation and give their SI units.

[Radioactivity – PH5.4]

Questions to test understanding

12. The momentum of a body is given by $p = mv$.

The momentum of a photon is given by $p = \dfrac{h}{\lambda}$.

Show that these two equations give the same units for p.

[Momentum concepts – PH4.2]

13. A planet is detected at a distance of 8×10^{10} m from a star. It orbits the star at a constant speed of 5×10^4 m s^{-1}.

(a) Explain clearly how you can tell that the orbit is circular.

(b) Find the following information about the planet and its orbit:

    (i) its angular speed,

    (ii) its orbital period,

    (iii) the frequency of the orbit

    (iv) the centripetal acceleration

    (v) the mass of the star

[Orbits – PH4.5]

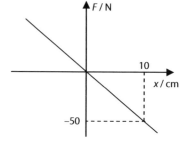

14. The graph shows the resultant force, F, on a body of mass 2 kg when displaced by x from its equilibrium position.

It is held at $x = 10.0$ cm and released at time $t = 0$.

Find its position and velocity at time $t = 1.5$ s.

[Vibrations – PH4.1]

15. Newton's law of gravitation can be expressed in the following equation:

$$F = G\frac{M_1 M_2}{r^2}$$

(a) Identify the symbols used in the equation.

(b) The Moon orbits the Earth at a mean distance of 384 000 km. The orbital period is 27.3 days. Use this information to obtain a value for the mass of the Earth. [You may assume that $M_{Earth} \gg M_{Moon}$.]

(c) The gravitational field strength at the surface of the Earth is 9.81 N kg^{-1}. The radius of the Earth is 6370 km. Use this information to obtain a second value for the mass of the Earth.

(d) Newton's law of gravitation refers to point masses. Explain how you were able to apply it when answering parts (b) and (c).

[Electrostatic and gravitational fields of force – PH4.4]

16. The craters of the Moon have mainly been caused by the impact of orbiting bodies. This question concerns the energy released in such an impact.

A small asteroid, of diameter 50 m and mean density 2500 kg m^{-3}, approaches the Earth–Moon system. Its speed at a large distance from the Earth–Moon is 1 km s^{-1}. It impacts on the Moon and causes a crater.

(a) Calculate the initial kinetic energy of the asteroid.

(b) Use the following data to calculate the gravitational potential at the surface of the Moon due to:

    (i) the gravitational field of the Moon;

    (iii) the gravitational field of the Earth.

        Data: Mass of Moon = 7.35×20^{22} kg; radius of Moon = 1740 km

          Mass of Earth = 5.97×10^{24} kg; mean radius of Moon's orbit = 384 000 km

(c) Calculate the kinetic energy of the asteroid when it impacts the Moon.

[Electrostatic and gravitational fields of force – PH4.4]

17. An electronic clock has a 0.2 F backup capacitor in case its power supply is interrupted. The capacitor is initially charged to 3.3 V. The clock needs a minimum voltage of 1.3 V to function.

    When the supply is interrupted the capacitor starts discharging with a current of 1.0 µA. Estimate the number of hours before the clock stops working.

    [Hint: Assume that the clock acts as a constant resistance load.]

    [Capacitance – PH5.1]

18. (a) The internal energy, U, of a capacitor can be calculated from the equation $U = \frac{1}{2}CV^2$. Starting from a definition of capacitance, show that the units of this equation balance.

    (b) A 5 F capacitor is charged to 3 V and then isolated from the power supply.

       (i) Calculate the internal energy of the capacitor.

       (ii) A second, initially uncharged, 5 F capacitor is connected in parallel with the first capacitor. Calculate the total internal energy of the two capacitors.

       (iii) Comment on your answers to (i) and (ii).

    [Capacitance – PH5.1]

Data analysis questions

19. A group of Physics students investigated the oscillations of a 1.5 m long wooden beam. To do this they drilled a series of small holes at different distances, y, from the centre of mass. They suspended the beam from a nail at each of the holes in turn, released the beam from a small angle to the side measured the period, T, of oscillation using a stopwatch.

    They read that T and y are related by the equation

    $$T = 2\pi\sqrt{\frac{k^2 + y^2}{gy}}$$

    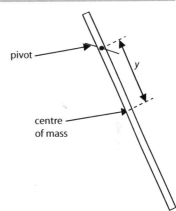

    where g is the acceleration due to gravity and k is a constant called the radius of gyration of the beam.

    They repeated their measurements several times and obtained these data.

    They estimated the uncertainty in T to be ±0.05 s and the uncertainty in y to be ±3 mm, because of the difficulty in estimating the positions of the centre of mass and the pivot.

y/m	T/s
0.700	1.98
0.600	1.89
0.500	1.90
0.400	1.87
0.300	1.93
0.200	2.15

    (a) From the data, describe the relationship between T and y and relate it to the equation given above.

    (b) Show that a graph of yT^2 against y^2 should be a straight line and state the relevance of the gradient and intercept to the quantities in the above equation.

(c) Complete the following table for each of the values of y and T given above.

y^2/m^2	$yT^2/m\ s^2$
0.490 ± 0.004	$\pm$
0.360 ± 0.004	$\pm$
0.250 ± 0.003	$\pm$
0.160 ± 0.002	$\pm$
0.090 ± 0.002	$\pm$
0.040 ± 0.001	$\pm$

(d) On the grid, plot the values of yT^2 against y^2. Plot the error bars in yT^2 [the error bars in y^2 can be omitted] and draw the steepest and least steep lines consistent with the data.

(e) Use your graph to determine values for k and g together with their absolute uncertainty.

[Data analysis – PH6]

Note: This question is longer than the one you can expect to meet in PH6 because of the number of uncertainty calculations in part (c).

20. [Experimental task – PH6]

For a certain class of thermistor, the resistance R varies with the kelvin temperature T according to the relationship:

$$R = Ae^{\frac{\varepsilon}{2kT}},$$

Where k is the Boltzmann constant, 1.38×10^{-23} J K^{-1}, and ε is the band gap, which is the energy gap between electrons which are bound to atoms and those which are free to move in the thermistor.

(a) Plan an experimental procedure to investigate the relationship between R and T between 273 K (0°C) and 373 K.

(b) The following results were obtained.

T/K	R/Ω
273	380
298	100
323	38.5
348	14.7
373	6.2

Plot a suitable graph to test the relationship.

(c) Comment on whether the results support the suggested relationship.

(d) Use your graph to determine ε.

Exam Practice and Technique

Exam Practice and Skills

The exam papers are written by Principal Examiners well in advance of the date of the examination. A committee of experienced examiners and teachers checks and modifies the papers to ensure they have suitable content and wording.

Exam tips

Remember that A2 units are **synoptic** in nature, i.e. the exam papers can draw on material which is in the AS units or, in the case of PH5, from PH4. This is not a 'free hit' for the examiners; they will always base a question around a topic in the A2 unit but some parts of the questions involve AS or previous A2 work.

Examples: PH4. Momentum is introduced here. A question involving a collision could explore whether kinetic energy is lost. This requires use of the kinetic energy equation, $E_k = \frac{1}{2}mv^2$, which is found in PH1.

PH5: The Hall Effect is introduced here. This requires knowledge of $I = nAve$, from PH1 and electric fields from PH4.

Look at the mark allocation

Each part of a question is allocated a number of marks. In written answers, this total gives a hint as to how much detail you need in your answer. In calculations, some marks will be for the working and some for the answer (see below).

Understand the command words

These are the words which show the sort of answer which the examiner expects in order to give you credit.

State (a fact)

A short answer with no explanation.

State (a law or definition)

This requires you to recall a law or definition that you have learnt, e.g. 'State Ohm's Law'

Explain

Give a reason or reasons. Look at the mark allocation: 2 marks usually means that you need to make two distinct points. It may be worth making an extra point 'just to be sure' but be careful you do not contradict yourself.

State . . . and explain

There may be a mark for the statement but the first mark may be for an explanation of a correct statement, e.g. 'State which resistor, A or B, has the higher value and explain your reasoning.' It is unlikely that the examiner will give you a mark for a 50/50 choice!

Calculate

A correct answer will score all the marks, unless the question includes the instruction to 'show your working.' **Warning**: An incorrect answer without working will score 0.

Always give the units of your answer – missing or incorrect units will be penalised.

Show that (in a calculation question)

For example, 'Show that the half-life is approximately 200 years.' There is no mark here for just the correct answer; the working must be shown in sufficient detail for the examiner to be convinced you know what you are doing!

Hint: In this case, calculate an accurate answer, e.g. 185 years and say that this is approximately the value stated.

Describe

A series of statements is required. These may be independently marked but care may be needed with sequencing, e.g. in the description of how to carry out an experiment.

Compare

There must be a clear comparison, not just two separate statements. It is also not safe just to state one thing and leave the examiner to infer another; e.g. 'Compare the Hall voltages of metals A and B.'

Answer 1: Metal A has a low Hall voltage – not enough

Answer 2: Metal A has a lower Hall voltage **than metal B** – this answer would gain credit (if correct!) unless the question makes it clear that a numerical comparison is required.

Suggest

This command word often comes at the end of a question. You are expected to put forward a sensible idea based upon your physics knowledge and the information in the question. There will often be more than one correct answer.

Name

A single word or phrase is expected; e.g. 'State the name of this effect' (*in a situation with large vibrations produced*). Answer: *Resonance*. Note that, especially in this kind of question, a correctly spelt answer may be required.

Estimate

This does not mean 'guess'. It usually involves one or more calculations with simplifying assumptions. The question may ask you to state any assumptions you make, e.g. '*Estimate the number of grains of sand on a beach, stating any assumptions you make.*'

Tips about diagrams

Questions sometimes ask for diagrams. For example, in PH4 a question may require you to sketch electric field lines and equipotentials. It is important for your diagram to convey the relevant information, e.g. it should be labelled (in the example, which line is a field line and which an equipotential?). Straight lines should be drawn using a ruler. Even if the question does not demand one, some of the marks may be awarded for information included in a well-drawn diagram.

Tips about graphs

Graphs from data: Where the axes and scales are not drawn, make sure that you choose the scale so that the points occupy at least half of the given grid (on theory papers, the examiners usually choose a grid size which makes this easy). Label the axes with the name, or symbol, of the variable with its unit – e.g. time/s, or F/N – and include scales.

Plot points as accurately as possible; for points requiring interpolation between grid lines, the usual tolerance is $\pm \frac{1}{2}$ a square. Unless the question instructs differently, draw in the best-fit graph.

Sketch-graphs (in PH4 and PH5 papers): A sketch-graph gives a good idea of the relationship between the two variables. It needs labelled axes but often it will not have scales and units. It is **not** an untidy ('hairy') graph. If the graph is intended to be a straight line, it should be drawn using a ruler. Sometimes significant values need to be labelled.

Tips about calculations

1. If the command word is **calculate** or **find** or **determine**:

    Full marks are given for the correct answer **but** an incorrect answer with no working scores 0 and there are usually marks available for correct steps in the working, even if the final answer is incorrect. Points the examiner will look for will include:

    - Selection of equation or equations and writing them down.

    - Statement of any principles used.

    - Conversion of units, e.g. hours into seconds, mA into A.

    - Insertion of values into equation(s) and manipulation of equations.

    - Stating the answer – **remember the unit**.

    Example: *An isolated charged metal sphere of diameter 10 cm, has an electric field at its surface of 9.00×10^5 V m^{-1}.*

    Calculate its charge, showing your reasoning.

    Working: The field at the surface of a spherical conductor is the same as that due to a point charge of the same size, placed at its centre.✓

    $$E = \frac{Q}{4\pi\varepsilon_0 r^2}$$

    So $Q = 4\pi\varepsilon_0 r^2 E = 4\pi \times 8.864 \times 10^{-12}$ F m^{-1}
    $\times (0.10 \text{ m})^2 \times 9 \times 10^5$ V m^{-1}
    $= 1.00 \text{ }\mu\text{C}$ ✓

(1 mark for stating the principle, 1 mark for correct use of equations (with a unit conversion); 1 for conversion of diameter to radius; 1 mark for correct answer with unit)

2. If the command phrase is **show that**, the basic rules for the setting out are the same. You **must** give clear convincing steps.

Example: *A planet orbits a star of mass M in a circle of radius r. Show that the speed, v, of the planet is given by $v = \sqrt{\dfrac{GM}{r}}$.*

Working: The centripetal force on the planet $= \dfrac{mv^2}{r}$, where m is the mass of the planet.

The centripetal force is provided by the gravitational field of the star:

$$F = \frac{GMm}{r^2}$$

So $\dfrac{mv^2}{r} = \dfrac{GMm}{r^2}$

Dividing by m and multiplying by r:

$$v^2 = \frac{GM}{r}, \text{ so } v = \sqrt{\frac{GM}{r}} \text{ QED.}$$

Comment: The statement 'Dividing by m and multiplying by r' would probably not be needed for the marks.

Tips about questions involving units

There are several sorts of questions involving units:

1. Expressing a derived unit in terms of the SI base units: kg, m, s, A:
   - Start with the defining equation or equations of the quantity with the derived unit.
   - Insert the units of the simpler quantities.
   - Simplify the resulting expression.

   Example: *Express the unit of electric field strength in terms of the SI base units, kg, m, s and A.*

- Electric field strength is defined by the equation:

$$E = \frac{F}{q},$$

where q is a small charge and F is the force exerted on it by the field.

- Force is calculated by mass × acceleration.
- Charge is calculated by current × time.

So: Unit of electric field strength $= \dfrac{\text{kg m s}^{-2}}{\text{A s}} = \text{kg m s}^{-3}\text{A}^{-1}$.

2. Suggesting a unit for a quantity.

The question will always give an equation involving the quantity.

- Manipulate the equation to make the unknown quantity the subject.
- Insert the known units for the other quantities.
- Simplify.

Example: *The drag on a sphere of radius a moving slowly with a velocity v through a fluid is given by: F = 6 πηav where η is a constant called the coefficient of viscosity. Suggest a unit for η.*

Make η the subject: $\eta = \dfrac{F}{6\,\pi a v}$

Rewrite in terms of units:

$$\therefore \text{unit of } \eta = \frac{\text{N}}{\text{m} \times \text{ms}^{-1}} = \text{N m}^{-2}\text{ s.}$$

Note: The question did not ask for any particular form, e.g. reducing it to the base units, so it can be left like this. The pascal, Pa, is equivalent to N m^{-2} so another equivalent is Pa s.

3. Showing that an equation has consistent units.

An equation is given and the candidate is required to show that the units of the two sides are the same. If any quantities are added or subtracted, these need also to have the same units, e.g. in the equation:

$\ln Q = \ln Q_0 - \dfrac{t}{RC}$, the two terms on the right-hand side have the same units – no units in this case.

- Start with the complicated side of the equation – usually the right-hand side.
- Put in the units of all the quantities.

- Manipulate to show whether it is the same as the unit of the left-hand side.

Example: *The period of oscillation, T, of a simple pendulum is given by*

$$T = 4\pi \sqrt{\frac{l}{g}},$$

where l is the length of the pendulum. Show that this equation is homogeneous.

Starting with the complicated side:

Units of r.h.s. $= \sqrt{\dfrac{m}{m\ s^{-2}}}$

Now simplify $= \sqrt{s^2}$

$\qquad\qquad\quad = s =$ units of l.h.s.

So the equation **is** homogeneous.

Questions and answers

This part of the guide looks at actual student answers to questions. There is a selection of questions covering a wide variety of topics. In each case there are two answers given; one from a student (Seren) who achieved a high grade and one from a student who achieved a lower grade (Tom). We suggest that you compare the answers of the two candidates carefully; make sure you understand why one answer is better than the other. In this way you will improve your approach to answering questions. Examination scripts are graded on the performance of the candidate across the whole paper and not on individual questions; examiners see many examples of good answers in otherwise low scoring scripts. The moral of this is that good examination technique can boost the grades of candidates at all levels.

PH4: Oscillations and Fields

page 162 Q1 Kinetic theory of gases   *(10 marks)*

page 163 Q2 Thermodynamics   *(10 marks)*

page 164 Q3 Resonance   *(4 marks)*

page 165 Q4 Electrostatic fields   *(12 marks)*

page 167 Q5 Conservation of momentum   *(6 marks)*

PH5: Magnetism, Nuclei and Options

page 168 Q6   Nuclear binding energy   *(10 marks)*

page 169 Q7   Radioactive decay   *(10 marks)*

page 171 Q8   Hall Effect   *(10 marks)*

page 172 Q9   Electromagnetic induction   *(10 marks)*

page 173 Q10 Capacitance   *(20 marks)*

A bubble of krypton (Kr) gas is formed underwater. The bubble has a volume of 2.14×10^{-6} m^3 and contains 1.70×10^{20} krypton molecules, each of mass 1.39×10^{-25} kg. The pressure of the gas inside the bubble is 300 kPa.

Kr bubble
Volume = 2.14×10^{-6} m^3
Pressure = 300 kPa
No. of molecules = 1.70×10^{20}
Mass of a Kr molecule = 1.39×10^{-25} kg

(a) Calculate:
  (i) The rms speed of the Kr molecules in the bubble. [3]
  (ii) The relative molecular mass of Kr. [2]
  (iii) The temperature of the gas inside the bubble. [3]
(b) The bubble is initially 20 m below the surface of the water. Explain, giving your reasoning, what happens to the size of the bubble as it rises. [2]

Tom's answer

(a) (i) $p = \frac{1}{3} \rho \overline{c^2}$ ✓ used

$$300 \times 10^3 = \frac{1}{3}(6.495 \times 10^{-20}) \times \overline{c^2}$$

$\rho = \frac{m}{V}$ $\overline{c^2} = 1.39 \times 10^{25}$

$$= \frac{1.39 \times 10^{-25}}{2.14 \times 10^{-6}} = 6.495 \times 10^{-20} \quad \therefore c = 3.72 \times 10^{12} \text{ m/s}$$

(ii) $RMM = \frac{mass}{no. \text{ of molecules}}$

$$= \frac{(1.39 \times 10^{-25}) \times 1000}{1.70 \times 10^{20}} = 8.17 \times 10^{-14} \text{ moles.} ✗$$

(iii) $pV = nRT$ ✓ used
$(300 \times 10^3) \times (2.14 \times 10^{-6}) = (8.176 \times 10^{-14}) \times 8.13 \, T$
$\therefore T = 9.658 \times 10^{11}$ K

(b) As $p \propto \frac{1}{V}$ the volume of the bubble will increase ✓ as the

pressure acting on the bubble decreases ✓.

Examiner commentary

(a) (i) The first mark is for using the relevant equation. Tom has substituted values of p and ρ into the equation which qualifies him for the first mark. Unfortunately the value of ρ is incorrect – he should have used the total mass of the gas in the bubble to work it out.

  (ii) Tom's initial equation is incorrect.

  (iii) Tom has substituted relevant quantities into the equation and gains the first mark. The value of n is the value he worked out for the relative molecular mass so, in spite of his giving this the unit 'moles' in part (ii), he doesn't qualify for e.c.f.

(b) A good answer – Tom has mentioned both marking points: pressure decreasing leading to volume increasing.

Tom scores 4 out of 10 marks.

Seren's answer

(a) (i) $\overline{c^2} = \dfrac{3p}{\rho}$

$\rho = \dfrac{1.70\times10^{20}\times1.39\times10^{-25}}{2.14\times10^{-6}}$

$rms = \sqrt{\dfrac{3\times300\times10^3}{11.04}}$ ✓

$= 11.04 \text{ kg m}^{-3}.$ ✓

$= \sqrt{81,522} = 285.5 \text{ m s}^{-1}$✓

(ii) $M_r = 1.39\times10^{-25}\times6.02\times10^{23}$

$= 0.084 \text{ kg mol}^{-1}$

$= 84 \text{ g mol}^{-1}$ ✓✓ [no unit penalty]

(iii) $pV = nRT$ $\qquad n = \dfrac{N}{N_A} = \dfrac{1.70\times10^{20}}{6.02\times10^{23}}$ ✓ $= 0.0002823$

$T = \dfrac{pV}{nR} \; \dfrac{300000\times2.14\times10^{-6}}{8.31\times0.0002823}$ ✓ $= 273.6 \text{ K}$ ✓

(b) Pressure is inversely proportional to volume. Therefore the size of the bubble increases ✓ as the pressure is less ✓ towards the top surface of the water.

Examiner commentary

Seren has produced almost textbook answers to this question. Her one mistake, which wasn't penalised here, was in (a) (ii) where she calculated the molar mass rather than the relative molecular mass. This slip and hence the use of the units [g mol⁻¹] was not penalised on this occasion.

One point of **good practice** is that in (a) (i) and (iii), Seren has written the equation she wants to use and done separate calculations to find ρ and n, which she needed. In (i) she put a vertical line to separate the calculation.

Seren scores 10 out of 10 marks.

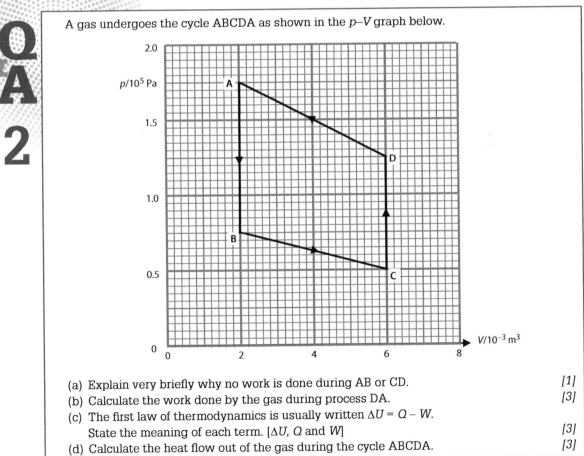

A gas undergoes the cycle ABCDA as shown in the p–V graph below.

(a) Explain very briefly why no work is done during AB or CD. [1]

(b) Calculate the work done by the gas during process DA. [3]

(c) The first law of thermodynamics is usually written $\Delta U = Q - W$. State the meaning of each term. [ΔU, Q and W] [3]

(d) Calculate the heat flow out of the gas during the cycle ABCDA. [3]

Tom's answer

(a) There is no change in volume. ✓

(b) Work done $= p\Delta V = \frac{1}{2}bh + bh = \frac{1}{2}(4\times 0.5) + 4\times 1.25$ ✓

$$= 6\,\text{J}$$

(c) ΔU: The change in internal energy ✓

   Q: Internal heat flow ? ✗

   W: Work done ✗

(d) D→A: 6 J

   B→C: 2.5 J

   Total heat $= 3.5\,\text{J}$ ✓ [just]

Seren's answer

(a) Because the volume remains constant. ✓ There is no volume change so work done $= 0$ since $W = p\Delta V$.

(b) Work done = area under graph =

$$\frac{1.75\times 10^5 \times 1.25\times 10^5}{2}\times 4\times 10^{-3}\ ✓ = 600\,\text{J}\ ✓$$

Work is negative because ΔV is negative, so work done by gas $= -600\,\text{J}$ ✓

(c) ΔU: The change in internal energy ✓

   Q: The heat flow into the system ✓

   W: The work done by the system ✓

(d) $\Delta U = 0, \therefore Q = W$ ✓

   $W = W_{DA} - W_{BC} = -600 + \frac{1}{2}\times(0.755\times 10^5 + 0.50\times 10^5)$
   $\times 4\times 10^{-3} = -350\,\text{J}$

   $\therefore Q = -350\,\text{J}$ ✓, so heat flow out of the gas $= +350\,\text{J}$ ✓

Examiner commentary

(a) Tom hits the marking point.

(b) Tom has made a good attempt to calculate the area so has obtained the first mark, but he has failed to spot the multiplying factors on the scales of the graph. He also fails to understand that the work is done **on** the gas and so he needs to introduce a minus sign.

(c) The examiner hesitated by 'internal heat flow' but Tom hasn't clearly stated that Q is the heat flowing into the system. Similarly Tom needs to give a direction to W.

(d) Tom appears to be calculating work. He notices that the two quantities of energy flow are in different directions and the difference needs to be found, for which he gains the mark. He does not relate Q to W. He would not be penalised twice for the multiplying factors [see part (b)].

Tom scores 4 out of 10 marks.

Examiner commentary

(a) On this occasion, the examiner was only looking for the statement about volume, hence the instruction to explain 'very briefly'. Seren gave more details which is a good idea.

(b) The first mark is for an attempt to calculate the area – in this case it was successful! The final mark is for the negative sign.

(c) All correct. '. . . of the system' would have been good to see in the explanation of ΔU, but was not required.

(d) The statement that $Q = W$ is an important part of the answer.

   Again, the sign of the answer is important. Because net work is done **on** the gas in taking it round the cycle, heat must flow **out**.

Seren scores 10 out of 10 marks.

Q&A 3

Describe an everyday circumstance where resonance occurs. Your example of resonance may be useful or it may be an example where resonance should be avoided. You should explain what your oscillating system is, what provides the driving force and the result of the resonance. A diagram may (or may not) assist your answer.   [4]

Marking scheme

Diagram/statement of application [e.g. bridge, car rattle...] ✓

Description of plausible oscillating driving force ✓

Description of system ✓

Large amplitude because of same frequency [or graph showing resonance, with labelled axes] ✓

Tom's answer

Everyday example of resonance can be that in the bridges ✓ where driving force is equal to the natural frequency (Millennium Bridge). People's footsteps, when they walk in time, provide the driving force ✓. The bridge will collapse as it disturbs.

Examiner commentary

Tom has identified that the situation involves a bridge and has gained the first mark. He has also indicated that it is the walking people that provide driving force. He has not indicated clearly what the oscillating system is, or the conditions under which resonance occurs. The statement about the bridge collapsing is too vague to achieve the 'effect' mark.

A better answer, in the context of the Millennium Bridge, would have included: the effect of the footsteps was to make the bridge oscillate from side to side; because the frequency of the footsteps coincided with the natural frequency of the bridge, large amplitude oscillations occurred.

Tom scores 2 out of 4 marks.

Seren's answer

Resonance occurs when a child is being pushed on a swing ✓ by an adult. The adult provides the driving force ✓ and the swing oscillates about a central equilibrium position. ✓ If the adult provides a force [pushes!] with the same frequency as the natural frequency of the swing, large amplitude oscillations will occur, i.e. the swing will swing high!✓

Examiner commentary

Seren's answer is not perfect. The second point should perhaps have stated 'The regular pushes of the adult...'. The third point, which required identification of the oscillating system, is a little incomplete too: better would be 'the child, the swing seat and the supporting wires form the oscillating system, which swings to and fro'. However, the examiner considered she had done enough for the marks!

Seren scores 4 out of 4 marks.

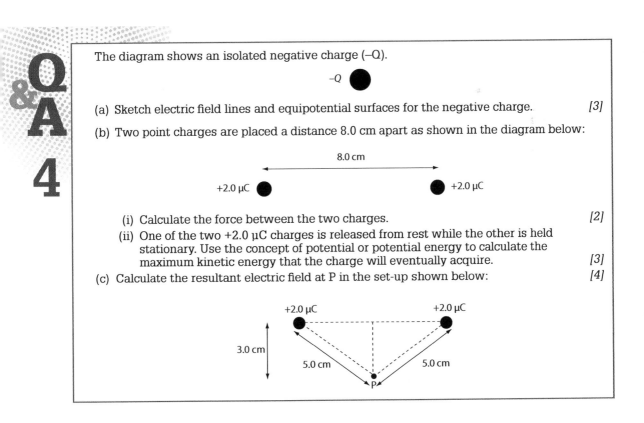

Q&A 4

The diagram shows an isolated negative charge (–Q).

−Q ●

(a) Sketch electric field lines and equipotential surfaces for the negative charge. [3]

(b) Two point charges are placed a distance 8.0 cm apart as shown in the diagram below:

8.0 cm

+2.0 µC ●   ● +2.0 µC

(i) Calculate the force between the two charges. [2]

(ii) One of the two +2.0 µC charges is released from rest while the other is held stationary. Use the concept of potential or potential energy to calculate the maximum kinetic energy that the charge will eventually acquire. [3]

(c) Calculate the resultant electric field at P in the set-up shown below: [4]

+2.0 µC   +2.0 µC
●   ●
3.0 cm
5.0 cm   5.0 cm
●
P

Tom's answer

(a)

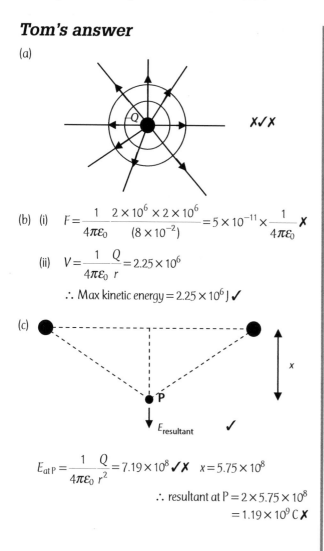

$X \checkmark X$

(b) (i) $F = \dfrac{1}{4\pi\varepsilon_0} \dfrac{2\times10^6 \times 2\times10^6}{(8\times10^{-2})} = 5\times10^{-11} \times \dfrac{1}{4\pi\varepsilon_0}$ X

(ii) $V = \dfrac{1}{4\pi\varepsilon_0}\dfrac{Q}{r} = 2.25\times10^6$

$\therefore$ Max kinetic energy $= 2.25\times10^6$ J $\checkmark$

(c)

$E_{\text{resultant}}$ $\checkmark$

$E_{\text{at P}} = \dfrac{1}{4\pi\varepsilon_0}\dfrac{Q}{r^2} = 7.19\times10^8$ $\checkmark X$ $x = 5.75\times10^8$

$\therefore$ resultant at P $= 2 \times 5.75\times10^8$

$= 1.19\times10^9$ C X

Seren's answer

(a)

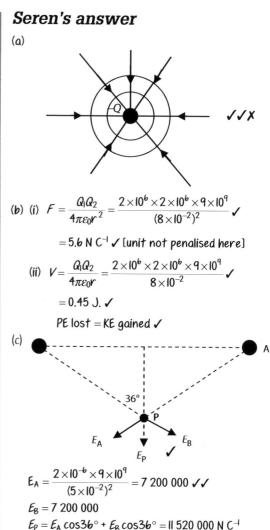

$\checkmark\checkmark X$

(b) (i) $F = \dfrac{Q_1 Q_2}{4\pi\varepsilon_0 r^2} = \dfrac{2\times10^6 \times 2\times10^6 \times 9\times10^9}{(8\times10^{-2})^2}$ $\checkmark$

$= 5.6$ N C^{-1} $\checkmark$ [unit not penalised here]

(ii) $V = \dfrac{Q_1 Q_2}{4\pi\varepsilon_0 r} = \dfrac{2\times10^6 \times 2\times10^6 \times 9\times10^9}{8\times10^{-2}}$ $\checkmark$

$= 0.45$ J. $\checkmark$

PE lost $=$ KE gained $\checkmark$

(c)

E_P $\checkmark$

$E_A = \dfrac{2\times10^{-6} \times 9\times10^9}{(5\times10^{-2})^2} = 7\ 200\ 000$ $\checkmark\checkmark$

$E_B = 7\ 200\ 000$

$E_P = E_A \cos36° + E_B \cos36° = 11\ 520\ 000$ N C^{-1}

Examiner commentary

(a) Tom has drawn field lines but they are in the wrong direction. He has drawn two equipotentials. He has not identified the field lines and equipotentials.

(b) (i) Tom has used an incorrect formula – the 8×10^{-2} should be squared – so no marks are given.

(ii) Tom has calculated a potential and thinks this is the potential <u>energy</u>. He gains a mark for realising that the drop in potential energy is the gain in kinetic, even though the figure is wrong.

(c) Tom realises that the resultant field at P is vertically downwards – 1 mark. His second mark is for the use of the formula for the electric field at P due to one of the 2.0 µC charges – his answer is wrong as is the use of the x distance subsequently.

Tom scores 4 out of 12 marks.

Examiner commentary

(a) The missing mark is because Seren has not identified the equipotentials and the field lines.

(b) (i) Seren has used the correct formula. She has used the very good approximation, not given in the data sheet, that $(4\pi\varepsilon_0)^{-1} = 9\times10^9$ F^{-1}m. This is acceptable here and in the subsequent working.

(ii) Seren has made a slip in writing '$V =$' rather than 'Potential energy $=$' at the start of her answer. She goes on to treat the answer as PE, so it is accepted.

(c) Seren realises that the resultant field at P is vertically downwards – 1 mark. She correctly calculates the contribution to E_P from A and B [her labels] but unfortunately has miscalculated the angle at P [see diagram] – it is 53°.

Seren scores 10 out of 12 marks

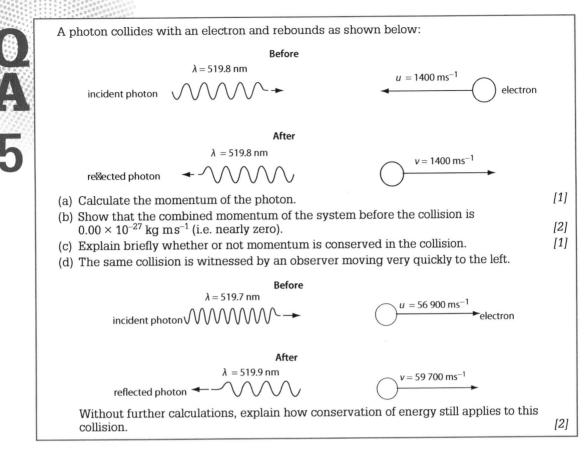

Q&A 5

A photon collides with an electron and rebounds as shown below:

(a) Calculate the momentum of the photon. [1]
(b) Show that the combined momentum of the system before the collision is 0.00×10^{-27} kg m s^{-1} (i.e. nearly zero). [2]
(c) Explain briefly whether or not momentum is conserved in the collision. [1]
(d) The same collision is witnessed by an observer moving very quickly to the left.

Without further calculations, explain how conservation of energy still applies to this collision. [2]

Tom's answer

(a) $p = \dfrac{h}{\lambda} = \dfrac{6.63 \times 10^{-34}}{519.8 \times 10^{-9}} = 1.28 \times 10^{-27}$ kg m s^{-1}. ✓

(b) Momentum of electron $= 9.11 \times 10^{-31} \times 1400$ ✓

Total momentum $= \dfrac{6.63 \times 10^{-34}}{519.8 \times 10^{-9}} - 9.11 \times 1400$

$= 9.05 \times 10^{-32}$

(c) Momentum is conserved in the collision as the momentum was negligible.

(d) Energy has been transferred from the photon to the electron. ✓

Examiner commentary

(a) Tom has selected and correctly used the photon momentum formula and given the correct units [N s would also have been accepted].

(b) A good start – the first mark was given for the method of calculating the momentum of the electron. Writing '..= .00009 × 10^{-27} = 0.00 × 10^{-27} [3 s.f.]' would get the second mark.

(c) Tom needed to say that the <u>total</u> momentum before and after the collision was roughly zero.

(d) Tom is on the right lines but he needed to be clearer that the loss in photon energy was the same as the gain in electron energy. An examiner might have given Tom the benefit of the doubt but did not on this occasion.

Tom scores 3 out of 6 marks.

Seren's answer

(a) $p = \dfrac{h}{\lambda} = \dfrac{6.63 \times 10^{-34}}{519.8 \times 10^{-9}} = 1.28 \times 10^{-27} \text{ kg m s}^{-1}.$ ✓

(b) Combined momentum = momentum of photon + momentum of electron

$$= 1.28 \times 10^{-27} - m_e v_e$$
$$= 1.28 \times 10^{-27} - 9.11 \times 10^{-31} \times 1400 ✓$$
$$= 1.28 \times 10^{-27} - 1.28 \times 10^{-27}$$
$$= 0.00 \times 10^{-27}$$

(c) Momentum is conserved as the speed of the electron is the same before and after and the wavelength of the photon is also the same ✓

(d) Conservation of energy still applies to this collision as no energy is lost. The energy of the electron has increased but the energy of the reflected photon is less. ✓

Examiner commentary

(a) As Tom's – a good answer.

(b) The second mark is just there. Ideally, Seren would have taken both the electron's and the photon's momenta to 4 s.f. [they are both 1.275×10^{-27} Ns].

(c) Strictly this answer also relies on the previous one; there was no requirement to say that the total momenta before and after were virtually zero.

(d) This is less good than Tom's answer. Seren needed to say that the decrease in the photon's energy was the same as the increase in the electrons.

Seren scores 4 out of 6 marks.

PJHS

Q & A 6

(a) Calculate the binding energy per nucleon of $^{14}_{6}$C. [4]

[1u = 931 MeV, $m_{\text{neutron}} = 1.008665$u, $m_{\text{proton}} = 1.007276$u, mass of $^{14}_{6}$C nucleus = 13.999950u]

The following reaction can be regarded as evidence for the existence of neutrinos (or an anti-neutrino in this case).

$$^{14}_{6}\text{C} \longrightarrow {}^{14}_{7}\text{N} + {}^{0}_{-1}\beta^- + \overline{v}_e$$

Mass of $^{14}_{6}$C nucleus = 13.999950u; Mass of $^{14}_{7}$N nucleus = 13.999234u
Mass of β^- particle = 0.000549u; The mass of the anti-neutrino $\overline{v}_e$ is negligible.

(b) Calculate the energy released in this reaction (1u = 931 MeV). [3]

The evidence for the existence of the anti-neutrino came from the (unexpected) wide variation of the energies of the β-particles emitted. However, you should now ignore the existence of the anti-neutrino.

(c) Explain briefly, using conservation of momentum, which particle (N or β^-) receives most of the energy of the reaction. [3]

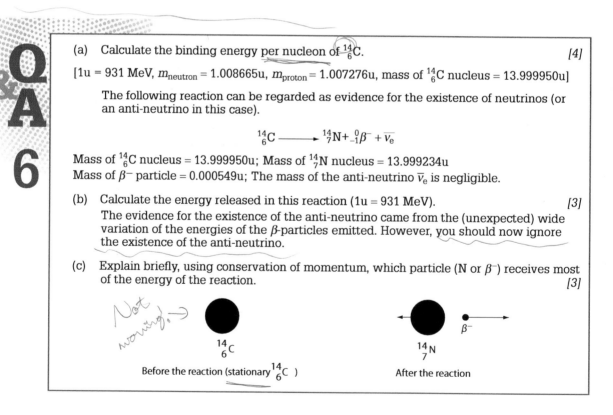

Not moving.→

$^{14}_{6}$C

Before the reaction (stationary $^{14}_{6}$C)

$^{14}_{7}$N

β^-

After the reaction

Tom's answer

(a) $m_{total} = 6 \times 1.007276 + 8 \times 1.008665 \checkmark = 14.112976u$

$m_{lost} = 14.112976 - 13.99950 = 0.113026u \checkmark$

$E = mc^2 = 0.113026 \times (3 \times 10^8)^2 = 1.017234 \times 10^{16} \text{ eV} \times$

(b) $13.999950 - (13.999234 + 0.000549) = 1.67 \times 10^{-4}u \checkmark$

$E = mc^2 = 1.67 \times 10^{-4} \times (3 \times 10^8)^2 = 1.503 \times 10^{13} \text{ eV}$

(c) The nitrogen nucleus receives most of the energy from the reaction because it is a lot heavier than the β / electron emitted $\checkmark$ and the $^{14}_{7}N$ still has a fair bit of velocity. $\therefore$ the $^{14}_{7}N$ has the most energy from the collision.

Examiner commentary

(a) Tom has calculated the mass of the 14 nucleons correctly and the mass deficit of the nucleus in u – giving him the first two marks. He wants to use $E = mc^2$, so he should have converted the u to kg. He also fails to divide by the number of nucleons.

(b) Tom's first step is correct but he makes the same mistake as in part (a).

(c) Tom correctly identifies the significant fact of the relative masses of the $^{14}_{7}N$ and the β-particle but fails to draw the correct conclusion.

Tom scores 4 out of 10 marks.

Seren's answer

(a) $6 \times 1.007276 + 8 \times 1.008665 \checkmark = 14.11297 6u$

$14.112976 - 13.99950 = 0.113026u \checkmark$

$\dfrac{0.113026 \times 931}{14} \checkmark = 7.52 \text{ MeV} \checkmark$

(b) $13.999950 - (13.999234 + 0.000549) = 1.67 \times 10^{-4}u \checkmark$

Energy released $= 931 \times 1.67 \times 10^{-4} \checkmark = 0.155 \text{ MeV} \checkmark$

(c) The momentums of the nucleus and the β particle, ie mv for the two particles are the same and so v for the lighter β particle $\checkmark$ is much higher $\checkmark$. Kinetic energy is $\frac{1}{2}mv^2$ which is $\frac{1}{2}mv \times v$, so the β particle with the bigger velocity has the bigger KE $\checkmark$.

Examiner commentary

(a) Seren has done all the steps and has received the marks. Her communication is not perfect because she doesn't say what each line of the answer means. Her answer is correct [the units MeV, MeV/nucleon were accepted].

(b) Again correct with better communication.

(c) Seren has come to the correct conclusion with good reasoning. Even easier would be to note that the relationship between KE and momentum is $KE = \dfrac{p^2}{2m}$, so if the momenta are the same, the lighter particle gets the lion's share of the energy.

Seren scores 10 out of 10 marks.

Caesium-137 is a radioactive by-product from fission nuclear power stations. It has a half-life of 30 years and emits β^- radiation.

(a) Complete the following reaction equation: [2]

$$^{137}_{55}\text{Cs} \longrightarrow {}_{\cdots\cdots}^{\cdots\cdots}\text{Ba} + {}_{\cdots\cdots}^{\cdots\cdots}\beta^-$$

(b) Show that the decay constant of caesium-137 is approximately $7 \times 10^{-10} \text{ s}^{-1}$. [2]

(c) Show that the initial activity of 1.0 kg of caesium-137 is approximately 3×10^{15} Bq. [2]

(d) Explain why 1.0 kg of caesium-137, although it has an activity of 3×10^{15} Bq, would be quite safe in a sealed metal box of thickness 1 cm. [1]

(e) When the activity of 1.0 kg of caesium has dropped to 1000 Bq (comparable to soil) it can be disposed of by mixing with soil and scattering on the ground. Calculate how long it takes for the caesium sample to reduce its activity from 3×10^{15} Bq to 1000 Bq. [3]

Tom's answer

(a) $^{137}_{55}C \longrightarrow \ ^{137}_{56}Ba + \ ^{0}_{0}\beta^- \ \boldsymbol{xx}$

(b) $\lambda = \dfrac{\ln 2}{T_{\frac{1}{2}}} \checkmark = \dfrac{0.693}{30 \times 365 \times 24 \times 60 \times 60} = 2.198 \times 10^{-8} \, s \ \boldsymbol{x}$

(c) $A = \lambda N \checkmark = 3 \times 10^{15} \, Bq$

(d) The beta particles would be absorbed by the metal. $\checkmark$

(e) $A = A_0 e^{-\lambda t}$

$\ln A = \ln A_0 - \lambda t \checkmark$

$\lambda t = \ln A_0 - \ln A$

$t = \dfrac{\ln\left(\dfrac{A_0}{A}\right)}{\lambda} = \dfrac{\ln\left(\dfrac{3 \times 10^{15}}{1000}\right)}{2.198 \times 10^{-8}} \checkmark = 567\,657\,927 \, s = 18 \ years.$

Examiner commentary

(a) Tom misses both marks. The first was for applying the conservation of A and Z and the second was for all the numbers being correct.

(b) The incorrect answer was down to a calculator slip. The mark was actually for the correct expression, which Tom gave – unfortunately his answer contradicted this expression.

(c) The first mark was for the selection of the correct equation, which earned the mark.

(d) Correct.

(e) Another calculator slip. One mark was for taking logs correctly; the second for the correct identification of A and A_0.

Tom scores 5 out of 10 marks.

Seren's answer

(a) $^{137}_{55}C \longrightarrow \ ^{137}_{56}Ba + \ ^{0}_{-1}\beta^- \ \checkmark\checkmark$

(b) $\lambda = \dfrac{\ln 2}{T_{\frac{1}{2}}} \checkmark = \dfrac{0.693}{30 \times 365 \times 24 \times 60 \times 60} \checkmark = 7.33 \times 10^{-10} \, s^{-1}$

(c) $A = \lambda N \checkmark \quad N = \dfrac{1000}{137} \times 6.02 \times 10^{23} = 4.394 \times 10^{24}.$

So $A = 7 \times 10^{-10} \times 4.394 \times 10^{24} = 3.0758 \times 10^{15} \, Bq \ \checkmark$

(d) It only emits β radiation

(e) $A = A_0 e^{-\lambda t} \checkmark \quad 1000 = 3 \times 10^{15} e^{-\lambda t}$

$1000 = 3 \times 10^{15} \times e^{-7 \times 10^{-10} t}$

so $\ln 1000 = \ln 3 \times 10^{15} - 7 \times 10^{-10} \, t \checkmark$

So $t = \dfrac{\ln 3 \times 10^{15} - \ln 1000}{7 \times 10^{-10}} = 4.104 \times 10^{10} \, s \checkmark$

Examiner commentary

(a) The totals of A and Z on the two sides are equal and the figures are all correct.

(b) Correct working.

(c) Seren's working is correct. She has used the approximate value for λ, which is acceptable. In this 'show that' type of question it is best to give the asked-for figure to at least one more s.f. than requested.

(d) Seren should have related the question to the penetrating powers of β-particles.

(e) Again, Seren has used the given approximate values for λ and A_0.

Seren scores 9 out of 10 marks.

Q&A 8

Electrons move through a metallic conductor as shown and experience a force due to the applied magnetic field (B perpendicular to the front face as shown).

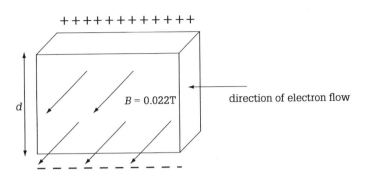

(a) Explain why charges accumulate on the upper and lower face of the conductor as shown. [2]

(b) Indicate on the diagram how you would connect a voltmeter in order to measure the Hall voltage (V_H). [1]

(c) By equating the electrical and magnetic forces acting on an electron in the conductor, show that $V_H = Bvd$. [3]

(d) (i) The magnetic field ($B = 0.022$ T) is produced by a solenoid of length 2.00 m and with 15000 turns. Calculate the current in the solenoid. [2]

(ii) Where must the conductor be placed and how should it be oriented in relation to the solenoid to obtain the maximum Hall voltage? [2]

Tom's answer

(a) The force produced by the electrons moving through the conductor and the B-field generated push the electrons down to the lower face. ✓

(b)

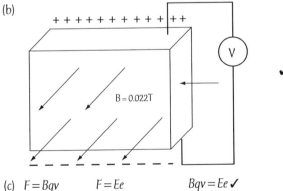

(c) $F = Bqv$ $F = Ee$ $Bqv = Ee$ ✓

(d) (i) $B = \mu_0 n \ell$

$$\rightarrow I = \frac{B}{\mu_0 n} \checkmark = 1.167 \text{ A} \times$$

(ii) It should be parallel to the solenoid ✗ and placed inside the coil ✓

Examiner commentary

(a) Tom has communicated that the electrons experience a downward force and thus gains one mark. He needs to give more detail, e.g. referring to Fleming's LH rule to gain the second.

(b) Correct – voltmeter connected between the upper and lower surfaces.

(c) A good start, Tom equates the electric and magnetic forces but makes no further progress.

(d) (i) The incorrect use of ℓ rather than l is ignored as l is used in the manipulated form of the equation. Tom's mistake is not to realise that n is the number of turns per metre. He therefore needs to divide n by 2, so the value for l should be double his answer.

(ii) The plane of the conductor should be perpendicular to the field and hence to the axis of the solenoid.

Tom scores 5 out of 10 marks.

Seren's answer

(a) The electrons feel a force downwards ✓ due to Flemming's left-hand rule✓. This causes the top to become positive and the bottom to become negative.

(b)

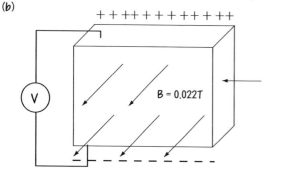

(c) $Ee = Bev$ ✓

$E = \dfrac{V}{d}$, so $\dfrac{V_H}{d}e = Bev$ ✓, ∴ $V_H = \dfrac{Bevd}{e}$ ✓$= Bvd$

(d) (i) $B = \mu_0 nI$.

$I = \dfrac{B}{\mu_0 n} = \dfrac{0.022}{\mu_0 \times 7500} = 2.33$ A ✓✓

(ii) The conductor should be placed perpendicular to the B-field to obtain a max Hall voltage – perpendicular ✓ (b.o.d.) inside the solenoid ✓.

Examiner commentary

(a) The misspelling of Fleming is ignored.

(b) Seren has placed the voltmeter correctly.

(c) A good clear derivation.

(d) (i) Seren has remembered to divide the number of turns by the length to find n.

(ii) Only just. It is not very clear the large flat surfaces of the conductor should be placed perpendicular to the axis of the solenoid – the examiner had to infer this – but she has been given the benefit of the doubt on this occasion.

Seren scores 10 out of 10 marks.

Q & A 9

A magician's metallic wand can spring apart into the shape of a circular hoop (see below).
$B = 58$ mT

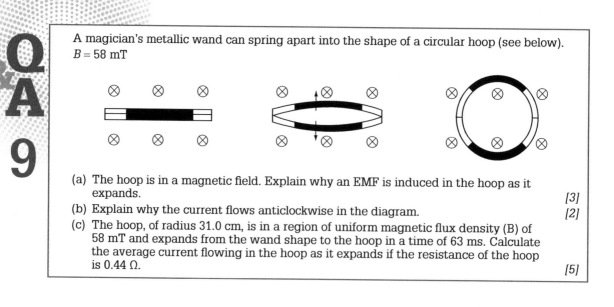

(a) The hoop is in a magnetic field. Explain why an EMF is induced in the hoop as it expands. [3]

(b) Explain why the current flows anticlockwise in the diagram. [2]

(c) The hoop, of radius 31.0 cm, is in a region of uniform magnetic flux density (B) of 58 mT and expands from the wand shape to the hoop in a time of 63 ms. Calculate the average current flowing in the hoop as it expands if the resistance of the hoop is 0.44 Ω. [5]

Tom's answer

(a) The sides of the hoop move through ✗ magnetic field lines ✓ as the hoop expands. This induces a current.

(b) The current flows anticlockwise because the B-field is directed at a right angle to the hoop and is flowing towards the top of the hoop.

(c) Area $= \pi r^2 = \pi \times 0.31^2$ ✓

$\Phi = BA$ ✓ $= 58 \times 10^{-3} \times \pi \times 0.31^2 = 1.75 \times 10^{-2}$

Change of flux per second $= \dfrac{1.75 \times 10^{-2}}{63 \times 10^{-3}} = 0.2779$ ✓

$I = VR$ ✗ $= 0.2779 \times 0.44 = 0.122$ A

Examiner commentary

(a) Tom has not mentioned that the hoop sides <u>cut</u> the field lines. Moving along field lines produces no current. For the third mark a correct mention of a law of induction or a relevant equation is needed.

(b) Tom's answer lacks any substance. He could have considered the top of the hoop and applied the right-hand rule to show that the induced current is to the left, which is anticlockwise.

(c) Tom has correctly worked out the area of the expanded loop and the flux which links it. Unaccountably he has made a mistake with the well-known equation $V = IR$ and so failed to calculate the current correctly.

Tom scores 4 out of 10 marks.

Seren's answer

(a) EMF is the rate of change of flux linkage✓. As the area of the wand increases✓, the flux linking the loop increases✓, so inducing an EMF.

(b) The current must oppose the change, e.g. on the top of the loop the force must be downwards, so the current must be to the left by the left-hand rule. ✓✗

(c) $V_{induced} = B \dfrac{dA}{dt}$ ✓ $= 58 \times 10^{-3} \times \dfrac{\pi \times 0.31^2}{63 \times 10^{-3}}$ ✓✓ $= 0.278$ V

$I = \dfrac{V}{R} = \dfrac{0.278\text{V}}{0.44\Omega}$ ✓ $= 0.632$ A ✓

Examiner commentary

(a) Seren has used a different approach from Tom. Both are valid. Seren has mentioned the general point relating EMF to change of flux and pointed out how these apply to the hoop.

(b) If Seren had said that the current in the bottom of the loop was to the right she'd have received the second mark.

(c) Seren's answer uses calculus notation correctly. This is not required. Tom's approach would have gained all 5 marks if he had used the correct equation for his final step.

Seren scores 9 out of 10 marks.

Q & A 10

(a) Calculate the capacitance of the capacitor shown. Area = 0.163 m² vacuum [2]

(b) The capacitor is charged so that there is a pd of 1.2 kV across the plates. Calculate:
  (i) the charge stored, [1]
  (ii) the energy stored in the capacitor. [1]

(c) The capacitor is discharged through a 670 kΩ resistor. Calculate the time the capacitor takes to lose half its charge. [3]

(d) Explain briefly whether or not the time the capacitor takes to lose half its energy is longer or shorter than your answer to (c). [2]

(e) An electron is located between the plates of the charged capacitor. Show that the acceleration experienced by the electron is approximately 6×10^{17} m s⁻². [3]

(f) The electron starts from rest halfway between the plates.
  (i) Use the acceleration (6×10^{17} m s⁻²) to calculate the speed of the electron when it strikes the upper plate of the capacitor [2]
  (ii) Show that the speed of the electron (when it strikes the upper plate of the capacitor) corresponds to a kinetic energy of 0.6 keV and explain briefly another method for obtaining this answer of K.E. = 0.6 keV. [3]
  (iii) Calculate the time the electron takes to travel to the upper plate. [3]

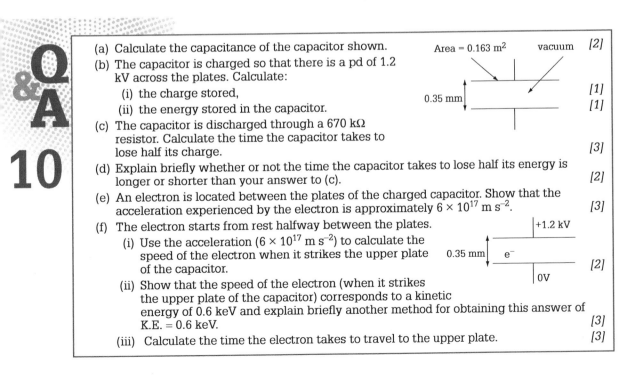

0.35 mm

+1.2 kV

0.35 mm   e⁻

0V

Tom's answer

(a) $C = \dfrac{\varepsilon_0 A}{d}$

$C = \dfrac{8.85 \times 10^{-12} \times 0.163}{0.33 \times 10^{-3}}$ ✓ (only) $= 4.37 \times 10^{-9}$

(b) (i) $Q = CV = 4.37 \times 10^{-9} \times 1.2 \times 10^3$

$\qquad = 5.244 \times 10^{-6} \, C$ ✓ e.c.f.

(ii) $E = \tfrac{1}{2} QV$

$\qquad E = 5.244 \times 10^{-6} \times 1.2 \times 10^3 = 6.293 \times 10^{-3} \, J$ ✗

(c) $Q = Q_0 e^{-t/RC}$. $RC = 670 \times 10^3 \times 4.37 \times 10^{-9} = 2.93 \times 10^{-3} \, s$ ✓

$\ln Q = \ln Q_0 - \dfrac{t}{RC} \qquad \dfrac{\ln Q}{\ln Q_0} = -\dfrac{t}{RC}$ ✗

$t = \dfrac{\ln 2.62 \times 10^{-6} \times 2.93 \times 10^{-3}}{\ln 4.95 \times 10^{-6}} = 3.08 \times 10^{-3} \, s$

(d) Shorter, as energy is released to the outside, extra escapes ? ✗

(e) $F = \dfrac{1}{4\pi\varepsilon_0} \dfrac{1.2 \times 10^3 \times 1.6 \times 10^{-19}}{(0.35 \times 10^{-3})^2} = 14.9 \, N$ ✗

$a = \dfrac{14.9}{9.11 \times 10^{-31}} =$

(f) (i) $v^2 = u^2 + 2ax$ ✓

$\qquad v^2 = 2 \times 10^{17} \times 0.00035 \, m = 4.2 \times 10^{14}$ ✗

$\qquad v = 2.05 \times 10^7 \, m \, s^{-1}$

(ii) $ke = \tfrac{1}{2} m v^2 = \tfrac{1}{2} \times 9.11 \times 10^{-31} \times (2.05 \times 10^7)^2$ ✓

(iii) $v = u + at; t = \dfrac{v}{a} = \dfrac{2.05 \times 10^{-7}}{6 \times 10^{17}}$ ✓✓ ecf

$\qquad t = 3.42 \times 10^{-11} \, s$ ✓

Examiner commentary

(a) Tom started well and obtained the mark for using the capacitor equation. Unfortunately he made a slip, used an incorrect values for d, and paid for it. He lived dangerously by omitting the unit!

(b) (i) Good – note that Tom used his (incorrect) value for C but was credited on the error carried forward principle.

(ii) Another slip – this time Tom omitted the factor of $\tfrac{1}{2}$ in his calculation.

(c) Tom correctly calculated the value of the time constant, RC, and received a mark. He incorrectly manipulated the equation after correctly taking logs. He might have done better to simplify the first equation – using Q and $\tfrac{1}{2} Q$ and cancelling the Qs – to start with. It would have produced an easier equation to work with.

(d) The answer 'shorter' is correct but it needs to arise from correct reasoning.

(e) Tom appears to be attempting to apply the equation for the force between two point charges, which is inappropriate. No credit can be given.

(f) (i) Correct equation – on this occasion, this was enough for the first mark.

His value of x was incorrect – it should have been $\tfrac{1}{2} \times 0.35 \, mm = 0.175 \, mm$.

(ii) Tom could have earned a second mark by converting his value of energy to eV. It would have been incorrect but ecf would have come to his rescue!

(iii) A good final answer. It is worth persevering to the end of a question – the last part is not always the most difficult and Tom snapped up 3 marks.

Tom scores 8 out of 20 marks.

Seren's answer

(a) $C = \dfrac{\varepsilon_0 A}{d} = 4.1216 \times 10^{-9} \, \text{F}$ ✓✓

(b) (i) $Q = CV = 4.1216 \times 10^{-9} \times 1.2 \times 1000 = 4.946 \times 10-6 \, \text{C}$ ✓(b.o.d.)

   (ii) $E = 0.5QV$

$$= 0.5 \times 4.946 \times 10^{-6} \times 1.2 \times 1000 = 2.968 \times 10^{-7} \, \text{J} \; ✗$$

(c) $Q = Q_0 e^{-t/RC}$ $R = 670$

$$\dfrac{Q_0}{2} = Q_0 e^{-t/RC} ✓ \qquad \dfrac{-t}{RC} = \ln \dfrac{1}{2}$$

$$t = -\ln\dfrac{1}{2} \times 670 \times 1000 \times 4.1216 \times 10^{-3} = 1.91 \times 10^{-3} \, \text{s} \; ✓✓$$

(d) The rate of charge loss is exponential. The energy is the product of charge and voltage ✓: when the charge is halved, voltage is also halved so the energy is more than halved. So the time for the energy to halve is shorter. ✓

(e) In between the capacitor plates $E = \dfrac{V}{d} = \dfrac{1.2 \times 10^3}{0.35 \times 10^{-3}}$

$$= 3.42 \times 10^6 \, \text{N C}^{-1}.$$

$F = EQ$ ✓ $= 3.42 \times 10^6 \times 1.6 \times 10^{-19} = 5.49 \times 10^{-13} \, \text{N}$

$a = \dfrac{F}{m}$ ✓ $= \dfrac{5.49 \times 10^{-13}}{9.11 \times 10^{-31}}$ ✓ $= 6.02 \times 10^{17} \, \text{m s}^{-2}.$

(f) (i) $v^2 = u^2 + 2as$ ✓

$$v^2 = 0 + 2 \times 6 \times 10^{17} \times \dfrac{0.35 \times 10^{-3}}{2} = 2.1 \times 10^{14} \, \text{ms}^{-1}$$

$$v = \sqrt{2.1 \times 10^{14}} = 1.449 \times 10^7 \; ✓$$

   (ii) $\dfrac{1}{2}mv^2 = \dfrac{1}{2} \times 9.11 \times 10^{-31} \times (2.1 \times 10^{14})$ ✓ $= 9.56 \times 10^{-17} \, \text{J} = 0.6 \, \text{keV}$?

An eV is the amount of energy to accelerate an electron

through 1 V. $\dfrac{1.2 \, \text{kV}}{2} \rightarrow 0.6 \, \text{keV}$ ✓

   (iii) $v = u + at$ ✓

$$1.449 \times 10^7 = 0 + 6 \times 10^{17} \, t \; ✓$$

$$t = \dfrac{1.449 \times 10^7}{6 \times 10^{14}} = 2.41 \times 10^{-11} \, \text{s} \; ✓$$

Examiner commentary

(a) Seren is living slightly dangerously – the first mark is often for the correct substitution in the equation – as she obtained the correct answer, this was awarded 'by implication'.

(b) (i) Writing 10–6 instead of 10^{-6} was considered a slip and ignored.

   (ii) Seren has made a mistake in the power of 10. It should be 10^{-3}.

(c) Almost an ideal answer: writing $R = 670$ instead of $670 \times 10^3 \, \Omega$ on the first line was a little alarming, but Seren used the correct value later.

(d) Good reasoning – even nicer would have been to say that the time for energy to halve is half the time for the charge to halve, but this was not needed for full credit.

(e) This question was answered correctly by only a few candidates. Seren's solution is well expressed: in a 'show that' question, all the steps must be shown and fully described. It also helps to give a more precise answer than the one asked for. Note that this question relates to PH4. As this is an A2 unit, it contains synoptic aspects.

(f) (i) Seren has actually made three slips of expression here – but none was considered serious enough to cause the loss of a mark:

- writing the unit of v^2 as m s^{-1}
- writing m s^{-1} as ms^{-1} [i.e. milliseconds^{-1}]
- omitting the unit of v in the final answer.

   (ii) Seren's lost mark is in the conversion of J to eV: She wrote '$9.56 \times 10^{-17} \, \text{J} = 0.6 \, \text{keV}$'. This is not clear enough for a 'show that' answer. We needed to see something like:

$$9.56 \times 10^{-17} \, \text{J} = \dfrac{9.56 \times 10^{-17} \, \text{J}}{1.6 \times 10^{-19} \, \text{C}} = 597 \, \text{eV}$$

$$= 0.6 \, \text{keV}$$

   (iii) Good.

Seren scores 18 out of 20 marks.

Quickfire answers

PH4

① 1.71 Ns west, 11.4 N west
② 130 N
③ A body's velocity stays constant, unless the body is acted upon by a resultant external force.
④ 9.0 m s^{-1} east
⑤ 13.75 J
⑥ (a) 1. 47 $\times 10^{-21}$ J s (b) 37 km s^{-1}
⑦ (a) 3.3 $\times 10^{21}$ s^{-1} (b) 1.0 kW
⑧ π, $\pi/2$, $\pi/4$, $\pi/6$
⑨ 314 rad s^{-1}
⑩ 2.7 m s^{-2}
⑪ 97 kN from the rails
⑫ –gradient
⑬ 9.2 N m^{-1}
⑭ –0.032 m
⑮ 0
⑯ (a) 0.67 s, (b) 1.33 s
⑰ (a) 0.26 m s^{-1} (b) –0.13 m s^{-1}
⑱ $E_p = 0.013$ J, $E_k = 0.040$ J
⑲ 1/8, 1/64
⑳ 2.0 Hz
㉑ 5.32 $\times 10^{-26}$ kg
㉒ 0.066 kg
㉓ 667 kPa
㉔ 600 K
㉕ 0.024 mol, 1.45 $\times 10^{22}$
㉖ 326 kPa
㉗ 432 m s^{-1}
㉘ (a) 0.195 kg (b) 7.81 kg m^{-3}
(c) 480 m s^{-1} (d) 296 K
(e) 6.13 $\times 10^{-21}$ J (f) 5.32 $\times 10^{-26}$ kg
㉙ 113 K, 188 K
㉚ 375 J, 0
㉛ (a) 10.5 J of work done on gas
(b) 275 J [$\pm$ 25 J] of work done by gas
㉜ (a) 60 K (b) +38 J (c) 25 J by gas
(d) 63 J into gas
㉝ (a) 120 K (b) –360 J
(c) 360 J by gas
㉞ Heat inflow = work done by gas = area under graph
㉟ Work is done by gas over AB, but no work involved over BC
㊱ 2.4 $\times 10^{-7}$ N
㊲ It quarters
㊳ 445 N C^{-1}
㊴ 6.0 kV with A at higher potential
㊵ (+)5.4 nJ
㊶ 11.1 $\times 10^4$ m s^{-1}
㊷ 1.0 kN C^{-1}
㊸ 1.47 kN C^{-1}
㊹ 2.54 kN C^{-1} away from midpoint of AB
㊺ 1.47 kN C^{-1} parallel to displacement AB
㊻ +205 V
㊼ 0
㊽ (a) 2.3 $\times 10^{-22}$ N (b) 5.5 $\times 10^{-65}$ N
㊾ 6.0 $\times 10^{24}$ kg
㊿ 5500 kg m^{-3} (2 s.f.) (density of water = 1000 kg m^{-3})
(51) (a) 6.3 $\times 10^{-4}$ N kg^{-1}
(b) –0.50 $\times 10^9$ N kg^{-1}
(52) Random molecular
(53) 2.37 km s^{-1}
(54) (a) –1.34 MJ kg^{-1} (b) –1.36 MJ kg^{-1}
(55) 27 earth-years
(56) 6.0 $\times 10^{24}$ kg
(57) 2.0 $\times 10^{30}$ kg
(58) Because within central bulge mass within *r* of galactic centre rises rapidly with *r*.
(59) It's constant
(60) 12. 12 times more mass within 1.5 $\times 10^{21}$ m of galactic centre than predicted.
(61) 1.26 (which is $\sqrt[3]{2}$)
(62) 9.4 m s^{-1} away from us
(63) 471 m s^{-1} away, 2.14 $\times 10^7$ m
(64) (a) 4.25 $\times 10^9$ (b) 6.58 $\times 10^{10}$ m
(c) 6.16 $\times 10^{10}$ m (d) 5.46 $\times 10^{28}$ kg
(e) 26.5 km s^{-1}
(65) It's circular

PH5

① (i) 2.5 nF
(ii) 85 V
② 47 pC
③ 1.8 μm
④ (i) 4.5 mC
(ii) 21 mJ
(iii) 40 A
⑤ 0.55 mm
⑥ 3.1 nF, area = 190 m^2, not achievable using tin foil in the lab – you won't be able to keep 14 m $\times$ 14 m of foil separated by 0.55 mm of air!
⑦ 1.0 nF
⑧ 56.9 pF
⑨ 0.37 $\times$ 18 μC = 6.7 μC, reading from graph gives time = RC = 0.7 s, hence R = 0.7/1.5 $\times 10^{-6}$ = 470 kΩ
⑩ (i) Move switch up then down
(ii) 150 s
(iii) 2.04 mC
(iv) 104 s
(v) 25%
⑪ 2.68 mN
⑫ 44°
⑬ (i) To the right
(ii) To the right
⑭ for *N* electrons, $F = N \times Bqv \sin\theta$
but $N = n \times$ volume $= n \times Al$
hence $F = n \times Al \times Bqv \sin\theta = Bl \sin\theta \times nAvq$
but $I = nAvq$, hence
$F = BI\ell \sin\theta$
⑮ 7.8 $\times 10^{-15}$ N
⑯ $m\omega^2 r = Bqv$ but from circular motion $v = \omega r$
$m\omega^2 r = Bq\omega r$
$$m\omega = Bq \quad \rightarrow \quad \omega = \frac{Bq}{m}$$
⑰ Attach to the top and bottom face

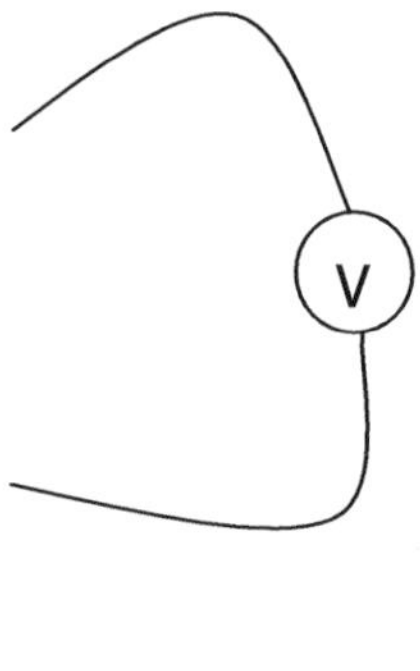

⑱ 1.2 mV m^{-1}

⑲ Attach to left and right sides

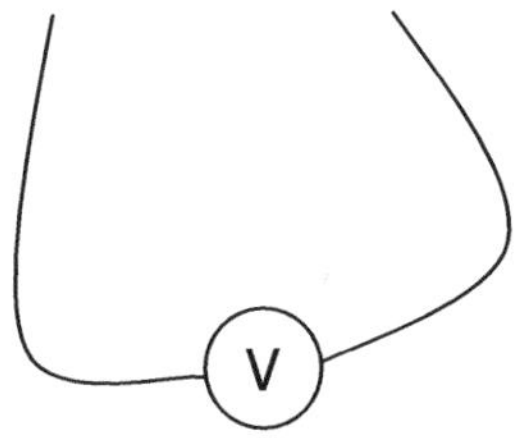

⑳ The force on electrons is to the left from FLHR which means that the right side is depleted of electrons.

㉑ (i) 0.435 mV m^{-1}
(ii) 1.3 mm s^{-1}

㉒ 2.1×10^{24} m^{-3}

㉓

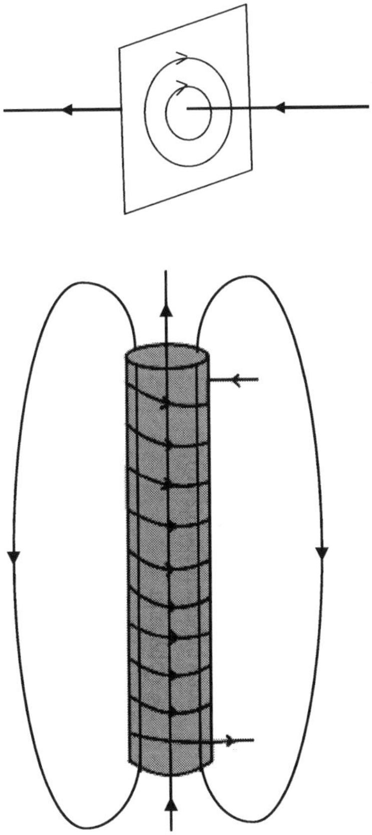

㉔ 5800 (turn m^{-1})

㉕ When the distance from the wire is less than 4.28 cm.

㉖ Field is out of paper at bottom wire (right-hand grip)
Force is down on bottom wire (FLHR)
Also, field is out of paper at top wire (right-hand grip)
Force is up on top wire (FLHR)

㉗ 1.14 mN m^{-1}

㉘ Top wire gives 0.168 mT out of paper (at position of middle wire). Bottom wire gives 0.168 mT into paper.
Hence B-field is zero at position of middle wire.

㉙ $F = ma = Eq \rightarrow ma = \frac{V}{d}q \rightarrow a = \frac{Vq}{md}$

㉚ Speed = 5.9×10^{6} m s^{-1}

㉛ (i) 5.78 eV
(ii) 9.25×10^{-19} J

㉜ (i) 5.7 kV
(ii) 9.12×10^{-16} J

㉝ 3.2 GHz

㉞ 6 tubes (6×125 keV = 750 keV)

㉟ (i) same answer (6 tubes) because same charge
(ii) 3 tubes because double the charge

㊱ Neutrons are neutral and won't be accelerated by an E-field.

㊲ Particles are negative (force must be toward centre and current in opposite direction to the motion).

㊳ (i) The frequency doubles.
(ii) The B-field doubles $\left(B = \frac{mv}{qr} \text{ and } m, q, r \text{ all constant}\right)$.
(iii) The KE quadruples (unless Einstein's theory of relativity must be used which isn't on the syllabus).

㊴ 1.4 mWb

㊵ 0.092 Wb

㊶ 15 ms

㊷ 5.3×10^{-4} m^{2}

㊸ Either – the flux first increases then decreases so the direction of the EMF changes. Or – the direction of the cutting of flux changes so the EMF changes direction.

㊹ 0.11 V

㊺ No change in flux (or no flux cutting)

㊻ 14.6 mA

㊼ The magnetic force opposes the forces pulling the coat hanger, i.e. in the opposite direction to the arrows.

㊽ Clockwise (FRHR, right-hand grip or forces on free electrons using FLHR, or the induced current produces a B-field into the paper).

㊾ Either – the direction of flux cutting is opposite. Or – the flux is zero and becoming negative in one and becoming positive in the other.

㊿ 3.96 A

(51) 32.5 V

(52) (i) 2.54 kW
(ii) 223 V

(53) 2000 W

(54) (i) 0.52 V
(ii) 0.37 V
(iii) 0.45 s
(iv) 2.22 Hz

(55)

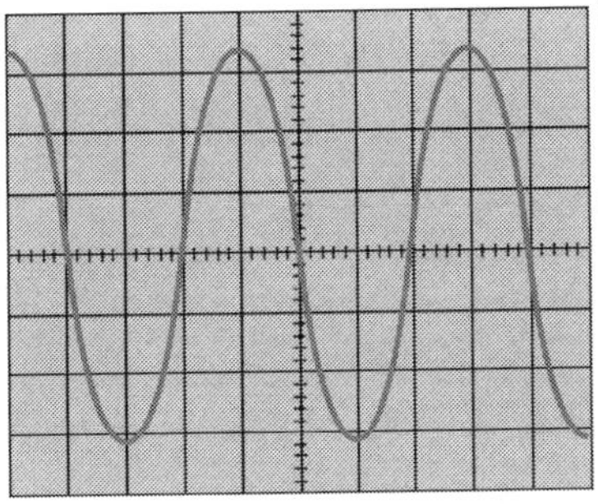

(56) top = 175 µV, bottom = 130 µV

(57) $^{241}_{95}Am \rightarrow ^{237}_{93}Np + ^{4}_{2}He$
$^{7}_{4}Be \rightarrow ^{7}_{3}Li + ^{0}_{+1}\beta$ i.e. positron not an electron
$^{99}_{43}Tc^{*} \rightarrow ^{99}_{43}Tc + ^{0}_{0}\gamma$

⑤⑧ No α (insignificant drop with paper – either a little β absorbed or a random variation is enough to account for a 150 s^{-1} drop). β present (3000 s^{-1} drop with 2mm Al). γ present (6700 s^{-1} penetrating 2mm of Al).

⑤⑨ Not at danger from α because none present. Although the γ count is around twice that of β, β radiation is far more ionising than γ radiation, hence the greatest danger is from β.

⑥⓪ 2.1 mJ

⑥① Yes, this is around 20 times greater than background radiation (0.5 s^{-1}).

⑥② 542 counts in 20 min = 0.45 counts s^{-1}, which is less than the background radiation. It would appear that the radioactive sample is not radioactive and that background radiation was slightly lower than average over the 20 minutes of the experiment.

⑥③ (i) 4.92×10^{-18} s^{-1}
(ii) 6.37×10^{25} nuclei
(iii) 3.14×10^{8} s^{-1}
(iv) 3.92×10^{7} s^{-1}
(v) 1.45×10^{8} s^{-1}
(vi) 7.86 billion years

⑥④ Place a detector around 1 cm from the α-source. When smoke enters, the count rate decreases due to extra absorption by the air and an alarm rings.

⑥⑤ 505 MeV

⑥⑥ (i) 1.99×10^{-26} kg
(ii) 242 u

⑥⑦ (i) 59.9 MJ
(ii) 7.35 MeV

⑥⑧ 12.1 MeV

⑥⑨ 8.81 MeV/nucleon

⑦⓪ 5250 J and 5.83×10^{-14} kg

⑦① Products have more BE/nucleon and are more stable hence they lose mass (and PE) and give off energy.

⑦② Fission and alpha emission result in moving towards greater BE/nucleon. Hence, products have more BE/nucleon and are more stable, hence they lose mass (and PE) and give off energy.

⑦③ 176 MeV

PH5 Option A

① (i) 41 000 V
(ii) 0.19 A
(iii) 32.5 A

② (i) 32 W
(ii) 0.13 A

③ $V = -\dfrac{\Delta(BAN)}{\Delta t}$

$= -\dfrac{\Delta\left(\dfrac{\mu_0 NI}{2r}AN\right)}{\Delta t} = -\dfrac{\mu_0 AN^2}{2r}\dfrac{\Delta I}{\Delta t}$

cf   Induced EMF $= -L\dfrac{\Delta I}{\Delta t}$

$L = \dfrac{\mu_0 AN^2}{2r} = \dfrac{\mu_0 \pi r^2 N^2}{2r} = \dfrac{1}{2}\mu_0 \pi r N^2$

QED

④ 1.2 H

⑤

⑥

⑦ (i) 11.9 kΩ
(ii) 663 Ω
(iii) 11.2 kΩ
(iv) 3.0×10^{-4} A
(v) Almost 90° (89.8°)
(vi) 5.66 kHz

⑧ (i) 0.133 A
(ii) 4.09 nF
(iii) 430 V (across both)
(iv) Zero (because $Z = R$)

⑨ 4.9×10^{-4} A
Both currents are the same because in $(X_L - X_C)^2$ the values of X_L and X_C swap (1620 Ω and 6480 Ω becomes 6480 Ω and 1620 Ω) and $(1620 - 6480)^2 = (6480 - 1620)^2$.

⑩ 5.3 MHz and 0.53 MHz

⑪ 500 and 50

⑫ L and C haven't changed from Quickfire 10, hence 5.3 MHz and 0.53 MHz.

⑬ 1000 and 10

⑭ At low frequencies $\dfrac{1}{\omega C}$ is large so nearly all the pd is across C and none across the output resistor. At high frequencies $\dfrac{1}{\omega C}$ is small so nearly all the pd is across R.

⑮ 590 Hz

⑯
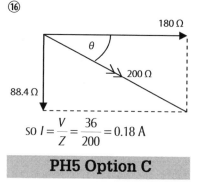

so $I = \dfrac{V}{Z} = \dfrac{36}{200} = 0.18$ A

PH5 Option C

① 19.6 N

② 25 cm

③ (a) 0.001 m, (b) 0.001 km, (c) 0.053 cm

④ (a) 2500 N cm^{-2}, (b) 2.5×10^{7} Pa, (c) 25 MPa.

⑤ 0.75 J

⑥ 200 kJ

⑦ (a) $\sigma_X = 560$ MPa [5.6×10^8 Pa]
   (b) $\varepsilon_X = 5.6 \times 10^{-3}$
   (c)

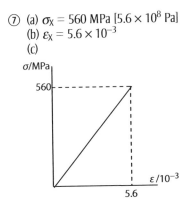

PH5 Option D

① 60 keV!

② 21 pm [2.1×10^{-11} m]

③ The equation gives 8900 V but the voltage will need to be higher to actually see the line.

④ The power of e has no unit, i.e. μx has no unit.

So unit of $\mu = \dfrac{1}{\text{unit of } x} = \text{m}^{-1}$

⑤ $\frac{1}{2}I_0 = I_0 e^{-10x}$, so $e^{-10x} = 0.5$.

Taking logs: $-10x = \ln 0.5 = -0.69$
So $x = 0.069$ cm.

⑥ 1.7×10^6 kg m^{-2} s^{-1}

⑦ 5×10^{-5}

⑧ Yes: 15 m s^{-1}

⑨ No units – the gray and the sievert are both J kg^{-1}.

⑩ $1 < Q < 20$
   [Actually $Q \sim 2$]

⑪ 2.7×10^{-22} Ns

⑫ $^{82}_{38}\text{Sr} + \,^{0}_{-1}\text{e} \rightarrow \,^{82}_{37}\text{Rb}$

$^{82}_{37}\text{Rb} \rightarrow \,^{82}_{36}\text{Kr} + \,^{0}_{+1}\text{e}^{+}$

PH6

① 36.0 ± 0.5 cm^3

② Diameter of coil along the centre line of wire

$= \dfrac{(2.54 \pm 0.02) + (2.68 \pm 0.02)}{2}$

$= \dfrac{5.22 \pm 0.04}{2}$

$= 2.61 \pm 0.02$ cm.
Length of 40 turns $= 40 \times \pi \times (261 \pm 0.02$ cm$) = 328 \pm 3$ cm

③ (a) $\dfrac{4\pi}{g}$ (b) $\dfrac{4\pi k^2}{g}$ (c) m

④ (a) 1.28
   (b) 14.5
   (c) 10.4
   (d) 12.2
   (e) 2.50 [because $e^{2.5} = 12.2$]

⑤ (a) A graph of $\ln I$ against $\ln V$ [a graph of $\log_{10} I$ against $\log_{10} V$ could be used.
   (b) $\ln k = $ intercept on $\ln I$ axis, so $k = e^{\text{intercept}}$. Gradient $= n$.

(c)

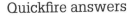

⑥ The graph is $\ln A$ against t. The gradient is $-\lambda$ so minus the gradient is λ.

⑦ $\ln A = \ln A_0 - n \ln 2$, so the gradient $= -\ln 2 = -0.693$.

⑧ $L = 1.5 L_\odot \left(\dfrac{M}{M_\odot} \right)^{3.5}$

So $\ln L = \ln 1.5 + \ln L_\odot - 3.5 \ln M_\odot + 3.5 \ln M$ or

$\ln\left(\dfrac{L}{L_\odot} \right) = \ln 1.5 + 3.5 \ln\left(\dfrac{M}{M_\odot} \right)$

So plotting $\ln L$ against $\ln M$

$\left[\text{or } \ln\left(\dfrac{L}{L_\odot} \right) \text{ against } \ln\left(\dfrac{M}{M_\odot} \right) \right]$

would give a straight line of gradient 3.5.

⑨ $y = 12.2\, x^2$

⑩ $1.64 \rightarrow 1.90$ m s^2 [$yT^2 = 1.77 \pm 0.13$ m s^2]

⑪ $u = 2.5 \pm 0.3$ m s^{-1}
   $a = 1.60 \pm 0.05$ m s^{-2}

Practice question answers

① A body undergoes <u>simple harmonic motion</u> if its acceleration is always directed towards a fixed point and is proportional to its distance from that point. The <u>period</u> is the time for 1 cycle of the motion. The <u>amplitude</u> of the motion is the maximum distance of the body from the central point.

Commentary

A better definition of the period would be the shortest interval between times in which the body is in the same position and moving with the same velocity [i.e. same speed in the same direction].

②

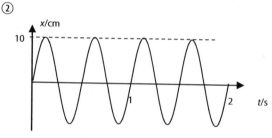

Commentary

A sketch-graph is not necessarily accurately plotted but it often needs numerical information. The axes need to be labelled and given units – but not given an accurate scale. In this case, the amplitude is 10 cm so this needs to be labelled on the x axis. The period is 0.5 s, so that information needs including on the t axis. The sin curve need not be accurately drawn but does need to be recognisable – it helps to mark the places where it crosses the axis [0, 0.25, 0.5 . . . . s].

③ A system which can oscillate undergoes free oscillations if it is displaced and then released. The frequency of the free oscillations is called the system's natural frequency. Forced oscillations occur if the system is subject to a periodic driving force – in this case the system oscillates with the frequency of the driving force.

④

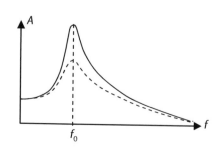

Commentary

The only feature of interest is the frequency of the peak, which is the resonance frequency. The value of this is actually slightly less than the natural frequency but this distinction can be ignored as it is so small.

The second curve should have the same amplitude at very low frequencies, the peak should be in the same place [or <u>very</u> slightly lower frequency], be below the first curve at all frequencies and have the same shape.

⑤ The vector sum of the momenta of the bodies of a system stays constant, providing that no resultant external force acts on the system.

Alternative answer

In any interaction between bodies, the total momentum of the bodies remains constant provided no resultant external force acts on the system.

Commentary

The use of 'vector sum' rather than just 'sum' is usually ignored: momentum is a vector quantity so can only be summed in a vector fashion. Similarly 'total momentum' is taken to imply a [vector] sum of the momenta. Writing 'provided no external forces' rather than 'no resultant external force' is not quite as good but is usually accepted.

⑥ This is the number of particles per mole of substance, which is the number of atoms in exactly 12 g of carbon-12, approximately 6.0×10^{23}.

Commentary

Going on to say what is meant by a mole is a good idea, although the question does not specifically require it.

⑦ ΔU – this is the change in internal energy of the system.

Q – this is the heat flow into the system [from the surroundings]

W – this is the work done by the system [on the surroundings]

Commentary

'Change' is by definition positive if there is an increase. Generally the change in a quantity is 'final value – initial value', i.e. $\Delta U = U_2 - U_1$. Candidates often make the mistake of writing 'heat flow into or out of the system'. This is incorrect. Writing the equation in this way requires Q to be algebraically the flow <u>into</u> the system, e.g. if 10 kJ of heat flowed out of the system, then Q would be -10 kJ, not $+$ 10 kJ. Similarly, if a gas is compressed, it does a negative amount of work <u>on</u> the surroundings.

⑧ The temperature rise, ΔT when a substance, of mass m is heated by Q is given by $Q = mc\Delta T$. The quantity c is the specific heat capacity.

The statement says that it takes 4200 J of heat per kg of water to raise its temperature by 1 K.

Commentary

An equation is a good way of defining a quantity – if all the terms in the equation are defined.

⑨ Kepler's 3rd law states that the square of the period of the orbit is proportional to the cube of the orbital radius.

Consider a planet of mass m orbiting a star of mass M, with $M \gg m$, at a *distance r*. The gravitational force, F, on the planet is given by: $F = \dfrac{GMm}{r^2}$.

F provides the centripetal force, $mr\omega^2 = mr\left(\dfrac{2\pi}{T}\right)^2$

i.e. $\dfrac{GMm}{r^2} = mr\left(\dfrac{2\pi}{T}\right)^2$

Dividing by m and re-arranging: $T^2 = r^3 \times \dfrac{4\pi^2}{GM}$,

i.e. $T^2 \propto r^3$ as required.

Commentary

Strictly, Kepler's 3rd Law refers to the semi-major axis, rather than the radius, but the above answer would be accepted.

⑩

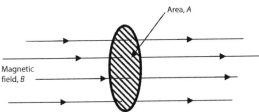

Area, A

Magnetic field, B

The magnetic flux, Φ, linking the circuit is defined by $\Phi = BA$.

⑪ A is the **activity** of a radioactive material, which is the number of radioactive decays per unit time. Its unit is the becquerel – Bq.

N is the number of undecayed nuclei in the radioactive material. It is a number and has no units.

The symbol λ is the **decay constant** of the material. Its unit is s^{-1}.

Commentary

The unit s^{-1} would be acceptable instead of Bq as the unit of activity.

Questions to test understanding

⑫ $p = mv$, so the unit of p is kg $\times$ m s^{-1}, i.e. kg m s^{-1}.

$p = \dfrac{h}{\lambda}$: The unit of h is J s = kg m^2 s^{-2} $\times$ s = kg m^2 s^{-1}

The unit of λ is m

So the unit of $p = \dfrac{\text{kg m}^2\ \text{s}^{-1}}{\text{m}} = $ kg m s^{-1}, which is

the same.

Commentary

With 'show that' questions, you should always make it clear what your working means and fill in all the steps. This answer has used the fact that the joule is equivalent to kg m^2 s^{-2}. If you are not confident of this, work it out using:

$$W = Fd \text{ and } F = ma.$$

⑬ (a) The speed is the same so the kinetic energy of the planet is constant. Because energy is conserved, this means that the planet's gravitational potential energy is constant and so it must always be the same distance from the star.

(b) (i) Angular speed $= \dfrac{\text{speed along orbit}}{\text{radius}}$

$= \dfrac{5\times10^4\ \text{m s}^{-1}}{8\times10^{10}\text{m}} = 6.3 \times 10^{-7}$ rad s^{-1}

(ii) Orbital period, $T = \dfrac{2\pi}{\omega} = \dfrac{2\pi}{6.3\times10^{-7}}$

$= 1 \times 10^7$ s.

(iii) Orbital frequency $= \dfrac{1}{T} = 1 \times 10^{-7}$ s

(iv) Centripetal acceleration $\dfrac{v^2}{r} = \dfrac{(5\times10^4)^2}{8\times10^{10}}$

$= 0.031$ m s^{-2}

(v) Centripetal acceleration $=$ gravitational field strength

So 0.031 m s$^{-2} = \dfrac{GM}{r^2}$

So $M = \dfrac{0.031\times\left(8\times10^{10}\right)^2}{6.67\times10^{-11}} = 3.0 \times 10^{30}$ kg

⑭ The equation of the graph is

$F = -kx$, where $k = 5$ N cm^{-1} = 500 N m^{-1}.

So the acceleration $a = \dfrac{F}{m} = -250\ x$. Compare this

with $a = -\omega^2 x$, which is the equation for simple

harmonic motion. So the subsequent motion is simple harmonic motion with amplitude 10.0 cm and $\omega = \sqrt{250} = 15.8\ s^{-1}$.

The equation of shm with initial velocity zero is: $x = A\cos(\omega t)$, so in this case $x = 10.0\cos(15.8t)$, where x is in cm and t in seconds.

When $t = 1.5\ s$, $x = 10.0 \times \cos 23.7 = 1.38$ cm.

The velocity, v, is given by $v = -A\omega\sin(\omega t) = -158\sin 23.7 = -156$ cm s^{-1} = -1.56 m s^{-1}.

Commentary

For all calculations involving oscillations, it is important that the calculator mode is 'rad' (radians) and not 'deg' (degrees).

⑮ (a) M_1 and M_2 refer to the masses of two point objects [i.e. ones which are very small compared to their separation]. F is the force of attraction between the objects, r their separation and G the universal constant of gravitation.

(b) The centripetal force on the Moon $= M_{Moon}r\left(\dfrac{2\pi}{T}\right)^2$

So $\dfrac{GM_{Earth}M_{Moon}}{r^2} = M_{Moon}r\left(\dfrac{2\pi}{T}\right)^2$

And, cancelling M_{Moon} and rearranging:

$M_{Earth} = \dfrac{4\pi^2 r^3}{GT^2}$

$= \dfrac{4\pi^2 \times (384\,000 \times 10^3)^3}{6.67 \times 10^{-11} \times (27.3 \times 24 \times 3600)^2}$

$= 6.02 \times 10^{24}$ kg

(c) From Newton's law of gravitation, $g = \dfrac{GM_{Earth}}{r^2}$, where r = radius of the Earth.

So $M_{Earth} = \dfrac{9.81 \times (6370 \times 10^3)^2}{6.67 \times 10^{-11}} = 5.97 \times 10^{24}$ kg.

(d) For a spherically symmetric object, the gravitational field outside the object is the same as it would be if all the mass of the object were concentrated in a point at the centre. In both (b) and (c) the Earth can thus be treated as a point mass. The Moon is quite small compared to its distance from the Earth, so it can be treated as a point mass for the purposes of the calculation in (b).

Commentary

It is unlikely that the examiner would require identification of the objects as point masses in part (a). You should study the answer to part (d) carefully.

⑯ (a) Mass of asteroid = density × volume

$= 2500 \times \frac{4}{3}\pi \times 25^3$

$= 1.64 \times 10^8$ kg

KE of asteroid $= \frac{1}{2} \times 1.64 \times 10^8 \times 1000^2$

$= 8.2 \times 10^{13}$ J

(b) (i) Potential due to Moon

$= -\dfrac{GM}{r} = -\dfrac{6.67 \times 10^{-11} \times 7.35 \times 10^{22}}{1.74 \times 10^6}$

$= -2.82 \times 10^6$ J kg^{-1}

(ii) Potential due to Earth

$= -\dfrac{GM}{r} = -\dfrac{6.67 \times 10^{-11} \times 5.97 \times 10^{24}}{3.84 \times 10^8}$ J

$= -1.04 \times 10^6$ J kg^{-1}

(c) Total energy = initial kinetic energy $= 8.2 \times 10^{13}$ J

Total potential energy at impact

$= -(2.82 + 1.04) \times 10^6 \times 1.64 \times 10^8$ J

$= -6.33 \times 10^{14}$ J

Total PE at impact + KE at impact $= 8.2 \times 10^{13}$ J

∴ KE at impact $= 8.2 \times 10^{13} + 6.33 \times 10^{14}$ J

$= 7.15 \times 10^{14}$ J

[Note this is equivalent to about 150 000 tonnes of TNT]

⑰ First calculate the resistance of the clock:

$R = \dfrac{V}{I} = \dfrac{3.3}{1.0 \times 10^{-6}} = 3.3 \times 10^6\ \Omega.$

The capacitor decay equation: $Q = Q_0 e^{-t/RC}$,

Dividing by C and remembering that $V = Q/C$:

$V = V_0 e^{-t/RC}$ with $V = 1.3$ V and $V_0 = 3.3$ V

Taking logs: $\ln V = \ln V_0 - \dfrac{t}{RC}$, so

$\ln 1.3 = \ln 3.3 - \dfrac{t}{3.3 \times 10^6 \times 0.2}$

i.e. $t = 3.3 \times 10^6 \times 0.2 \times (1.194 - 0.262) = 615\,000$ s $=$ 170 hours (2 s.f.)

Commentary

An alternative method would have been to calculate the charge Q, when the voltage was 3.3 V and 1.3 V and then to use $Q = Q_0 e^{-t/RC}$ directly.

⑱ (a) Capacitance is defined by $C = \dfrac{Q}{V}$.

So $\frac{1}{2}CV^2 = \frac{1}{2}\dfrac{Q}{V}V^2 = \frac{1}{2}QV.$

V is defined by $V = \dfrac{W}{Q}$, so the volt is equivalent to J C^{-1}; Q has units of C,

So Units of $\frac{1}{2}QV = $ C J C^{-1} = J, which is the unit of internal energy. QED.

(b) (i) $U = \frac{1}{2}CV^2 = \frac{1}{2} \times 5 \times 3^2 = 22.5$ J.

(ii) When the second capacitor is placed across the first, charge is transferred until the pd's are equal. Because the capacitances are equal, each capacitor will have half the total charge and so the pd across each will be 1.5 V.

Total internal energy $= \frac{1}{2} \times 5 \times 1.5^2 + \frac{1}{2} \times 5 \times$
$1.5^2 = 5.625 + 5.625 = 11.25$ J

(iii) Half of the initial energy has been lost from the capacitors. It could be lost as: heating in the connecting wires, e-m radiation emitted from a spark when the connection is made, radio waves given out from the sudden surge of current.

Data analysis questions

⑲ (a) For y between 0.6 m and 0.3 m, T is approximately constant [at 1.90 s]. For the extreme values of y the period is greater, but the difference is very small [but more than the uncertainty].

The equation agrees with this: because of the y at the bottom of the fraction, small values of y should give large values of T; because of the y^2 at the top of the fraction, large values of y should give large values of T.

(b) Squaring the equation: $T^2 = 4\pi^2 \dfrac{k^2 + y^2}{gy}$

Multiplying by y: $yT^2 = 4\pi^2 \dfrac{k^2 + y^2}{g}$

So $yT^2 = \dfrac{4\pi^2}{g}y^2 + \dfrac{4\pi^2 k^2}{g}$

Comparing this with the straight line relationship $y = mx + c$, this shows that a graph of yT^2 against y^2 should be a straight line with gradient $\dfrac{4\pi^2}{g}$ and intercept $\dfrac{4\pi^2 k^2}{g}$ on the yT^2 axis.

(c)

$(y/m)^2$	$(y\,T^2/m\,s^2)$
0.490 ± 0.005	2.74 ± 0.15
0.360 ± 0.004	2.14 ± 0.12
0.250 ± 0.003	1.81 ± 0.10
0.160 ± 0.002	1.40 ± 0.08
0.090 ± 0.002	1.09 ± 0.06
0.040 ± 0.001	0.92 ± 0.05

(d)

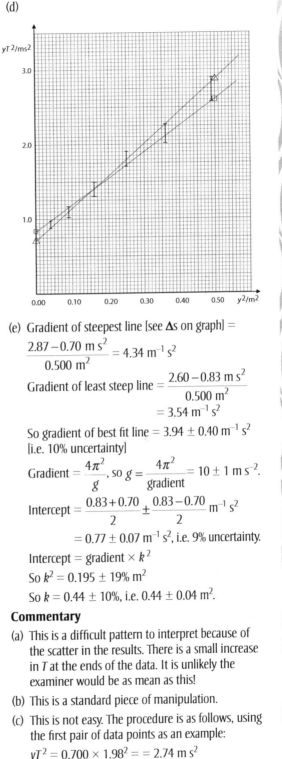

(e) Gradient of steepest line [see Δs on graph] =
$\dfrac{2.87 - 0.70 \text{ m s}^2}{0.500 \text{ m}^2} = 4.34 \text{ m}^{-1}\text{ s}^2$

Gradient of least steep line $= \dfrac{2.60 - 0.83 \text{ m s}^2}{0.500 \text{ m}^2}$
$= 3.54 \text{ m}^{-1}\text{ s}^2$

So gradient of best fit line = $3.94 \pm 0.40 \text{ m}^{-1}\text{ s}^2$ [i.e. 10% uncertainty]

Gradient $= \dfrac{4\pi^2}{g}$, so $g = \dfrac{4\pi^2}{\text{gradient}} = 10 \pm 1 \text{ m s}^{-2}$.

Intercept $= \dfrac{0.83 + 0.70}{2} \pm \dfrac{0.83 - 0.70}{2} \text{ m}^{-1}\text{ s}^2$
$= 0.77 \pm 0.07 \text{ m}^{-1}\text{ s}^2$, i.e. 9% uncertainty.

Intercept = gradient × k^2

So $k^2 = 0.195 \pm 19\%$ m^2

So $k = 0.44 \pm 10\%$, i.e. 0.44 ± 0.04 m^2.

Commentary

(a) This is a difficult pattern to interpret because of the scatter in the results. There is a small increase in T at the ends of the data. It is unlikely the examiner would be as mean as this!

(b) This is a standard piece of manipulation.

(c) This is not easy. The procedure is as follows, using the first pair of data points as an example:
$yT^2 = 0.700 \times 1.98^2 = = 2.74 \text{ m s}^2$

% uncertainty in $y = \dfrac{0.003}{0.700} \times 100 = 0.43\%$

% uncertainty in $T = \dfrac{0.05}{1.98} \times 100 = 2.53\%$

So % uncertainty in $T^2 = 5.06\%$

So % uncertainty in $yT^2 = 0.43 + 5.06 = 5.49\%$

So uncertainty in $yT^2 = 5.49\% \times 2.74 = 0.15$ m s^2

Note that it makes sense to keep several s.f. in the calculations of uncertainty before reducing to 1 or 2 s.f. at the end.

(d) The scales are chosen so that the error bars occupy at least half the available vertical height – the horizontal axis is the obvious one. The axes are labelled and the units stated.

(e) In PH6 the examiner is likely to split (e) into several parts:

✓ Calculation of mean gradient and uncertainty

✓ Calculation of mean intercept and uncertainty

✓ Calculation of g and k.

You will not be penalised for omitting units on the gradient and intercept – but you are likely to lose marks if you leave out the unit of g and k. In this case, the unit of k must be the same as the unit of y because k^2 is added to y^2.

The value of g is clearly consistent with the standard value of 9.81 m s^{-2}. The value of k for this beam should be 0.43 m^2.

㉑ (a)

1. Place the thermistor into a glass beaker containing melting ice and a thermometer, and connect it up to a resistance meter. Allow time for the temperature to become steady. Record the temperature and resistance.

2. Discard the ice and replace with water at approximately room temperature. Replace the thermistor and proceed as in step 1.

3. Heat the water using a Bunsen burner until its temperature has increased by approximately 25°C. Remove the Bunsen, allow time for equilibration and measure the resistance using the resistance meter.

4. Repeat step 3 in approximately 25°C steps up to 100°C.

Method of analysis: If $R = Ae^{\varepsilon/2kT}$, then taking

logs: $\ln R = \ln A + \dfrac{\varepsilon}{2kT}$, so a graph of $\ln R$ against

$\dfrac{1}{T}$ should be a straight line with a gradient $\dfrac{\varepsilon}{2k}$. The

value of ε can be found from the gradient.

Results:

T/K	R/Ω	ln (R/Ω)	1/(T/K) × 10⁻³
273	380	5.89	3.66
298	100	4.61	3.34
323	38.5	3.65	3.10
348	14.7	2.69	2.87
373	6.2	1.82	2.68

(b) Graph

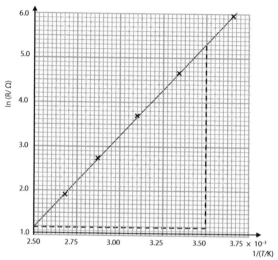

(c) The graph is a straight line, allowing for a small amount of experimental uncertainty. This supports the suggested relationship.

(d) Gradient of graph $= \dfrac{(5.24 - 1.12)}{(3.50 - 2.50) \times 10^{-3}\text{K}^{-1}}$

$= \dfrac{4.12}{1.00 \times 10^{-3}\text{K}^{-1}} = 4.12 \times 10^3$ K

So $\dfrac{\varepsilon}{2k} = 4.12 \times 10^3$ K

and $\varepsilon = 2 \times 1.38 \times 10^{-23}$ J K^{-1} $\times 4.12 \times 10^3$ K

$= 1.14 \times 10^{-19}$ J

Commentary

(a) In this case a diagram isn't necessary – all the details are clearly given in the written plan. It is not clear from the question whether the analysis of the relationship by taking logs and comparing to $y = mx + c$ is necessary here, but it needs to be done before the graph is plotted.

(b) Be careful when putting in units where logs are involved. The log of a quantity has no unit. The safest way is always to put the units with the variable – in this case ln (R/Ω). Similarly with

$1/T$: write this as $1/(T/K)$. Alternatively the unit of $\ln R$ could be omitted and $\frac{1}{T}(K^{-1})$ written.

The graph needs careful thought – the points should occupy as much of the grid as possible. Particularly with log graphs, there is no need to include 0 on either axis unless the intercept needs to be found.

(c) No comment.

(d) The points used for calculating the gradient must be identified clearly, either by drawing the triangle as shown here, or by labelling the points – see the data analysis question.

The unit of the gradient does not need to be included but the unit of the derived quantity, ε in this case, must be given.

Index

absolute
  temperature 26
  zero 26
absorbed dose 138–139
acceleration 10, 16–19, 21, 36, 42, 47, 50, 73–76, 132
acoustic impedance 134
air resistance 11
alpha (α) radiation 90–92
amorphous
  materials 126
  phase 130
ampere 72
angle in radians 15
angular velocity 15–16, 50, 85
annihilation 141
A-scan 134
Avogadro constant 25

background radiation 93
baryonic mass 49
beta (β) radiation 90–92
B-field (magnetic flux density) 65–72, 77–83, 105–107
binary system 50, 52
binding energy 98–101
Boyle's law 26–27
brittle fracture 128
Brownian movement 27
B-scan 134

capacitance 57–64, 115
capacitor 57–63, 68, 73, 108–117
  discharging 62–64
  in parallel 61
  in series 60–61
  time constant 63–64
centripetal
  acceleration 16–17
  force 17
circular orbit 47–48, 50
collision 12–13
Coulomb's law 37
coupling medium 134
creep 127
critical damping 23
crystalline material 126
cyclotron 74

dark matter 49
decay constant λ 93–95
dielectric 57

displacement 18–23
Doppler
  effect/shift 49, 51–52, 135
  probe 135
driving force 24
ductile material 127

$E = mc^2$ 97, 99
Eddy current 105–106
edge dislocation 126–127
elastic
  collision 13
  hysteresis 129–130
  limit 125
electric field (E-field)
  direction 37, 40, 41
  inside a capacitor 59
  lines 41
  source 37
  strength 36, 38, 40, 41, 46
electric potential 38–41
electrical potential energy 38
electrocardiogram (ECG) 137
electron capture 139
electron-volt (eV) 73
energy
  flow 31–32
  interchange in SHM 22
equilibrium 18, 19, 21, 22, 23, 68, 101
equipotential 41
error bars 147–150
escape speed (escape velocity) 45
exponential
  fall/decay 23, 62–63, 94
  relationship 146

Faraday's law 79–82, 107
fission reactor 101–102
Fleming's left-hand rule (FLHR) 66–69, 72, 81–83
Fleming's right-hand rule 82
flux
  leakage 105–106
  linkage 78–79, 82–85
force
  between two wires carrying current 71–72
  of light 14
  on charge moving in magnetic field 66–68
  on wire carrying current in magnetic field 65–66
frequency of rotation 15

galaxy, rotation of 49
gamma (γ)
  camera 140
  radiation 90–92
gas
  cycle of change 34
  density 26, 28
  pressure 25–31, 33–34
gravitational
  field strength 42–44, 46
  force 10, 42–43
  potential (energy) 41–46

half-life (radioactive) 94–95
Hall effect/probe/voltage 68–70, 81
heart 137
heat flow 32–33
high-pass filter 117–118
Hooke's law 120, 124

ideal gas 26–27, 30
  equation 27
impedance 109–112
inelastic collision 13
internal energy 30, 32–35
investigations, planning 151
ion beam 73
isothermal
  change 30–31
  expansion 33

Kepler's laws 47–48, 50
kinetic
  energy (KE) 13, 22, 29, 30, 45, 75, 102
  theory of gases 27–28

LCR circuit 111–115
Lenz's law 82–83
linear accelerator (Linac) 74
linearising equations 144
log plots 145–146
low-pass filter 116–117

magnetic
  field 65–68, 70–71, 84, 93, 107
  flux 77–78, 84–85; also see B-field
  flux density see B-field
magnetic resonance imaging (MRI) 135–136
mean square speed 28
metal
  fatigue 128
  structure of 126–128

molar mass 25
molecule 25–30
momentum 10–14
  conservation 13
  definition of 10
  of a photon 13–14
monatomic gas 25, 30

Newton's
  first law of motion 11
  law of gravitation 42–43, 48, 49
  second law of motion 10–11, 17, 28
  third law of motion 12, 28, 72
nuclear binding energy see Binding energy
nucleon 98–101
nucleus
  fission reaction 100–101
  fission reactor 101–102
  stable/unstable 98–101

oscillation 18–24, 115
  damped 23, 24
  forced 24
  natural 23, 24
oscilloscope 87–89

particle accelerator 67, 73–76, 141
periodic time 19, 23
permittivity of free space 37
phase constant 19
phasor diagram 108–109
photon, momentum of 13–14
point charge 37, 39–40
polycrystalline 126
polymer 129–130
polythene 130
positron emission tomography (PET) 141
potential energy (PE) 22, 43, 45, 98–99
potential gradient 39
power law relationship 145–146
prestressed 128
principle of conservation of
  energy 32, 45
  momentum 12–13
p–V diagram 30

quality (Q) factor 113–115, 138

radial velocity 51
radiation (nuclear)
  background 93
  effects of 138

in medicine 138–141
measuring 138–139
properties of 90–93
radioactive tracer 139–140
radioactivity, theory of 93–95
radioisotope 95–96, 139
reactance 109–112, 115
relative molecular mass (rmm) 25
relaxation time 136
resonance 24, 111–115, 135
root mean square (rms) 28–29, 85–87,
109–110, 113–114, 116
rotating coil 84–85
rubber 129–130

self-inductance 107–108
simple harmonic motion (SHM) 18–22
solenoid 70–71, 78, 107–108
specific heat capacity (SHC) 35
spring constant 18–21, 120
star
orbital radius 52
orbital velocity 51–52
strain energy 123–124
stress
lines 128
unit of 121–122

stress–strain graph 125
superalloys 127
surface potential 137
synchroton 75–76

terminal velocity 11
thermoplastic 129
thermoset 129
time constant 62–64
thermodynamics 30–35
first law of 32–33
transformer equations 105–106

ultrasound 133–136
uncertainties in quantities 143
unified atomic mass unit 98

velocity 10–11, 15–16, 19, 21, 23, 45, 50,
51, 52, 67–69, 74, 84–86

work
energy flow 31, 33
hardening 127

X-rays 132–133, 136

yield point 125
Young modulus 121–124